The Regulation of Cell Metabolism

Hermann, Publishers in Arts and Science
Molecular Biology Series

(Collection Méthodes)

Holt, Rinehart and Winston
Molecular and Cellular Biology Series

Consulting editors: James D. Ebert, Carnegie Institution of Washington; Ariel G. Loewy, Haverford College, Howard A. Schneiderman, Case Western Reserve University.

The Regulation of Cell Metabolism

GEORGES COHEN

Director Enzymology department
Centre national de la recherche scientifique
Gif-sur-Yvette, France

HERMANN, PUBLISHERS IN ARTS AND SCIENCE

115, boulevard Saint-Germain, Paris, France

HOLT, RINEHART AND WINSTON, INC.

New York Chicago San Francisco
Atlanta Dallas Montreal
Toronto London

Translated from the original French text: *Le métabolisme cellulaire et sa régulation,* published by Hermann, Paris, in 1967 in their series *Méthodes*.

Library of Congress Catalog Card Number: 69-19910

Printed in Great Britain

Contents

3. GLYCOLYSIS AND ITS REGULATION

4. TRICARBOXYLIC ACID CYCLE

5. GLUCONEOGENESIS. SYNTHESIS OF GLYCOGEN AND ITS REGULATION

6. BIOSYNTHESIS OF LIPIDS AND ITS REGULATION

7. BIOSYNTHETIC PATHWAYS. METHODS OF STUDY AND OUTLINE OF THE CONTROL OF ENZYME BIOSYNTHESIS

8. BIOSYNTHESIS OF ASPARTATE AND AMINO ACIDS DERIVED FROM IT

9. REGULATION OF BIOSYNTHESIS OF AMINO ACIDS DERIVED FROM ASPARTIC ACID IN *ESCHERICHA COLI*

10. REGULATION OF BIOSYNTHESIS OF AMINO ACIDS DERIVED FROM ASPARTIC ACID IN OTHER MICROBIAL SPECIES

11. BIOSYNTHESIS OF GLUTAMATE AND AMINO ACIDS DERIVED FROM IT AND ITS REGULATION

12. BIOSYNTHESIS OF AMINO ACIDS DERIVED FROM PHOSPHOGLYCERIC ACID AND PYRUVIC ACID

13. BIOSYNTHESIS OF AROMATIC AMINO ACIDS AND ITS REGULATION

14. BIOSYNTHESIS OF HISTIDINE AND ITS REGULATION

15. BIOSYNTHESIS OF PYRIMIDINE NUCLEOTIDES AND DEOXYNUCLEOTIDES AND ITS REGULATION

16. BIOSYNTHESIS OF PURINE NUCLEOTIDES AND DEOXYNUCLEOTIDES AND ITS REGULATION

17. BIOSYNTHESIS OF SOME WATER-SOLUBLE VITAMINS AND THEIR COENZYME FORMS

18. BIOSYNTHESIS OF CAROTENE, VITAMIN A AND STEROLS

19. BIOSYNTHESIS OF TETRAPYRROLE RING SYSTEM, ITS REGULATION AND AN OUTLINE OF THE FUNCTIONS OF VITAMIN B_{12}

Introduction

The ability of cells to multiply, leading to a net increase in mass, is due to a network of chemical reactions which can be classified as anabolic. Their study forms a chapter in biochemistry to which the name *biosynthesis* can be given. Biosynthetic reactions require energy; this is provided by another set of chemical reactions which are called catabolic.

A study of cellular metabolism must therefore concern itself with the reactions which produce energy and with the reactions of biosynthesis. This distinction, useful in a didactic way, must not obscure the fact that many intermediates involved in the classical degradation processes, glycolysis and the tricarboxylic acid cycle, are branch points from which purely biosynthetic pathways arise. The degradation sequences are therefore not only important in so far as they provide energy in the form of ATP, but also as they provide the carbon atoms which are necessary for the synthesis of cellular constituents.

Furthermore, if we consider the growth of a bacterium such as *Escherichia coli* on succinate as sole source of carbon, it is evident that this organism must be able to carry out the reactions of glycolysis in the reverse direction in order to obtain, for example, glucose 6-phosphate, which when transformed to erythrose 4-phosphate is required in the biosynthesis of the aromatic amino acids. In this instance, the glycolytic reactions have a purely biosynthetic role. The term "amphibolic" has been introduced to describe such reactions which function in both catabolism and anabolism.

Bacteria will be very frequently mentioned in this book devoted to intermediary metabolism. This choice is dictated not only by the preferences of the author, who for more than twenty years has been familiar with the study of such organisms, but also by the fact that the study of metabolism is easier if we examine unicellular organisms, free from the complications introduced by interactions with other cells and other organs. Let us consider the bacterium *E. coli*: it can grow exponentially on a mineral medium containing a usable carbon source. Table I gives the composition of one such medium and Table II is a very incomplete list of carbon sources for this bacterium. Such a bacterium will first of all have to be brought into contact with the carbon source of the medium. We shall see that this is generally achieved not by simple diffusion but by means of catalysts, probably localized in the cytoplasmic membrane, which are responsible for the ingress of metabolites into the intracellular space.

TABLE I

KH_2PO_4	13·6 g
$(NH_4)_2SO_4$	2·0 g
$MgSO_4, 7H_2O$	0·2 g
$FeSO_4, 7H_2O$	0·0005 g
Adjust to pH 7·0 with KOH.	
Redistilled water to 1 litre	

Phosphate is in great excess to act as a buffer against change in pH. Traces of zinc, molybdenum, cobalt, etc., which are found in some enzymes and vitamins are provided by impurities in the salts used.

TABLE II

Some carbon sources used by E. coli

Monosaccharides	Disaccharides	Acids	Polyols
Glucose	Maltose	Acetate	Glycerol
Fructose	Lactose	Succinate	Mannitol
Mannose			Dulcitol
Galactose			Sorbitol
Arabinose			
Xylose			
Rhamnose			

From the ingredients of the medium, E. coli *will need to synthesize the twenty amino acids found in proteins, the purine and pyrimidine nucleotides found in nucleic acids, the proteins and nucleic acids themselves, the sugars which are constituents of the cell membrane and cell wall, the polysaccharides, the growth factors and coenzymes, the fatty acids and the complex lipids. The bacteria will also need to obtain from these ingredients the energy necessary for these syntheses. Finally, it will need to ensure the coordination of all these reactions.*

1

Bacterial Permeases

PROTEIN NATURE OF β-GALACTOSIDE PERMEASE

Proof of the existence in microorganisms of stereospecific permeation systems, specialized in function and distinct from the so-called metabolic enzymes, has been obtained over the last twelve years. At the present time it seems likely that the entry into a bacterial cell of most organic metabolites and certain inorganic ions is catalyzed by these specific systems.

TABLE III

Inhibition of the synthesis of galactoside permease by chloramphenicol, β-2-thienylalanine, or deficiency of an amino acid

Additions to the culture medium	TMG accumulated as % of bacterial dry weight
Methionine, 10^{-4} M; TMG, 10^{-3} M	1·8
No methionine; TMG, 10^{-3} M	0·1
Methionine, 10^{-4} M; TMG, 10^{-3} M + chloramphenicol, 50 μg/ml	0·0
Methionine, 10^{-4} M; TMG, 10^{-3} M + β-2-thienylalanine, 10^{-4} M	0·0

A mutant of E. coli, *requiring methionine, is grown in synthetic media containing maltose with the additions noted. After one hour, the cultures are centrifuged, and the galactoside permease is measured using radioactive methyl-β-thiogalactoside (TMG).*

The generic name *permeases* has been adopted to designate the specific proteins involved in this catalysis (1). The definition of a permease implies: 1) the presence of a specialized protein, 2) its stereospecificity, 3) its functional specialization, that is, its distinctness from metabolic enzymes involved in the utilization of the substance under study.

The permease which has been studied most is β-galactoside permease (1, 2); we shall try to justify such a name in terms of the criteria listed above. β-galactoside permease, like β-galactosidase, is an inducible system. This means that it is demonstrable only in cells whose growth has taken place in the presence of a compound containing an unsubstituted galactoside radical. No other saccharide possesses this property of inducing the system. Measurement of the permease can be made with thiogalactosides (3), which are not substrates of β-galactosidase but excellent inducers of the permease and galactosidase. With the use of thiogalactosides, the activity of the permease can be measured by estimating the quantity of intracellular radioactivity, which can be attributed wholly to the unmetabolized thiogalactoside.

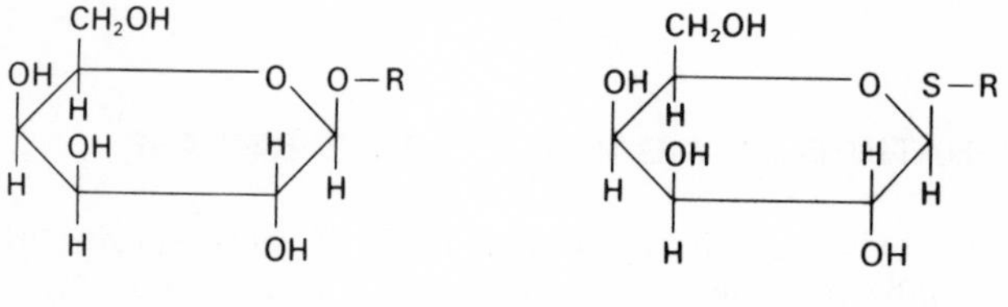

FIGURE 1 A galactoside A thiogalactoside

Induction of the permease is effective only under conditions which allow protein synthesis; it is blocked by chloramphenicol or deficiency of an amino acid. A significant fact is the inhibition of its synthesis in the presence of certain amino acid analogs, which do not inhibit protein synthesis but are incorporated in place of the natural amino acid, leading to the synthesis of inactive proteins (Table III).

It is therefore likely that induction corresponds to the synthesis of a specific protein, a necessary component of the permeation system. The kinetics of this induction follow a simple law: after a rapid acceleration phase due to synthesis of a specific messenger RNA, the permease activity increases linearly with bacterial mass (fig. 2). We can write:

$$\Delta Y = p\Delta x$$

where Y represents the quantity of permease, p the rate of synthesis and Δx the increase in bacterial mass after the addition of the inducer. This relationship is typical of inducible enzymes and suggests the possibility of a *de novo* synthesis of a protein.

Another characteristic of inducible enzymes, which also applies to β-galactoside permease, is the inhibition of their induction by the presence of glucose in the culture medium.

Amber mutants of β-galactoside permease are known: these mutants are

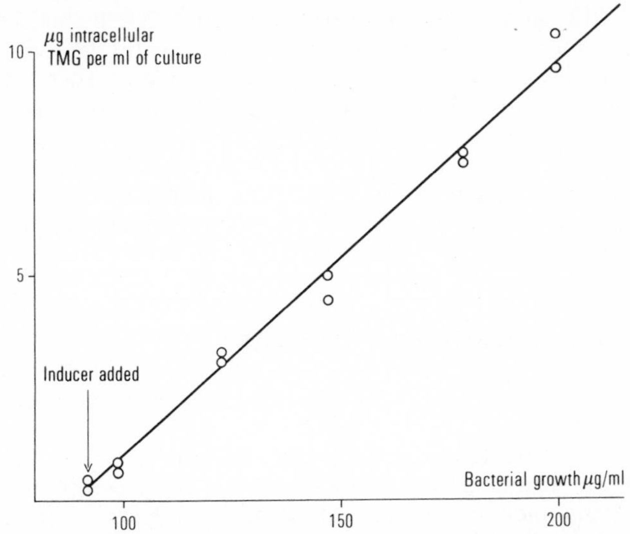

FIGURE 2

Induced synthesis of galactoside permease in growing *E. coli*. Carbon source: succinate. Inducer: methyl-β-thiogalactoside (TMG) 5×10^{-4} M. The increase in total permease activity is seen to be proportional to the increase in bacterial mass effectively from the moment of addition of inducer.

characterized by their inability to translate the genetic information of DNA into the corresponding protein sequence. This inability can be corrected if the bacterial genome contains a suppressor gene. The mode of action of the suppressor is to synthesize a modified transfer RNA capable of reading the nonsense codon determined by the *amber* mutation. This correction results in the synthesis of a protein which can be active, while differing from the protein of the wild type by one amino acid. The possibility of obtaining suppressions of the *amber* mutation in a cistron corresponding to the genetic locus of the permease is a powerful argument in favour of the protein nature of permeases (4).

Certain arguments are more direct: β-galactoside permease is a system which depends on the integrity of —SH groups; it is inhibited by *p*-mercuribenzoate, this inhibition being partially abolished by cysteine or reduced glutathione. Substrates of the permease, the thiogalactosides, protect against inactivation, the protection being in proportion to their affinity for the system, showing that the mercurial acts directly on the supposed protein component.

Quite recently, the hypothesis about the protein nature of the stereospecific permease component has received direct support from experiments carried out by Fox and Kennedy (5). We shall summarize the main results.

When intact cells are treated with N-ethylmaleimide, a reagent for —SH groups, the permease activity is strongly inhibited. Protection occurs with thiodigalactoside, a substrate with a very strong affinity for the permease.

Permease in the cells is labelled with radioactive N-ethylmaleimide as follows: non-radioactive N-ethylmaleimide reacts with the cells in the presence of thiodigalactoside which protects the permease. After centrifugation to remove excess N-ethylmaleimide and thiodigalactoside, the cells are treated with radioactive N-ethylmaleimide in the absence of the galactoside protector. Analysis shows that the labelled protein has the following properties: its synthesis is inducible; it is distinct from β-galactosidase and galactoside transacetylase; it is localized in the fraction containing proteins of the membrane.

KINETICS OF β-GALACTOSIDE PERMEASE (1,6)

The stereospecificity of this system cannot be studied without an outline of its kinetic properties.

Initial studies used the following technique: bacteria in exponential phase were exposed to a radioactive thiogalactoside, in the presence of a usable energy source but under conditions where protein synthesis was not possible (to avoid permease synthesis during the experiment). After a given time, samples were chilled, centrifuged, decanted and the intracellular thiogalactoside was extracted with hot water (2). It was quickly established that the value of the intracellular concentration (G_{in}) at equilibrium was related to the extracellular (G_{ex}) by a relationship of the Langmuir isotherm type:

$$G_{in} = Y\frac{G_{ex}}{K + G_{ex}} \qquad (Equation\ 1)$$

in which K is the apparent dissociation constant, Y another constant called "capacity", which expresses the maximum quantity that the cells can accumulate when the concentration of a given galactoside in the medium is saturating. The "specific capacity" is defined as the capacity in micromoles per gram dry cells.

Figure 3, in reciprocal coordinates, represents the hyperbolic relationship between the external and internal concentrations of galactoside at equilibrium.

During the induction of β-galactoside permease, the capacity Y per unit volume of culture increases in proportion to the increase in bacterial mass per unit volume, but the specific capacity tends towards a limiting value characteristic of the bacterial strain used, in a given set of conditions. On the other hand, the value of K remains constant throughout the induction.

The technique of rapid filtration on membranes (7) enabled kinetic studies to be done. As a result, it was possible not only to investigate the capacity at equilibrium, but to measure the initial velocity of the increase in concentration in the interior of the cells. Penetration begins without lag at its maximum rate, the rate finally diminishing to zero. The intracellular level

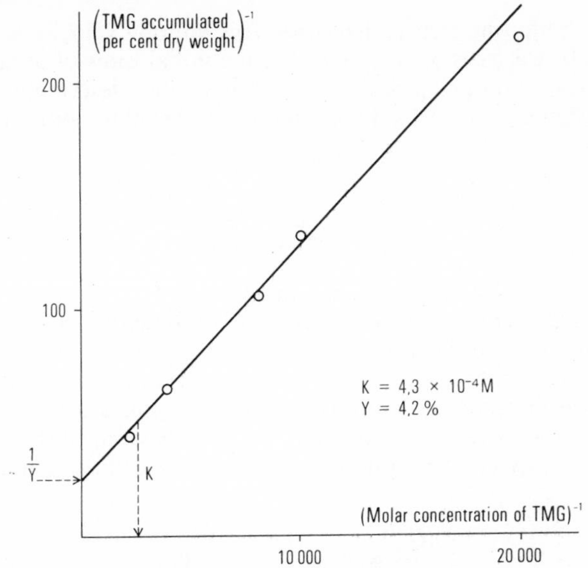

FIGURE 3

Accumulation of radioactive thiogalactoside (TMG) as a function of external concentration. Y and K are the constants of the preceding equation.

reached remains constant for at least one hour. The time required to reach half the maximum value of the intracellular concentration varies from 0·25 minute (for thiophenylgalactoside) to 2·5 minutes (for lactose) at 25°C. Turnover of intracellular thiogalactoside takes place during the steady state at the same rate as the initial uptake (fig. 4). The intracellular concentration reaches the same asymptote. The equality of the rates of the initial increase in concentration and the turnover tends to show that in these two

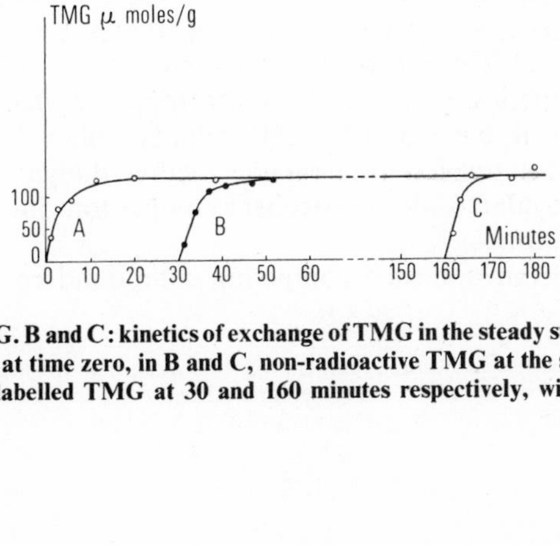

FIGURE 4

Kinetics of uptake of TMG. B and C: kinetics of exchange of TMG in the steady state. In A, radioactive TMG (10^{-3} M) is added at time zero, in B and C, non-radioactive TMG at the same concentration is added at time zero and labelled TMG at 30 and 160 minutes respectively, without change in final concentration.

cases the rate-limiting step is the same. This limiting velocity is referred to here as V_{in}. It was possible to show that the initial rates of uptake and exchange obey a relationship of the same form as that describing the plateau value of accumulation as a function of extracellular concentration (see equation 1).

$$V_{in} = V_{in}^{max} \frac{G_{ex}}{K_m + G_{ex}} \qquad (Equation\ 2)$$

In this equation, K_m is the same as K in equation 1.

Equation 2 represents a simplification of what actually occurs. In fact, the process of uptake into the cell is counter-balanced by an exit process, which behaves as a first order reaction, that is, one whose rate is proportional to the value of the intracellular concentration. However, this exit process does not seem to correspond to a free diffusion. To take account of this new factor, the equation describing the rate of uptake of intracellular galactoside can be written:

$$\frac{dG_{in}}{dt} = y\frac{G_{ex}}{K_m + G_{ex}} - cG_{in} \qquad (Equation\ 3)$$

In this equation, c represents the exit rate constant and y the activity of the permease. If one puts $y/c = Y$, equation 3 leads to equation 1 under steady state conditions (where $dG_{in}/dt = 0$). Under conditions where the rate constant is indeed constant, the steady state level of intracellular galactoside is found to be proportional to the activity of the permease.[1]

STEREOSPECIFICITY OF β-GALACTOSIDE PERMEASE

Once the steady state is reached, addition of a non-radioactive galactoside to the medium brings about a release of radioactive material into the medium (fig. 5). The replacement of labelled galactoside by non-radioactive galactoside follows the classical law observed in the case of competition for a common site (fig. 6). This allows measurement of apparent affinity constants for all the competing compounds. Only those having an unsubstituted galactoside radical have a detectable affinity; phenyl thioglucoside for example, does not displace radioactive methyl thiogalactoside; it differs from phenyl thiogalactoside, an excellent competitor, only by inversion of a hydroxyl in position 4.

The affinity constant for each competing compound can be measured in-

1. The reader who wishes to become familiar with the more detailed aspects of the kinetics of catalyzed permeation should refer to the general published reviews by Cohen and Monod (1) and Képès and Cohen (6).

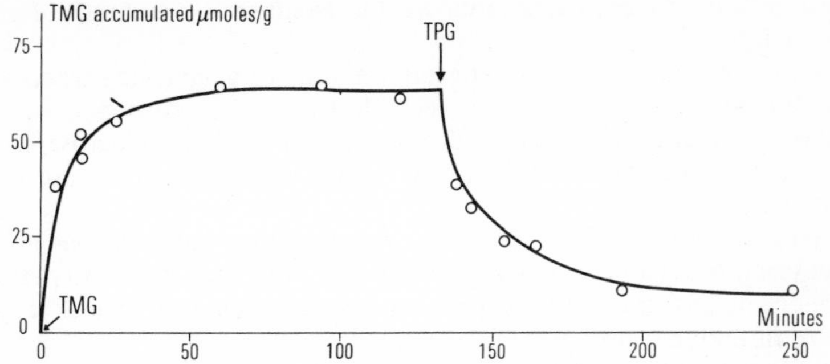

FIGURE 5

Accumulation of methyl-β-thiogalactoside by induced bacteria. Non-radioactive phenyl-β-thiogalactoside (TPG) was added at the point shown by an arrow. The experiment was carried out at 0°C to enable the kinetics to be followed.

dependently by using it as a substrate. The two values thus obtained are in excellent agreement.

FUNCTIONAL SPECIALIZATION OF β-GALACTOSIDE PERMEASE

The identification of the permease as an autonomous system poses the problem of distinguishing it from the hydrolytic enzyme, β-galactosidase.

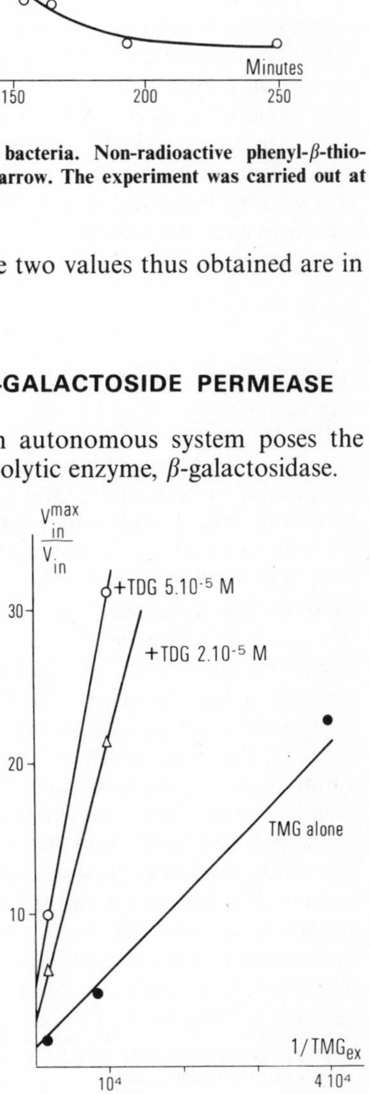

FIGURE 6

Representation in reciprocal coordinates of the rate of uptake of radioactive methyl thiogalactoside alone or in the presence of two different concentrations of thiodigalactoside.

This question has been answered by the isolation of mutants of *E. coli* of two kinds:

1) mutants which accumulate normal amounts of galactoside when grown on TMG but do not form any detectable traces of β-galactosidase. These organisms can accumulate up to 20% of their dry weight in lactose, without being able to metabolize it. They are unable to grow on lactose as sole carbon source.

2) cryptic mutants which when grown in very high concentrations of TMG synthesize normal amounts of β-galactosidase but very little or no permease. These organisms can no longer grow on lactose, because they lack a system capable of taking it up.

The existence of these two types of mutant shows that β-galactosidase and permease are genetically and functionally distinct and that they constitute a metabolic sequence *in vivo*. The genes which control the synthesis of the two systems have been named z and y respectively, the symbols z^- and y^- denoting mutants incapable of synthesizing galactosidase and permease respectively.

AMINO ACID PERMEASES (8)

At the same time as the work on β-galactoside permease was being carried out, the same group of investigators found evidence in *E. coli* of permeases specific for amino acids. One permease catalyzed the uptake of L-valine, L-leucine and L-isoleucine, amino acids with very similar structures[1]; another brought about the entry into the cells of L-methionine and its structural analog, L-norleucine. A third permease was later found, which catalyzed the permeation of the aromatic amino acids. Other systems have subsequently been described for histidine, arginine, proline, etc. . . .

Just as mutants lacking in β-galactoside permease activity have been isolated, mutants lacking in one or other of the specific amino acid permeases were easily selected by the following procedure (9). Advantage was taken of the fact that the same permease catalyzes the active transport of the natural amino acid and its structural analogs. These structural analogs are often inhibitors of bacterial growth, the inhibition being due to the incorporation of the antimetabolite into the protein in place of the natural counterpart. The desired mutants, lacking a specific amino acid permease, will no longer be able to bring about the uptake of the analog and will escape its toxic action. In practice, 10^9 bacterial cells are spread on a solid medium containing the nutrients required for their growth plus an inhibitory concentration of antimetabolite. Resistant cells produce colonies. Some of these bacteria are lacking in the corresponding permease; for example, it has been

1. This protein has recently been crystallized (8*a*) and shown to occur between the cell wall and the cytoplasmic membrane (8*b*).

possible to isolate bacteria without the permease specific for arginine from canavanine resistant colonies, bacteria unable to take up glycine by using D-serine, bacteria negative for histidine permease from triazole-alanine resistant colonies, etc.

Other techniques have been used (10) and nearly all the amino acid specific permeases have been identified and often the genes which control their synthesis have been localized.

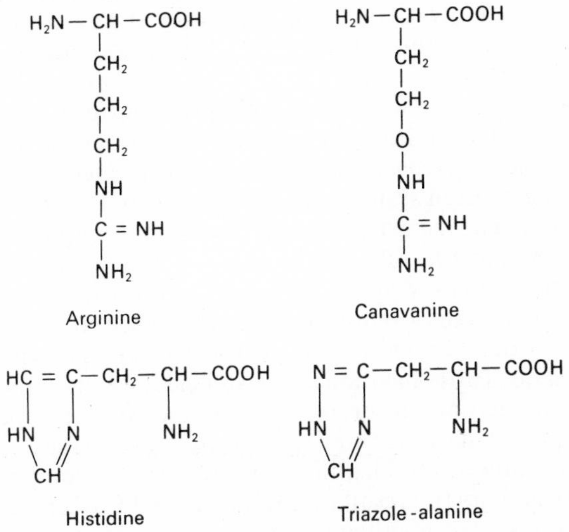

FIGURE 7

Structural formulas of some amino acids and their analogs which have allowed the selection of mutants negative for the specific permeases.

The experimental approach which could have been used if these permeases were inducible is not available: they are constitutive, and it is not possible to study easily the action of reagents which interfere with protein synthesis, in contrast to β-galactoside permease.

An attempt which has promise for the isolation of a protein specific for the permeation of proline has recently been made by Kaback and Stadtman (11). Isolated membranes were prepared from *E. coli*. The preparations appeared in the electron microscope as sacs of diameter varying from 0·1 to 1·5 μ. These sacs are surrounded by one to four membrane layers of thickness 65–70 Å. Chemical analysis of these preparations shows that they contain no cytoplasmic structures. These membranes are capable of taking up proline, a process which depends on an energy source. Membranes prepared from bacteria lacking in proline permease are incapable of concentrating proline. These results show that the preparation and the activity which can be measured *in vivo* are one and the same.

OTHER BACTERIAL PERMEASES

Transport and accumulation of galactose in *E. coli* has characteristics very similar to those described for β-galactosides (12). Almost all the work relating to this system has been carried out with mutants lacking in galactokinase, so that galactose is a substrate of the permease and is not further metabolized, a condition *sine qua non* for the rigorous characterization of a permease. A maltose permease has been similarly characterized in the same organism and in closely related organisms (13), as have a glucuronide permease (14), an α-glucoside permease (15, 16), an arabinose permease (17), etc.

Specific systems are responsible for the active transport of the K^+ ion in *E. coli*, the PO_4^{3-} ion in *Staphylococcus aureus*, the citrate ion in a *Pseudomonas* species and in *Aerobacter aerogenes*. In *Pseudomonas*, there probably exist specific permeation systems for each of the isomers of tartaric acid (18) and it is possible that the extraordinary discriminatory power which helped Pasteur to separate the different isomers of this acid using *Penicillium glaucum* was based mainly on the permeases of this organism.

A stereospecific uptake of biotin has been described in *Lactobacillus arabinosus* (19). It would be tedious to go through every permeation system described to date. Those mentioned are sufficient to show the generality of the existence in microorganisms of stereospecific systems of permeation.

One case however, the active transport of sulfate, deserves more attention, because it has allowed the identification of a protein component endowed with a positive activity (we recall that Kennedy and Fox's fraction is inactive due to the reaction of N-ethylmaleimide with a group necessary for the β-galactoside permease activity, and that the activity measured by Kaback and Stadtman is still bound to subcellular structures). The organism used for this study by Pardee, Prestidge and their co-workers (20, 21), is a mutant of *Salmonella typhimurium* bearing a deletion affecting the first two enzymes in the metabolism of sulfate, but retaining an active system for its uptake. The synthesis of sulfate permease is repressed if growth of this organism has taken place in the presence of cysteine. Other mutants are incapable of carrying out active transport but can regain this capacity by reversion or transduction. It is therefore possible to compare organisms with and without sulfate permease. Pardee and Prestidge used as a measure of the capacity to bind sulfate, the property of the cells or their extracts of displacing sulfate previously attached to a column of ion exchange resin. Only derepressed cells (grown in the absence of cysteine) and their extracts were able to bind sulfate. A protein fraction possessing this property can be purified from extracts by chromatography on DEAE-cellulose and hydroxylapatite. This fraction is homogeneous in gel electrophoresis. From the number of fixation sites per mg of protein and the behaviour of this protein during gel filtration on Sephadex, it can be deduced that the property of combination with sulfate ion is contained in a protein of molecular weight about 32,000.

This protein has recently been crystallized (21a). This work provides the first experimental data on a protein component in active transport, whose parameters can be measured by a method independent of the intracellular accumulation.

A recent observation (22, 23) suggests that other constituents of the permeation system, not possessing the same stereospecificity as the true permeases, will soon be demonstrated. A phosphotransferase has recently been isolated from several bacteria (22). It catalyzes the transfer of phosphate from phosphoenolpyruvate to certain hexoses. This phosphotransferase has been separated into three distinct protein fractions called Enzyme I, Enzyme II and phospho-HPr. The last is thermostable. Enzyme II is found in the membrane fraction, while the two other fractions appear to be cytoplasmic. Enzyme I has been purified 300 times and the thermostable protein 10,000 times. Enzyme II has not yet been solubilized; it seems to be responsible for the specificity for the monosaccharide phosphate acceptor, which varies with the composition of the growth medium. Enzyme II in fact represents a family of inducible enzymes, and fractions have been obtained which respectively catalyze the phosphorylation of α-methyl glucoside, galactose and methyl thiogalactoside. In the presence of Mg^{++}, enzymes I and II catalyze the following reactions:

$$
\begin{array}{rcl}
\text{Phosphoenolpyruvate} + \text{HPr} & \rightleftarrows & \text{Pyruvate} + \text{Phospho-HPr} \\
\text{Phospho-HPr} + \text{Sugar} & \longrightarrow & \text{HPr} + \text{Sugar phosphate} \\
\hline
\text{sum: Phosphoenolpyruvate} + \text{Sugar} & \longrightarrow & \text{Pyruvate} + \text{Sugar phosphate}
\end{array}
$$

The phosphate of the phosphorylated protein HPr is bound to a histidine residue. If *E. coli* is submitted to osmotic shock (23), the cells lose between 50 and 80% of their HPr fraction, and their capacity to accumulate α-methyl glucoside or methyl thiogalactoside is lost simultaneously to the same extent. When such cells are incubated with the purified thermostable protein, they recover their initial capacity for accumulation. These results suggest that the phosphotransferase system may be a component of the permease systems for glycosides. This point has been very recently substantiated by the finding that mutants unable to synthesize a normal Hpr or Enzyme I have lost simultaneously the capacity to utilize numerous carbohydrates (23a).

2

Regulation of Enzyme Activity
Allosteric Enzymes

One of the most remarkable properties of the cell is its capacity to coordinate its differential biochemical activities. A steady state is thus maintained between the different catabolic processes and the thousands of synthetic reactions necessary for reproduction of the species.

The last ten years has seen a striking advance in our knowledge of numerous regulatory processes, and in our understanding of their metabolic functions. The present chapter will be confined to an examination of the properties common to many enzymes whose activity is subject to metabolic regulation. In the following chapters, which will deal with particular catabolic or anabolic reactions, these controls will be examined in detail.

Other control mechanisms relating to the *de novo* synthesis of enzymes, induction and repression, will be dealt with briefly later.

It was evident from experiments carried out some fifteen years ago with *Escherichia coli* that each end product of a biosynthetic sequence is part of the system responsible for regulating its synthesis (24). The *de novo* synthesis of different amino acids from glucose is halted when these amino acids are added to the growth medium. The mechanisms which underlie this control by end products became clear when it was shown that each of these essential metabolites possesses the property of *repressing* the synthesis of one or several of the enzymes belonging to its biosynthetic pathway (25, 26, 27, 28) and also of *inhibiting* the activity of the early enzymes (often the first enzyme) in the pathway (29, 30).

These two distinct control mechanisms depend on separate genes, as shown by the existence of mutants with one or other of the controls modified. A recent review gives many examples (31).

The two mechanisms can function independently of each other; nevertheless they often occur in the regulation of the same metabolic pathway.

Which are the enzymes subject to control? Every highly complex metabolic system contains some reactions which produce intermediates occurring at branch points. The branches may be different biosyntheses, or mixtures of degradative and biosynthetic pathways. In this entangled network of reactions, certain enzyme activities occur at strategic points where their regulation becomes important for the preservation of the delicate equilibrium required to integrate the different metabolic functions. During evolution, natural selection retained those enzymatic species with structures best suited to act as targets for activations or inhibitions of a regulatory nature. The existence of control systems is probably the principal basis on which all teleological arguments are built. Natural selection of these systems can make every natural phenomenon appear useful.

PROPERTIES OF ENZYMES WHOSE ACTIVITIES ARE SUBJECT TO CONTROL

The examination of a large number of enzymes subject to control reveals certain common characteristics, structural as well as kinetic, which are not generally found for other enzymes.

Allosteric regulation 1.1.

The most fundamental characteristic of all the control enzymes is their ability to be activated or inhibited by metabolites other than their substrates (32). This is the property which enables them to be recognized and on which their functional classification is based. Often, there is no structural similarity between "effectors" (activators or inhibitors) and substrates. A few examples will be sufficient to substantiate this:

L-isoleucine is a specific inhibitor and L-valine a specific activator of L-threonine deaminase, the first enzyme involved specifically in the synthesis of isoleucine. It could be argued that these compounds are analogs of L-threonine because they share a carboxyl and an amino group in the same configuration. However, threonine deaminase is not inhibited by any amino acid other than isoleucine. The D-isomer of this amino acid has no inhibitory effect. Many other cases of strict specificity together with absence of structural relationship between effector and substrate can be quoted in order to make a general rule. Let us take the case of aspartate transcarbamylase, the first enzyme in the biosynthetic sequence for pyrimidines; in *E. coli*, this enzyme is inhibited by cytidine triphosphate and activated by adenosine triphosphate. Examination of the structural formulas of the substrates and the inhibitor (fig. 8) is enough to show that no similarity exists between them. Likewise, in the bacterium *Rhodopseudomonas spheroides*, hemin inhibits the synthesis of δ-aminolevulinic acid from glycine and succinyl CoA. This acid is the compound at which porphyrin synthesis diverges from the common catabolic path (see fig. 9 for the structures of the compounds cited).

The very fact that the effector is not a steric analog of the substrate has led

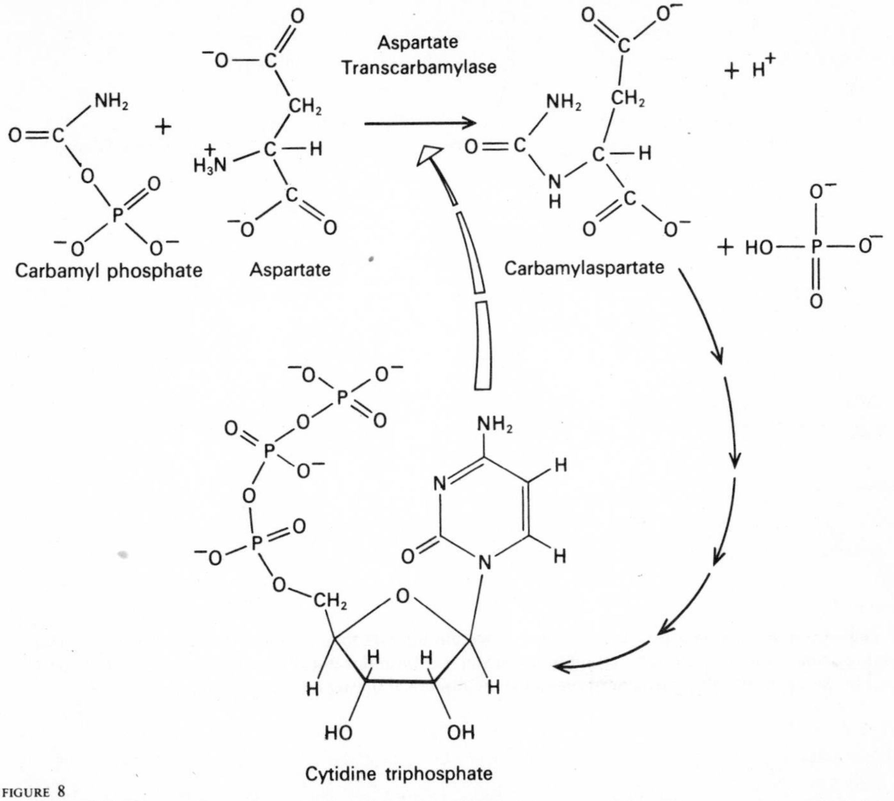

FIGURE 8

Scheme for feed-back inhibition in the synthesis of pyrimidines in *E. coli*.

to the name *allosteric effector* being given to it, and the name *allosteric site* to the sites on the enzyme for which these effectors have affinity. By extension, enzymes subject to control by these effectors are called *allosteric proteins or enzymes.* This terminology, proposed only a few years ago (33), has been universally adopted and the term *allosteric* is being increasingly used to describe the interaction of any small molecule, including substrates, with binding sites other than the site responsible for the catalytic activity of the enzyme.

Kinetic properties 1.2.

One of the most frequent characteristics (but not universal) of allosteric enzymes is the atypical relationships between the activity and the substrate or effector concentration. For the majority of enzymes, this relationship is described by a rectangular hyperbola, representing graphically the Henri-Michaelis equation (fig. 10). In the case of many enzymes subject to allosteric control, the relationship is represented by a sigmoid curve (fig. 11). Such a

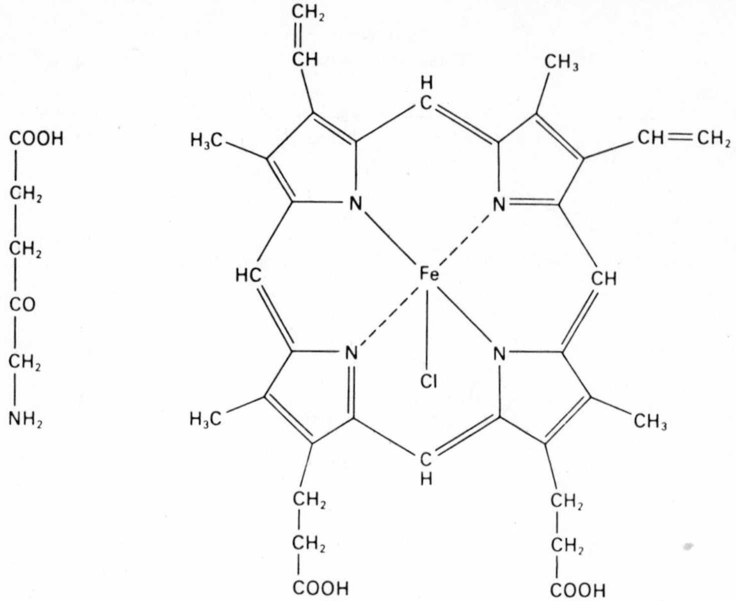

FIGURE 9

δ-aminolevulinic acid is a precursor of hemin. Hemin inhibits the synthesis of δ-aminolevulinic acid from simpler precursors. Examination of the structural formulas above shows that even with the best will in the world, no structural similarities can be discerned between these compounds.

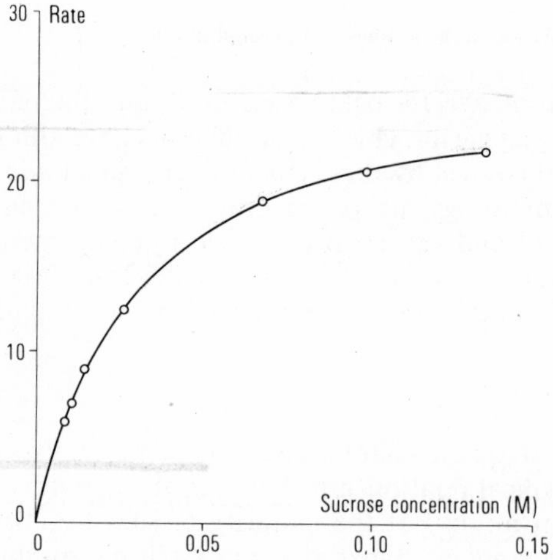

FIGURE 10

Hyperbolic relationship between the concentration of sucrose and its rate of hydrolysis by invertase.

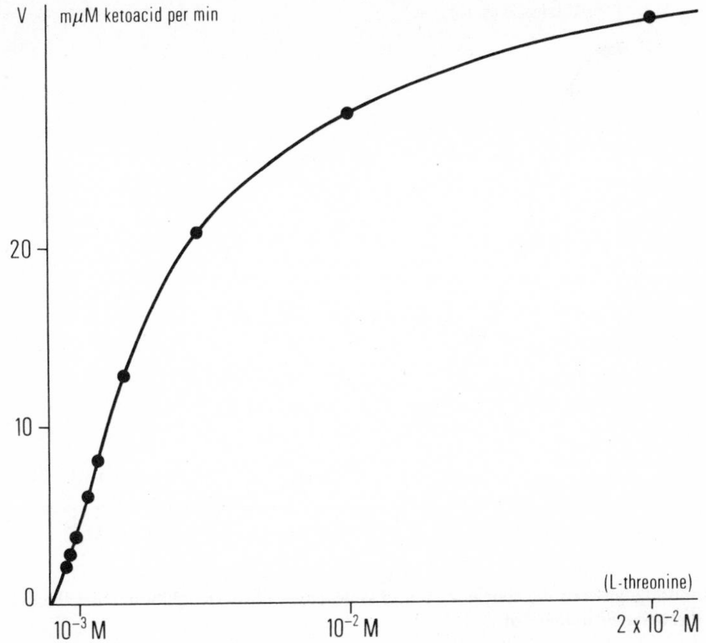

FIGURE 11

Sigmoid relationship between threonine concentration and the rate of its deamination by threonine deaminase.

curve indicates that at least two molecules of substrate react with the enzyme and the binding of one molecule of substrate in some way makes the binding of the second easier. Expressed in another way, there is a co-operative effect in binding more than one substrate molecule to the enzyme. One often finds similar co-operative interactions in the binding of allosteric effectors (fig. 12) which suggests that allosteric enzymes contain more than one allosteric site per molecule.

Although the molecular basis of co-operative interactions is still not known, it is certain that these interactions reflect some fundamental property. Whatever the mechanism may be, a sigmoidal response of the enzymatic activity to increasing concentrations of substrate or effector is in practice a "threshold" effect. At concentrations lower than the threshold, the enzymatic activity is effectively unaltered by changes in substrate or effector concentration, but on crossing the threshold, important activity changes are obtained by only slight changes in concentration. These threshold effects make the adjustment of enzymatic activity very sensitive to minimal variations in concentration within a narrow range.

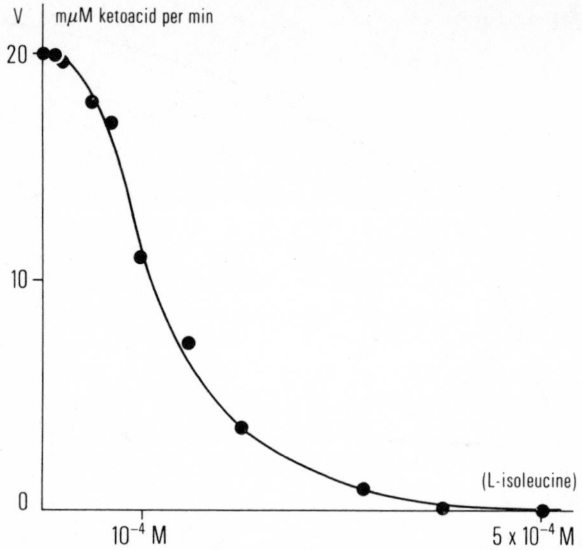

FIGURE 12

Sigmoid relationship between the concentration of isoleucine (allosteric inhibitor) and the activity of biosynthetic threonine deaminase of *E. coli*.

Allosteric inhibition 1.3.

Classical kinetic analysis (for example with the graphical method of Lineweaver and Burk) of the enzyme inhibitions caused by allosteric effectors shows that the inhibitions are reversible, and can be competitive, non-competitive or mixed, with kinetics quite often obeying very complex laws. When inhibition is non-competitive or mixed, the inhibitor clearly attaches itself to sites which are distinct from the catalytic site. Competitive inhibition is more difficult to explain. In the case of "classical" enzymes, competitive inhibitions are obtained with steric analogs of the substrate, and it is reasonable to assume that the substrate and the inhibitor compete with each other for occupation of the catalytic site. In some of the cases of interest here, the absence of structural similarity between the highly specific allosteric inhibitors and the substrates of the enzymes which they inhibit seems to exclude the possibility of such a competition, since the catalytic sites are usually characterized by a strict degree of specificity. In fact, allosteric effectors, even competitive ones, have been found to bind to sites separate from the catalytic sites; numerous allosteric enzymes can be made insensitive to their allosteric effectors (*desensitized*) without their catalytic activity being affected; in one case at least, it has been possible to physically separate the different sub-units of an allosteric enzyme subject to competitive inhibition, one kind of sub-unit bearing the catalytic site, and the other the allosteric site. This proves definitely that the two sites are situated on different parts of the enzyme macromolecule, and that the apparent competitive inhibition by these allosteric inhibitors does not result from a direct interaction with the catalytic site. Rather, the inevitable conclusion is that the binding of the inhibitor to its allosteric site causes a conformational change in the protein which results in a diminished affinity for substrate at the catalytic site.

Allosteric activators 1.4.

Some allosteric effectors act by causing conformational changes which increase the affinity for substrate.
In the case of enzymes showing a sigmoidal relationship between their activity and substrate concentration, the addition of these effectors (activators) changes the sigmoid relationship to a hyperbolic one. In some cases however, the transition from a higher order reaction to a unimolecular one is only an apparent change, and arises from a compression of the scale of the graph (36). In one case at least, it could be shown that the order of the reaction did not change although the kinetics passed from a typical sigmoidal nature to apparent Michaelis behavior.
In a number of cases, it is found that allosteric activators permit a "modulation" of the enzymatic activity to the advantage of the cell, as in the case of the threshold effects described above for allosteric inhibitors.

DESENSITIZATION WITH RESPECT TO ALLOSTERIC EFFECTORS

Allosteric enzymes can be desensitized by treatment with mercurials, by cold, dialysis, freezing, urea, treatment with proteolytic reagents, high ionic strengths, changes in pH, or heat treatment. Finally, the sensitivity to allosteric compounds can be modified or lost by mutation. The desensitization is often accompanied by a normalization of the kinetics to unimolecular type. As noted above, desensitization without loss of catalytic activity is an argument in favor of the independent existence of the two kinds of site.

THERMAL INACTIVATION

A number of allosteric enzymes are protected against thermal inactivation by their allosteric effectors (fig. 13). Such effects are thought to be attributable to an increased stability of the catalytic site due to conformational changes which accompany the reversible binding of allosteric ligands to their specific sites.

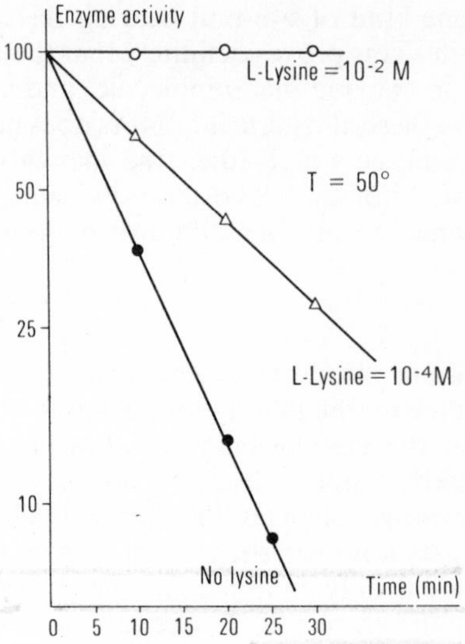

FIGURE 13

Protection of *E. coli* aspartokinase III against inactivation by heat. The enzyme is denatured by heat with first order kinetics; the inactivation can be completely prevented by the presence of L-lysine, a specific allosteric inhibitor of this aspartokinase (P. Truffa-Bachi and G. N. Cohen, Biochim. Biophys. Acta, 113 (1966) 531).

SENSITIVITY TO COLD

Some allosteric enzymes undergo a reversible inactivation on cooling to about 0°C. This inactivation is sometimes accompanied by a dissociation or association of the enzyme. The presence of allosteric effectors gives protection against the inactivation and molecular changes. It is thought that cold sensitivity is due to a change in conformation depending on interactions between hydrophobic regions in the protein.

POLYMERIC NATURE OF ALLOSTERIC ENZYMES

All carefully studied allosteric enzymes appear to be made up of sub-units. Reversible associations or dissociations are found with some of them, and these reactions may or may not be accompanied by inactivation or a number of changes in susceptibility to allosteric effectors. This absence of a general rule would indicate that association and dissociation are not inherent in the so-called allosteric effects. Nevertheless, it is possible that such an absence indicates that the strength of the interactions controlling the binding between sub-units differs from enzyme to enzyme in such a way as to allow or forbid an association or dissociation.

On the other hand, the polymeric nature of allosteric enzymes is a decisive element in the formation of ideas about the mechanism of allosteric regulation. We shall examine in turn some of the theories which have been put forward to account for the observed facts.

THE MODEL OF MONOD, WYMAN AND CHANGEUX (34)

The model proposed by these authors is described according to the following hypotheses:

1. Allosteric proteins are oligomers whose protomers are associated in such a way that they all occupy equivalent positions. This implies that the molecule possesses at least one axis of symmetry.
2. On each protomer there exists one and only one site capable of forming a stereospecific complex with a given ligand. In other words, the symmetry of each group of stereospecific sites is the same as the symmetry of the molecule.
3. The conformation of each protomer is constrained by its association with the other protomers.
4. There are at least two states in equilibrium in which allosteric oligomers can exist. These states differ in the distribution and/or energy of the inter-protomer bonds, and accordingly in the conformational constraints imposed on the protomers.
5. As a result, the affinity of one or several of the stereospecific sites for the corresponding ligand is modified when there is a transition from one state to the other.
6. During these transitions, the molecular symmetry and the symmetry of the conformational constraints is conserved.

Let us try to analyze the consequences of this model: in the absence of substrates or allosteric effectors, the distribution of molecular species among the different states will be a function of the free energies of formation of these states, which are in turn determined by the strength of the interactions between protomers of the different states. In the case where a given ligand has a greater affinity for one of the conformational states, the presence of this ligand at low concentration will result in the preferential binding of a single ligand molecule to the protomer in the state for which it has the greater affinity. This will bring about a displacement of the equilibrium in favor of that state, and will thus facilitate the subsequent binding of additional ligand molecules, because of the simultaneous formation of more than one reactive site (the exact number will depend on the number of identical protomers in the oligomer). It is evident that the sigmoid relationship between activity and substrate (or effector) concentration is explained perfectly by this model. Monod, Wyman and Changeux have elaborated a mathematical treatment of the model which accounts for most of the experimental observations obtained with a good many allosteric enzymes. However, other mathematical models, based on totally different assumptions, can also predict the kinetic behaviour of allosteric enzymes. The greatest quality of the model of Monod, Wyman and Changeux is that it takes into account the oligomeric nature of this class of enzyme. The model describes the tendency of certain allosteric enzymes to dissociate or associate under the influence of stereo-specific ligands or the medium (pH, temperature, mercurials, etc.). Nevertheless, as we noted above, the state of aggregation is not always connected with the effect of allosteric effectors on the catalytic activity, nor are co-operative effects always accompanied by allosteric transitions which involve changes in the substrate or effector affinity constants.

The main merit of the model is that it is suitable for experimental analysis. What more could one ask of a model?

OTHER MODELS (35, 36)

KOSHLAND

Other workers have proposed different models which account for sigmoid saturation curves. One theory, proposed by Koshland *et al.* (35), involves the flexibility of sites, coupled with classical Michaelis kinetics[1]. These theories differ in detail, but one of them concedes the existence of at least two sites able to combine with substrate, a catalytic site and a regulatory site (74a). There is a further hypothesis that the combination of substrate at the regulatory site induces a conformational change in the enzyme which results in a greater affinity of the substrate for the catalytic site. In this way, co-operative effects between substrate molecules are explained. To account for stimulatory or inhibitory effects of allosteric effectors, the model assumes that the regulatory ligand may complex with the regulatory site (normally occupied by substrate) or perhaps with other specific sites. In both cases, the net result is an increased affinity of the substrate for the enzyme catalytic site in the case of activators, or a decreased affinity in the case of inhibitors. Mathematical developments of these models have been carried out, and in general are compatible with the kinetic results.

COMPARISON OF THE TWO TYPES OF MODEL

If we examine the second kind of model (74a), it differs from that of Monod and co-workers only in one point, a very important one: the nature and number of binding sites for substrate. The M—W—C model predicts the existence of a single site per protomer, while the other model predicts two for the substrate, one of which is to be catalytically active, the other purely regulatory. An unambiguous choice between the two models cannot be made on the basis of kinetic measurements, and in each individual case, it is necessary to have a direct determination of the number and nature of stereo-specific binding sites.

There is no doubt that during the course of evolution, the selection of

1. This model assumes that there exist hybrid states, where some protomers exist in the constrained state and some others in the relaxed state, within the same oligomer.

enzymes whose activity can be regulated in a sigmoid manner in response to increasing concentrations of substrate or allosteric effector. has been advantageous for the species. The fundamental consideration for us here is the fact rather than the precise mechanism. Besides, there is no *a priori* reason for believing that all enzymes subject to allosteric control have become so by the same mechanism. Each case must be investigated individually, and only a study of many allosteric enzymes will decide whether there exists a general rule or whether multifarious mechanisms can lead to the same result.

APPENDIX

It is useful to define two classes of allosteric effects:
a) Homotropic effects, or interactions between identical ligands;
b) Heterotropic effects, or interactions between different ligands.
Homotropic effects seem to be present in most allosteric proteins for at least one type of ligand (substrate, activator or inhibitor). While heterotropic effects may be either co-operative or antagonistic, homotropic effects are always co-operative. Experimental conditions which change heterotropic interactions often change homotropic ones (e.g. the desensitization of threonine deaminase or aspartate transcarbamylase is invariably accompanied by the disappearance of co-operative effects between substrate molecules; in other words, desensitization of these enzymes is connected with a normalization of the kinetics to the Michaelis type (fig. 14)).

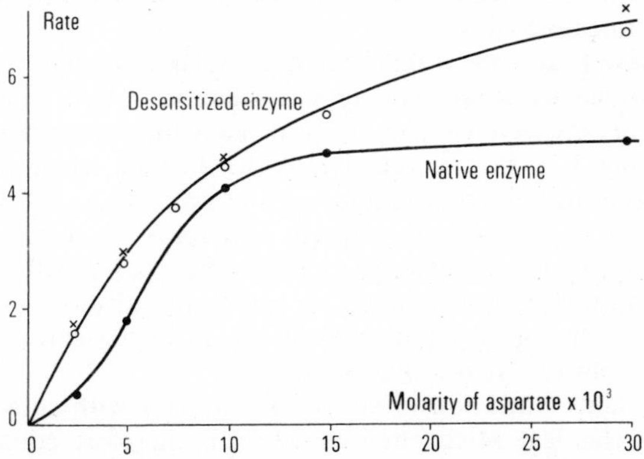

FIGURE 14

Kinetic differences between native *E. coli* aspartate transcarbamylase and the same enzyme desensitized by heating or by a mercurial. Whereas the rate is a sigmoid function of the substrate concentration in the first case, the kinetics are "normalized" in both the cases of desensitization.

In the model of Monod, Wyman and Changeux, two classes of allosteric enzymes can be defined:

1. Those in which the state with the weaker substrate affinity predominates in the absence of substrate. Since the other state has the greater affinity for substrate, the equilibrium is displaced in its favor when substrate is added. The affinity of the whole population of enzyme molecules for substrate thus increases progressively as more molecules of substrate are bound. In contrast, an allosteric inhibitor displaces the equilibrium in the direction of the state with the weaker affinity for substrate.

Enzymes in this category are called allosteric enzymes of type K. The substrate and the effector are both allosteric ligands which affect the equilibrium between the two enzyme states: it is this change in equilibrium that is defined as the allosteric transition. Co-operative homotropic effects are found for both substrate and effector. The presence of the effector modifies the apparent affinity of the enzyme for its substrate and conversely, the substrate concentration affects the value of the apparent affinity of the enzyme for the effector.

2. A second class where the two states of the allosteric enzyme have the same affinity for the substrate. In this case, there is no effect of substrate or effector on the combination of the other ligand with the enzyme. Consequently the effector is able to affect the enzymatic reaction only if the two states differ in their catalytic activity. Depending on whether the effector has a greater affinity for the active or the inactive (or less active) state, it will behave as an activator or an inhibitor.

From the fact that the effector influences only V_{max} in the reaction, and has no effect on the value of K_m, enzymes of this second class can be called allosteric enzymes of type *V*. Here the substrate is not an allosteric ligand, and co-operative interactions are not found between substrate molecules but only between effector molecules.

In practice, pure K systems will behave like enzymes inhibited competitively. The Henri-Michaelis curve will appear sigmoid rather than hyperbolic. Another useful representation is derived from an equation given by Hill in 1910. Letting V_{max} be the velocity of the enzyme when saturated with substrate, and v the velocity obtained at any non-saturating concentration, a plot of $\log[v/(V_{max} - v)]$ as ordinate and $\log S$ as abscissa will give a curve with a linear portion of slope n. The number n (or Hill coefficient) is a measure of the interaction between the different substrate-binding stereospecific sites of the enzyme molecule. If the substrate causes an allosteric transition, n is always greater than unity.

In pure *V* systems, variation of enzymatic activity with substrate concentration obeys classical Michaelis kinetics: n is therefore equal to 1. But if the enzymatic activity is plotted against the inhibitor concentration, a sigmoid relationship is obtained. Plotted as $\log[v/(V_0 - v)]$, where V_0 is the non-inhibited activity and v the activity measured with a given concentration of inhibitor, against log I, a curve is obtained which has a linear portion of negative slope n' which is a measure of the interaction between different inhibitor-binding stereospecific sites of the enzyme molecule.

3

Glycolysis
and its Regulation

We know that the bacterium *Escherichia coli* can grow at the expense of a large number of different carbon sources: glucose and other monosaccharides, disaccharides such as maltose and lactose, glycerol, succinate, glutamate, etc. Disaccharides are first hydrolyzed by specifically induced enzymes and further metabolized as monosaccharides. We shall see later how the individual carbon atoms of sources such as succinate give rise to the precursors necessary for biosyntheses which do not arise directly from the tricarboxylic acid cycle.

Other organisms, for example the genus *Pseudomonas*, can grow on a large variety of carbon sources (amines, tartaric acid, benzene, toluene, naphthalene, mandelic acid, catechol, etc.). The extreme capability of these organisms to adapt to such different carbon sources is described in the classical thesis of den Dooren de Jong (37). Other bacteria, generally anaerobic, can be isolated by enrichment on carbon sources such as uric acid, creatinine, choline, lysine, glutamate, etc., and can even use methane as sole source of carbon.

In all the above cases, the biochemical problem in using the carbon source is to secure useful energy for biosynthesis, usually as ATP. Within these pages, we shall place special emphasis on the utilization of glucose. In many organisms, the substance which is accumulated to provide for the energy requirements is a high polymer composed of glucose units, called glycogen. This polysaccharide is made up of a very long sequence of glucosyl residues linked $1 \rightarrow 4$. Throughout this single-chain structure there are branches, the result of a specific enzyme. The branches are bound to the principal structure by $1 \rightarrow 6$ links.

The utilization of glycogen can be schematically divided into two stages. The first stage produces pyruvic acid, and appears to be identical in mammalian muscle and liver and in yeast, at least so far as the intermediates involved are concerned.

PHOSPHORYLASES

These enzymes catalyze the decomposition of glycogen to glucose 1-phosphate in the presence of inorganic phosphate (38):

$$\text{(Glucosyl 1} \longrightarrow \text{4)}_n\text{-glucose} + \text{n P}_i \rightleftarrows \text{n glucose 1-phosphate}$$

Their main function is to carry out this reaction. We shall see later that another type of enzyme catalyzes the resynthesis of glycogen during gluconeogenesis. The following facts argue strongly in support of a purely degradative role for phosphorylases: *a*) the relative concentrations of inorganic phosphate and glucose 1-phosphate in muscle are in the ratio 300 to 1; *b*) the activation of phosphorylase (see below) is connected with glycogenolysis; *c*) in some muscular dystrophies, in which there is no phosphorylase in the muscle, there is an excess of glycogen.
Phosphorylases degrade and synthesize only linear chains; branches are introduced by the action of other enzymes.

Properties of phosphorylases 1.1.

These enzymes exist in two interconvertible forms, phosphorylase *a* and phosphorylase *b* (39). Phosphorylase *b* is practically inactive in the absence of AMP (40). The two forms of phosphorylase have been crystallized (41). They are characterized by the presence of pyridoxal phosphate (42), and, for phosphorylase *a*, residues of phosphoserine (43). Table IV summarizes some

TABLE IV

Properties of different phosphorylases[1]

Source	Molecular weight	Pyridoxal phosphate per mole of enzyme	Phospho-serine per mole of enzyme	Activity in the absence of AMP	Number of binding sites for AMP	Activation by AMP
Potato	207,000	2	0	100	?	Nil
Liver, *b*	240,000	2	0	0	+	Weak (15%)
Liver, *a*	240,000	2	2	70	+	Weak
Muscle, *b*	242,000	2	0	0	2	Strong
Muscle, *a*	495,000	4	4	65–85	4	Weak

of the properties of the phosphorylases: it is seen at once that muscle phosphorylase *a* has a molecular weight double phosphorylase *b*.

Dissociation of muscle phosphorylase *a* 1.2.

The dissociation can be followed by light scattering measurements on the pure enzyme. Different reagents transform the enzyme of MW 495,000,

1. The molecular weight of muscle phosphorylases has been re-measured recently with great care (43*a*). Values of 185,000 have been found for phosphorylase *b* and 370,000 for phosphorylase *a*. All the data given on these enzymes in this paragraph must be corrected accordingly.

which is a tetramer, to a dimer of MW 242,000, then to smaller sub-units of MW 125,000. The sedimentation coefficients are 13·2 S for the tetramer, 8·2 S for the dimer, and 5·6 S for the sub-units.
Table V summarizes some of the effects obtained upon dissociation of phosphorylase *a*.

TABLE V

Results of the dissociation of phosphorylase a

Cause of dissociation	Result	Enzymatic activity
p-mercuribenzoate	Tetramer *a* → sub-units (5·6 S) Dimer *b* → sub-units (5·6 S)	Inactivation, reversed by cysteine
Removal of pyridoxal phosphate by acid (pH 3·4)	Tetramer → sub-units	Inactivation, reversed by addition of pyridoxal phosphate
Hydrolysis of the phosphoserine by a specific phosphatase	Tetramer → dimer *b*	Reversed by a specific kinase with ATP and Mg^{++}
Limited action of trypsin	Tetramer → dimer *b′*	Irreversible. Product fully active in the presence of AMP
8 M urea	Tetramer → small sub-units (1·9 S)	Inactivation

When the enzyme —SH groups are reacted with *p*-MB or alkylated with iodoacetic acid, the enzyme is inactivated. The transitory formation of a dimer can be detected (44). On reduction by sodium borohydride, the pyridoxal phosphate becomes bound in a stable aldimine linkage with an ε-amino group of a lysine residue of the apoenzyme. Under these conditions, the enzymatic activity is retained (45).
Hydrolysis of the phosphoserine converts form *a* to form *b*. The enzyme catalyzing this conversion is *phosphorylase phosphatase*. It is present in muscle and liver. It is quite specific, and will not dephosphorylate any phosphoprotein other than phosphorylase (46).
Trypsin transforms the tetramer *a* to a dimer *b′*, removing a hexapeptide containing the phosphoserine residue (lys.gluNH_2.ile.serP.val.arg) (43).
Neither pyridoxal phosphate nor the phosphoserine residues are directly involved in the catalytic activity of the enzyme, since the borohydride-reduced Schiff's base is fully active and the phosphorus of the phosphoserine is not exchangeable with the phosphorus of inorganic phosphate or glucose 1-phosphate.

Role of AMP in the activation of phosphorylase 1.3.

Phosphorylase *b* binds two moles of AMP per mole of enzyme, while phosphorylase *a* binds four. The affinity of phosphorylase *b* for inorganic phosphate and glycogen increases with increasing concentrations of AMP; and conversely, increasing concentrations of one or other of the substrates increases the affinity for AMP. These mutual interactions are probably the result of conformational changes in the phosphorylase *b* molecule, as shown in Table VI (48).

TABLE VI

Association of bromothymol blue with muscle phosphorylases

	Moles dye per mole protein (MW 242,000)
Phosphorylase *b*	1·17
Same + 5′-AMP	3·22
Phosphorylase *a*	3·6
Same + 5′-AMP	3·25

The effect of AMP on phosphorylase *b* is reversed by ATP and glucose 6-phosphate (Table VII). In the presence of ATP, the saturation curve for glucose 1-phosphate becomes sigmoid, indicating allosteric interactions between the substrate sites (49).

TABLE VII

Activation of phosphorylase b *by AMP. Reversal of the activating effect of AMP by ATP and glucose 6-phosphate*

Additions	Activity (arbitrary units)
None	0
AMP $1{\cdot}5 \times 10^{-4}$ M	6·1
Same + ATP 8×10^{-3} M	2·2
Same + glucose 6-phosphate 10^{-3} M	2·8
Same + ATP + glucose 6-phosphate	0·6

AMP seems to be able to make good the loss of the serine phosphate, or the removal of the hexapeptide by the action of trypsin. Note that the potato enzyme contains no phosphoserine and is not activated by AMP.

Phosphorylase *b* kinase (50) 1.4.

This enzyme catalyzes the following reaction:

$$2 \text{ phosphorylase } b + 4 \text{ ATP} \xrightarrow{Mg^{++}} \text{Phosphorylase } a + 4 \text{ ADP}$$

The activation of phosphorylase kinase seems to be influenced by hormonal factors, for example adrenaline. The following scheme summarizes current ideas on this subject:

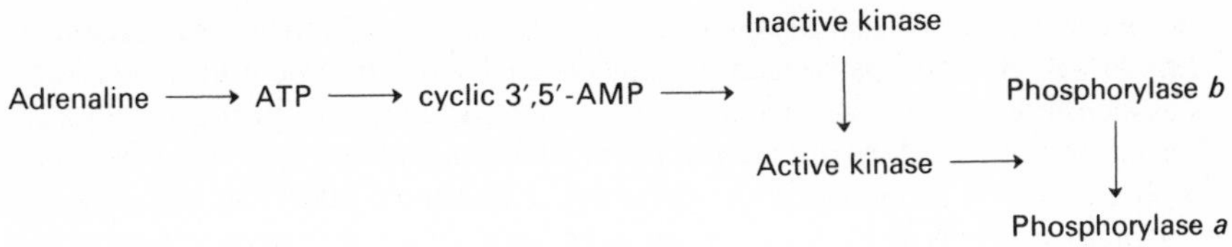

Muscular contraction has an analogous effect:

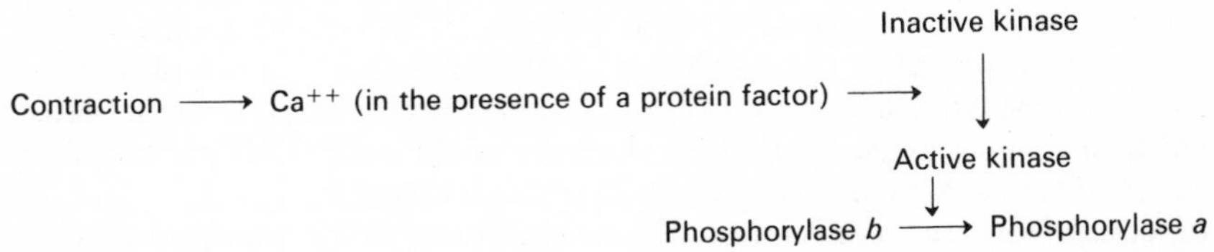

Regulation of glycogenolysis 1.5.

If we try to summarize the facts set out above, we notice the following points:

a) The activity of phosphorylase *b* demands the presence of 5′-AMP.

b) Phosphorylase *a* seems to be able to function without AMP (however, see below).

c) Phosphorylase *b* is converted to phosphorylase *a* by a specific kinase; ATP phosphorylates two serine residues of the *b* protein, the phosphorylation being accompanied by a dimerization of the phosphorylated product.

d) The reverse transformation of form *a* to form *b* involves the liberation of inorganic phosphate and is catalyzed by a specific phosphorylase phosphatase. Phosphorylase *b* has many of the characteristics required by the model of Monod and his co-workers for an allosteric protein: the enzyme can be dissociated into two identical monomers with molecular weights of 125,000, and its activity is influenced by a large number of metabolites (effect of glycogen or phosphate on the K_m for AMP, and of AMP on the K_m values for the substrates; effect of ATP and glucose 6-phosphate on the activation by AMP; co-operativity of glucose 1-phosphate in the presence of ATP).

The activation of phosphorylase *b* by AMP does not involve major changes in the state of aggregation of the enzyme of the order obtained by the action of phosphorylase kinase or phosphorylase phosphatase. Instead, the activation seems to be associated with a conformational change (there is an increase in binding of lipophilic dyes in the presence of AMP).

In contrast to phosphorylase *b*, phosphorylase *a* seems to be insensitive to activation by AMP, except at low substrate concentrations, where the activation is considerable.

It can be concluded that activation of phosphorylase *b* kinase and the subsequent conversion of the *b* form to the *a* form is of prime importance in the control of glycogenolysis in muscle. The following arguments strongly support this point of view:

The acceleration of glycolysis in muscle caused by electrical or chemical stimulation of frog gastrocnemius muscle or by adrenaline administration, is associated with a transformation of phosphorylase *b* to phosphorylase *a*. The effect of muscular contraction must be different from that of adrenaline, for the rates of transformation differ by a factor of 500. The response to contraction seems to depend on an activation of phosphorylase kinase by calcium ions, whereas the response to adrenaline requires an activation of the same enzyme by cyclic 3′,5′-AMP (the conversion $b \rightarrow a$ by adrenaline coincides with an increased amount of cyclic AMP in the tissue). Other factors are involved in the regulation of glycogenolysis; anoxia stimulates glycogenolysis; it is accompanied by an increase in the amount of inorganic phosphate in the muscle, and by a decrease in the ATP/AMP ratio. These two conditions stimulate the activity of phosphorylase *b*.
In conclusion, the conversion of phosphorylase *b* to phosphorylase *a* involves the activation of phosphorylase kinase by hormonal and metabolic effects. Upon this activation is superimposed the true allosteric regulation of phosphorylase *b* by AMP, ATP and glucose-6-phosphate.

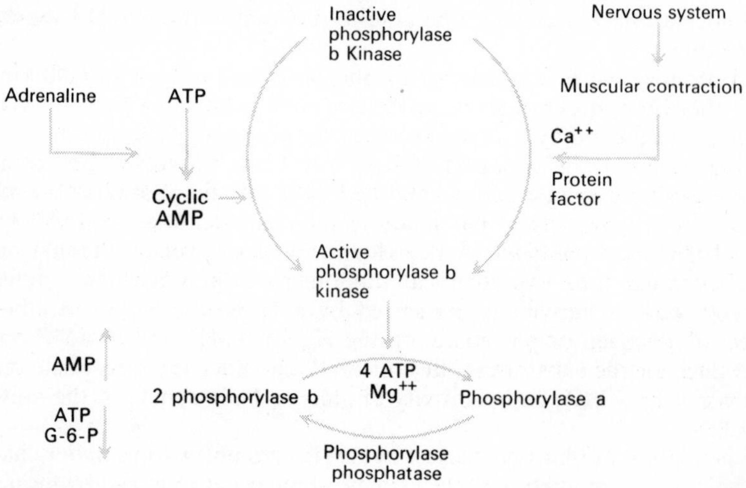

FIGURE 15

Scheme for the phosphorylase transformations.

HEXOKINASES

The reaction catalyzed by these enzymes is the phophorylation of hexose at position 1 or 6, in the presence of Mg^{++} ions:

$$\text{Hexose} + \text{ATP} \longrightarrow \text{Hexose phosphate} + \text{ADP}$$

Yeast hexokinase has been crystallized (51). It is a protein of molecular weight about 100,000, which catalyzes the phophorylation at position 6 not only of D-glucose, but also of D-fructose and D-mannose. It has no action on arabinose, xylose, rhamnose, galactose, sucrose, lactose, maltose, trehalose or raffinose. On the other hand, it catalyzes the phosphorylation of D-glucosamine to the corresponding 6-phosphate ester. Inhibition experiments with mixtures of sugars able to act as substrates show that the different phosphorylation reactions catalyzed are due to a single hexokinase. Soluble and particulate hexokinases have been obtained from different animal tissues. Their properties seem to vary with the source, and different tissues may contain more than one hexokinase. None of these enzymes has been obtained sufficiently pure for serious study of the kinetic or physico-chemical properties.

A fructokinase has been obtained from ox liver, and has the property of phosphorylating ketohexoses (fructose, sorbose and tagatose), but not aldohexoses. Phosphorylation is at position 1:

$$\text{Fructose} + \text{ATP} \longrightarrow \text{Fructose 1-phosphate} + \text{ADP}$$

There is an absolute requirement for Mg^{++} ions. It has been established that this ion forms an ATP complex which is the real substrate for the enzyme.

In the yeast *Saccharomyces fragilis* (52), adapted to grow on galactose, evidence has been found for a specific galactokinase which catalyzes the following reaction:

$$\text{Galactose} + \text{ATP} \longrightarrow \text{Galactose 1-phosphate} + \text{ADP}$$

Adaptation of the Enterobacteriaceae to utilization of pentoses such as ribose, xylose or arabinose, invariably results in the appearance of specific kinases to catalyze the initial reactions allowing pentose carbon atoms to be used by the existing constitutive enzymes of the cells.

Yeast hexokinase is only slightly inhibited by glucose 6-phosphate, the product of the reaction, which shows little affinity for the enzyme; in contrast, inhibition by glucose 6-phosphate of animal hexokinases does not seem to obey the law of mass action: it is non-competitive with respect to the substrates of the reaction (53). It has been suggested that these hexokinases contain at least two binding sites for glucose 6-phosphate: a catalytic site involved in the phosphorylation of glucose and an allosteric site involved in reversible inhibition of the enzyme (54). The inhibitory effect of glucose 6-phosphate is suppressed by inorganic phosphate in erythrocyte hexokinase (55). This antagonism is attributed to a decrease of the affinity of the enzyme for glucose 6-phosphate in the presence of orthophosphate. Thus it seems that inorganic phosphate plays a regulatory role in the activity of certain kinases as well. Although these studies *in vitro* with soluble systems suggest that hexokinases are subject to regulation, we have little data on the biological significance of these observations for intact cells. We should note, however, that the rate of utilization of glucose by intact human erythrocytes is inversely proportional to their glucose 6-phosphate content (56).

PHOSPHOGLUCOMUTASES

The mechanism of the reaction catalyzed by phosphoglucomutase has recently been elucidated (57):

$$\text{Enzyme-OH} + \text{glucose 1,6-diphosphate} \rightleftarrows \text{enzyme-O-phosphate} + \text{glucose (1 or 6)-phosphate}$$

This mechanism has been demonstrated in the following way: the enzyme is incubated with radioactive glucose 1,6-diphosphate (labelled in both phosphorus atoms) or with labelled glucose 1-phosphate in the presence of a catalytic amount of non-radioactive glucose 1,6-diphosphate. The enzyme is then isolated again and is found to be radioactive. Analysis shows that radioactive phosphorus is contained in a phosphate ester of a seryl residue of the protein. It is possible by enzymatic hydrolysis of the protein and suitable analytical procedures to isolate a radioactive peptide and study the phosphoserine environment. In *E. coli*, the sequence around the phosphoserine is —thr.ala.serP.his.asn—. Radioactivity recovered in this peptide accounts for all the radioactivity of the enzyme. The peptide isolated from rabbit muscle is identical. The presence of the same sequence at the active site of two proteins carrying out the same catalytic function, with identical molecular weights (62,000), isolated from two species as different as a mammal and a bacterium, would seem to argue for a genetic homology. However, the two enzymes differ considerably in their overall amino acid composition and in the peptide maps obtained after tryptic hydrolysis.

The phenomenon of labelling by the substrate for the phosphoglucomutases of *E. coli* and rabbit is repeated in the enzymes isolated from a fish, the flounder, and from yeast. In contrast, it has not been possible to discover an ester link between phosphate and serine for the enzymes isolated from two bacteria, *Micrococcus lysodeikticus* and *Bacillus cereus*. In order to explain these differences, it has been proposed that in the two last-named species, the phosphoglucomutases have lost the ability to bind their substrate covalently, but are still capable of forming enzyme-substrate complexes since they retain the necessary groups (sulfhydryl, aspartyl, histidyl, etc.) for effective functioning.

At this stage in glycolysis, glycogen has been transformed to glucose 6-phosphate by the successive action of phosphorylase and phosphoglucomutase. The direct utilization of glucose by means of hexokinase also leads to glucose 6-phosphate. Further steps in glycolysis are concerned with the metabolism of this glucose 6-phosphate.

PHOSPHOHEXOSE ISOMERASES

Under this heading are grouped enzymes catalyzing the reaction:

$$\text{Aldose 6-phosphate} \rightleftarrows \text{Fructose 6-phosphate}$$

One enzyme isolated from muscle uses mannose 6-phosphate as substrate, but the enzyme which has been studied most is phosphoglucose isomerase, obtained from rabbit muscle as well. At equilibrium, there is about 68 % glucose 6-phosphate and 32 % fructose 6-phosphate. Although this equilibrium is not very favorable for normal glycolytic functioning, the action of enzymes metabolizing fructose 6-phosphate displaces the reaction in the "physiological" direction.

PHOSPHOFRUCTOKINASES

These enzymes catalyze the phosphorylation of the fructose 6-phosphate formed in the preceding reaction:

$$\text{Fructose 6-phosphate} + \text{ATP} \longrightarrow \text{fructose 1,6-diphosphate} + \text{ADP}$$

Rabbit muscle phosphofructokinase (58) and sheep heart phosphofructokinase (59) have recently been crystallized. They are enzymes with a tendency to aggregate. They exhibit a similar affinity for ATP, ITP, UTP and CTP. Besides fructose 6-phosphate, they are capable of phosphorylating tagatose 6-phosphate and sedoheptulose 7-phosphate.

Regulation at the phosphofructokinase level 5.´

The effect of ATP concentration on the activity of phosphofructokinase from yeast deserves a special discussion (60). Figure 16 shows that excess ATP inhibits the reaction, no such effect being observed when ATP is replaced

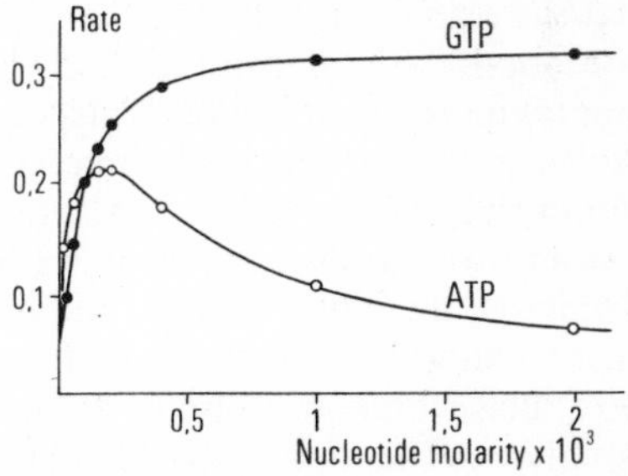

FIGURE 16

Activity of yeast phosphofructokinase in the presence of ATP and GTP. Concentration of fructose 6-phosphate: 9×10^{-4}M (24).

by GTP. This suggests that the enzyme has a regulatory site for ATP, different from the active site. Furthermore, fructose 6-phosphate is an antagonist of the inhibitory action of ATP, suggesting that occupation of the regulatory site by ATP interferes with occupation of the substrate site by fructose 6-phosphate. If it is agreed that ATP is the end product of glycolysis, phosphofructokinase can be considered as a key enzyme which leads irreversibly to ATP. Its inhibition is therefore a particular case of inhibition by the end product of a sequence, and on this evidence we are tempted to assume that it has a regulatory significance: when glycolysis produces an excess of ATP, the latter inhibits its formation by inhibiting phosphofructokinase; if the concentration of ATP falls below a certain level, it is restored by a greater activity on the part of phosphofructokinase. We are again faced with an *allosteric enzyme*, the class of proteins whose function in the regulation of metabolism is becoming more and more prominent.

The situation with ATP finds an analog in citrate, which can similarly be considered an end product of glycolysis (61). In actively growing yeast, it is only possible to detect a form of phosphofructokinase which is insensitive to its allosteric effectors. It is perhaps necessary for yeast in the growth phase to escape from control? Such an insensitive form may be obtained by *in vitro* desensitization of phosphofructokinase when extracts are treated with fluoride (62). The effects obtained with yeast are reproduced with slight differences in the phosphofructokinases of mammals or liver fluke (a parasite). Whatever the source of the phosphofructokinase, substances which consistently show an inhibitor effect are citrate and especially ATP. Substances which show an activator effect are fructose 6-phosphate, inorganic phosphate, AMP, ADP and sometimes fructose 1,6-diphosphate.

Physiological significance of the control of phosphofructokinase activity. The Pasteur effect 5.2.

The properties of phosphofructokinase, studied *in vitro*, form the basis of a rational control mechanism, which, if it operates *in vivo*, could present a very efficient means of controlling glycolysis. It has been shown very recently (63) that the transition from aerobic to anaerobic metabolism in brain (a transition obtained by decapitation of the animal which stops the blood oxygen supply) increases the rate of glycolysis seven times. This increase is accompanied by a decrease in the intracellular concentrations of glucose, glucose 6-phosphate and fructose 6-phosphate, and a concomitant increase in the concentrations of fructose 1,6-diphosphate and later intermediates of glycolysis, including citrate. The ATP concentration also decreases a little. These changes, associated with enzyme kinetic properties, suggest that hexokinase and phosphofructokinase are focal points for the control of glycolysis. The stimulation of the activity of phosphofructokinase, which follows the transition from aerobiosis to anaerobiosis, is attributed to increase in the concentrations of AMP, ADP and orthophosphate, which are antagonists of the inhibitory effect of ATP. Analogous studies with perfused rat hearts show that the intracellular concentrations of fructose 6-phosphate and ATP lie in the range within which the enzyme is very sensitive to inhibition by ATP. The increase in glycolysis which accompanies anoxia is also due to the reversal by increased AMP and inorganic phosphate concentrations of the inhibition caused by ATP.

The sequence of events may be summarized as follows:

1. Aerobiosis exhausts the intracellular reservoir of AMP, which renders isocitrate dehydrogenase inactive (see later); as a result, citrate accumulates.

2. ATP and citrate inhibit phosphofructokinase; as a result, fructose 6-phosphate and glucose 6-phosphate accumulate.

3. It is known from other work that glucose 6-phosphate is an inhibitor of the active transport of glucose into yeast cells.

It therefore appears that aerobiosis inhibits the use of glucose in fermentation. This is the same effect as was described earlier by Pasteur in yeast and by Meyerhof in muscle.

All this would lead to an arrest of growth in aerobiosis if the following mechanism did not exist: in growing cells, the effect of aerobiosis is suppressed by NH_4^+ ions. Further, under the influence of increasing concentrations of ATP, phosphofructokinase is transformed into a form insensitive to ATP and citrate.

FRUCTOSE DIPHOSPHATE ALDOLASES

These enzymes catalyze the transformation of fructose, 1,6-diphosphate into two molecules of triose phosphate:

$$\text{Fructose 1,6-diphosphate} \rightleftharpoons \text{D-glyceraldehyde 3-phosphate}$$

$$+ \text{ Dihydroxyacetone phosphate}$$

The aldolases of rabbit muscle, rat muscle and ox liver have been crystallized. The rabbit muscle enzyme has been studied in detail with regard to its mechanism of action: a covalent complex between the enzyme and one of its substrates, dihydroxyacetone phosphate, has been demonstrated. This complex can be stabilized by reduction with sodium borohydride, and the following amine has been isolated from hydrolysates of these reduced complexes:

$$\begin{array}{c} H_2COH \\ | \\ HC-NH-(CH_2)_4-CH-COOH \\ | \qquad\qquad\qquad | \\ H_2COH \qquad\qquad\quad NH_2 \end{array}$$

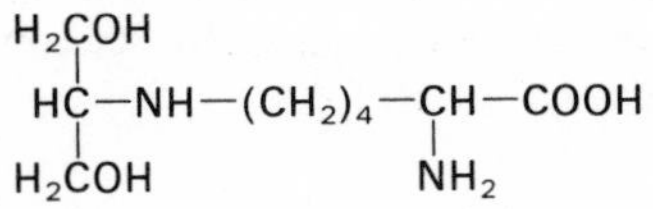

From this it is deduced that the active site of aldolase contains lysine, which condenses through its ε-amino group with the carbonyl group of the substrate to form an intermediate Schiff's base of the following structure:

$$\begin{array}{c} H_2COPO_3^{--} \\ | \\ C=N-(CH_2)_4-CH-CO-NH-R \\ | \qquad\qquad\qquad | \\ H_2COH \qquad\qquad\quad NH-CO-R' \end{array}$$

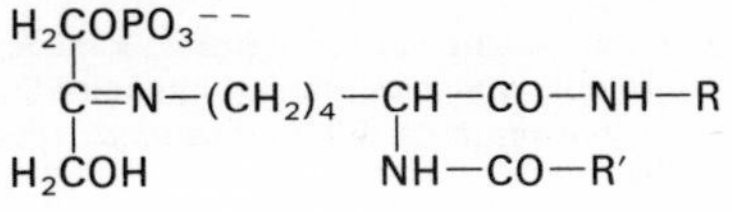

where R and R′ represent other residues bound to lysine in the protein chain. By using ^{14}C-dihydroxyacetone phosphate and measuring the number of N^6-β-glyceryllysine molecules per molecule of aldolase, it was deduced that this enzyme has two sites per molecule for combination with substrate. Other reactions have provided further information: on treatment with 1-chloro-2,4-dinitrobenzene, which reacts with the sulfhydryl groups of this enzyme, three of these groups react rapidly without loss of activity. Total inactivation requires the dinitrophenylation of twelve —SH groups. In the presence of substrate, four to six sulfhydryl groups are protected and the enzymatic activity is unimpaired. The deduction is that these four to six sulfhydryl groups are necessary for the enzymatic activity.

Aldolase has a molecular weight of 142,000 and can be dissociated by urea into several polypeptide chains without any apparent rupture of covalent bonds. On treatment with carboxypeptidase, two of the chains are much further degraded than the others, indicating that the *native* enzyme may contain two identical chains which are different from the others. The presence of several active sites suggests that they are located on the identical chains. Confirmation of this hypothesis requires the isolation of the individual chains.[1]

TRIOSE PHOSPHATE ISOMERASES

Dihydroxyacetone phosphate does not lie in the direct path of glycolysis; it is merely the other triose phosphate produced by the action of fructose 1,6-diphosphate aldolase, which can be metabolized in the direction of pyruvate. An enzyme, triose phosphate isomerase, catalyzes its transformation to D-glyceraldehyde 3-phosphate:

$$\text{Dihydroxyacetone phosphate} \rightleftarrows \text{D-glyceraldehyde 3-phosphate}$$

This enzyme has been crystallized from calf muscle. Its catalytic activity is extraordinary: 100,000 g of enzyme catalyze the transformation of 945,000 moles of substrate per minute at 26°C.

Triose phosphate isomerase is always found in association with fructose 1,6-diphosphate aldolase in all tissues. In its absence, the efficiency of glycolysis would be reduced by 50%.

D-GLYCERALDEHYDE 3-PHOSPHATE DEHYDROGENASES

These enzymes are often called triose phosphate dehydrogenases. They have been crystallized from rabbit muscle and bakers' yeast. The reaction catalyzed

1. Recent work (63*a*) suggests that rabbit muscle aldolase is made up of four sub-units; there appears to exist two types of sub-units which are similar, but non-identical. Both types were found to contain the lysine residue which forms the Schiff intermediate with dihydroxyacetone phosphate (63*b*).

is the following:

$$\text{Glyceraldehyde 3-phosphate} + NAD^+ + H_3PO_4 \rightleftharpoons \text{1,3-diphosphoglycerate} + NADH + H^+$$

The enzymes have a very high affinity for NAD. In particular, the enzyme crystallized from muscle contains 2 molecules of strongly bound NAD per molecule of enzyme, which can be removed by adsorption on charcoal. The NAD is held to the protein by two —SH groups, in a manner as yet not clear.

The mechanism assumed for the reaction catalyzed by these enzymes is as follows (64):

$$\text{Enzyme—SH} + NAD^+ \longrightarrow \text{Enzyme—S—NAD} + H^+$$

$$\text{Enzyme—S—NAD} + \text{R—CHO} \longrightarrow \text{Enzyme—S—CO—R} + NADH$$

$$\text{Enzyme—S—CO—R} + H_3PO_4 \longrightarrow \text{Enzyme—SH} + PO_3H_2\text{—O—CO—R}$$

It is presumed that the substrate aldehyde group undergoes a double decomposition with the enzyme —NAD complex, resulting in the transfer of the acyl group to the enzyme —SH group. This acyl group is next transferred to orthophosphate to form the corresponding acyl phosphate, the enzyme acting here as an acyl transferase. This scheme is supported by the fact that the muscle enzyme can readily catalyze other transacetylations, such as the transfer of the acetyl group from acetyl phosphate to different compounds containing thiol groups, or the transfer of an acyl group from one thiol compound to another, or even the arsenolysis of acetyl phosphate. However, these reactions occur with rates which vary from 0·006 to 0·02% of the normal dehydrogenase reaction.

A triose phosphate dehydrogenase requiring NADP in place of NAD has been discovered in pea leaves.

If the reaction is carried out in the presence of phosphate labelled with the heavy isotope ^{18}O, no change is found in the ^{18}O content of the phosphate, no matter in which direction the reaction has been carried out; this shows that it is the C—O bond which has been attacked and not the P—O bond, agreeing with the fact that the enzyme is specific for the aldehydic group (64a).

PHOSPHOGLYCERATE KINASES

These enzymes catalyze the reaction:

$$\text{D-1,3-diphosphoglycerate} + ADP \rightleftharpoons \text{D-3-phosphoglycerate} + ATP$$

Such a kinase has been crystallized from bakers' yeast. It should be noted that this enzyme mediates the synthesis of one molecule of ATP. Since aldolase has produced 2 molecules of triose, 2 molecules of ATP have been synthesized, which cancels the energy expended in the action of hexokinase and phosphofructokinase. By taking diphosphoglycerate labelled in its phosphate group (synthesized by triose phosphate dehydrogenase in the presence of ^{18}O) and submitting it to the action of phosphoglycerate kinase, the molecule of phosphoglycerate formed now contains the oxygen-18 in its carboxyl group. In fact, the oxygen atom which belonged initially to phosphate from now on remains bound to the carbon atom after the rupture (catalyzed by the kinase) of the P—O bond. The combined effect of triose phosphate dehydrogenase and phosphoglycerate kinase is therefore to transfer one of the oxygen atoms of phosphate to a carboxyl group (65).

PHOSPHOGLYCERATE MUTASES

This class of enzyme comprises two types which catalyze one or other of the following reactions:

$$\text{2,3-diphosphoglycerate} + \text{3-phosphoglycerate} \rightleftharpoons \text{2,3-diphosphoglycerate} + \text{2-phosphoglycerate} \quad (1)$$

$$\text{3-phosphoglycerate} \rightleftharpoons \text{2-phosphoglycerate} \quad (2)$$

The difference between the two types is the presence or absence of a requirement for 2,3-diphosphoglycerate.

Mutases requiring the presence of 2,3-diphosphoglycerate have been crystallized from bakers' yeast and muscle. A mutase independent of 2,3-diphosphoglycerate has been highly purified from wheat germ. At the present time, it has not been possible to demonstrate the presence of 2,3-diphosphoglycerate as a complex with the enzymes which require it for their activity.

ENOLASES (PHOSPHOPYRUVATE HYDRATASES)

These enzymes catalyze the reaction:

$$\text{D-2-phosphoglycerate} \rightleftharpoons \text{Phosphoenolpyruvate} + H_2O$$

Enolase from bakers' yeast has been crystallized, and is a protein with a molecular weight of the order of 60,000, whose activity depends on the presence of certain divalent ions (Mg^{++}, Zn^{++} or Mn^{++}).

PYRUVATE KINASES

The reaction catalyzed by these proteins is the following:

$$\text{Phosphoenolpyruvate} + \text{ADP} \rightleftharpoons \text{Pyruvate} + \text{ATP}$$

The rabbit muscle enzyme has been crystallized in 40% yield. Its molecular weight is 237,000. GDP, IDP, UDP and CDP can replace ADP, in decreasing order of effectiveness.

At this stage, two molecules of ATP have been used for the initial phosphorylation of glucose and the formation of fructose 1,6-diphosphate. Two molecules of triose phosphate have arisen from the latter. The phosphoglycerate kinase and pyruvate kinase reactions have produced two molecules of ATP from each molecule of triose phosphate, making four molecules of ATP in all. The net gain in the Embden-Meyerhof pathway is therefore two molecules of ATP per glucose molecule used. We shall see later that the reoxidation of the NADH produced by triose phosphate dehydrogenase provides additional molecules of ATP, except during anaerobiosis in muscle or yeast where the following fermentation reactions take place.

FORMATION OF LACTIC ACID BY MUSCLE DURING ANAEROBIOSIS

MUSCLE LACTATE DEHYDROGENASE

This enzyme catalyzes the reaction:

$$\text{Pyruvate} + \text{NADH} + \text{H}^+ \rightleftharpoons \text{L-lactate} + \text{NAD}^+$$

It has been crystallized from ox heart. Its molecular weight is 135,000. It must not be confused with the D- and L-lactate dehydrogenases found in aerobic yeast, which are flavin enzymes and cannot exchange electrons with the NADH + H^+ – NAD^+ system.

Pyruvate is the best substrate for this enzyme, which can also reduce a series of other α-keto acids or diketo acids. The muscle L-lactate dehydrogenases present an interesting problem from the point of view of protein structure and function. Their study however is outside the scope of this book.

ALCOHOLIC FERMENTATION IN ANAEROBIC YEAST

Pyruvate decarboxylase 14.1.

This enzyme decarboxylates pyruvate to acetaldehyde in two stages as follows:

a) an addition compound is formed between pyruvate and thiamine pyrophosphate:

$$CH_3\text{—CO—COOH} + \text{thiamine pyrophosphate} \longrightarrow CH_3\text{—CHOH—thiamine pyrophosphate} + CO_2$$

b) the compound formed, α-hydroxyethyl-thiamine pyrophosphate, is then decomposed to thiamine pyrophosphate and acetaldehyde:

$$CH_3\text{—CHOH—thiamine pyrophosphate} \longrightarrow CH_3CHO + \text{thiamine pyrophosphate}$$

The enzyme has not been obtained in the pure state; it contains thiamine pyrophosphate and magnesium, both indispensable for activity. On the basis of one molecule of thiamine pyrophosphate per molecule of enzyme, the molecular weight can be gauged approximately: 100,000. This figure is subject to a large uncertainty however. The mechanism of action envisaged is the following:

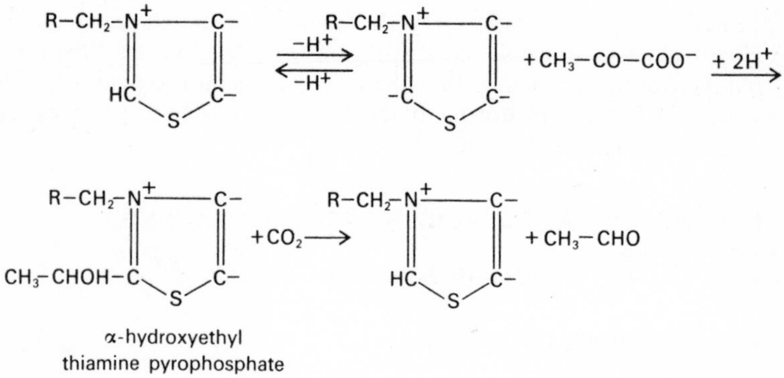

Alcohol dehydrogenase 14.2.

Crystallization of this enzyme from bakers' yeast in 1937 provided the first example of the crystallization of a protein whose action involves a pyridine nucleotide, and made possible fundamental investigations of its mechanism of action.

The reaction catalyzed is:

$$CH_3{-}CHO + NADH + H^+ \rightleftharpoons CH_3{-}CH_2OH + NAD^+$$

This enzyme has been found in every animal, plant, or microorganism in which it has been sought. In 1948, an alcohol dehydrogenase was crystallized from horse liver.

The molecular weight of the yeast enzyme has been estimated to be 129,000 by some workers, and 151,000 by others using different methods. The enzyme contains four or five zinc atoms bound strongly to the protein. Dialysis at acid pH causes a loss of zinc together with an irreversible inactivation of the enzyme. If the dialysis buffer contains zinc, the enzyme is protected.

Glycolysis, as described above, is the major pathway for the degradation of carbohydrates. It is by no means the only one, however. One of the first enzymes to be identified and studied, the *Zwischenferment* of Warburg and Christian, catalyzes the oxidation of glucose 6-phosphate to phosphogluconic acid, which itself is the substrate from which pentoses are synthesized. Figure 17 shows schematically the reactions which form ribose 5-phosphate and erythrose 4-phosphate, the precursors in numerous biosyntheses. Fructose 6-phosphate formed during this cycle of reactions can be recycled,

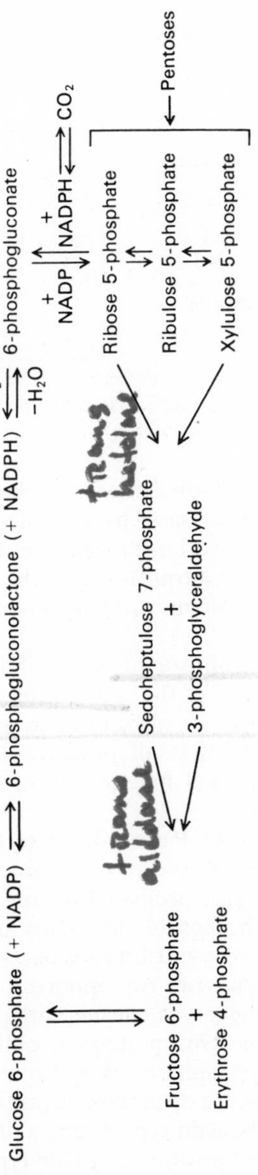

FIGURE 17

Hexose monophosphate cycle, so called in distinction from glycolysis, in which hexose diphosphates are involved. This cycle is also known by the name Warburg–Dickens–Horecker cycle.

TABLE VIII

		ATP	ADP	NADH
Glucose		−1	+1	
Glucose 6-P				
Fructose 6-P		−1	+1	
Fructose 1,6-diP				
D-glyceraldehyde 3-P + dihydroxy-acetone P				+2
D-1,3-diP-glycerate		+2	−2	
D-3-P-glycerate				
D-2-P-glycerate				
Phosphoenolpyruvate		+2	−2	
Pyruvate	acetaldehyde			−2
Lactate	ethanol			
		+2	−2	0

The energy balance sheet for glycolysis is slightly positive, and the net synthesis of reduced pyridine nucleotides is nil.

after transformation to glucose 6-phosphate by phosphohexose isomerase, or can be used in normal glycolysis. The enzyme which transforms two pentoses to a sugar with seven carbon atoms and a triose phosphate has been called transketolase; the one transforming the two products of transketolase action to fructose 6-phosphate and erythrose 4-phosphate has been called transaldolase.

As we shall see later, ribose 5-phosphate is an obligatory intermediate in the synthesis of nucleic acids and of the side chains of histidine and tryptophan; erythrose 4-phosphate is an obligatory precursor of the aromatic nucleus. It is therefore evident that all prototrophic organisms have an absolute requirement for a normal functioning of the pentose phosphate cycle in parallel with glycolysis.

We note that two molecules of NADP are reduced by the cycle, while we have seen that the net synthesis of reduced pyridine nucleotides is zero during glycolysis. NADPH, which is also produced during the functioning of the tricarboxylic acid cycle, is indispensable for many biosyntheses. Thus it is interesting to evaluate the relative contributions of glycolysis and the pentose cycle in the degradation of glucose. An opportunity is provided by the existence of a mutant of *Salmonella typhimurium* with practically no phosphohexose isomerase activity (66). This mutant is obliged to make fructose 6-phosphate from glucose 6-phosphate taken from the pentose cycle. Its growth rate is considerably reduced on glucose, while on glycerol the division time is identical with that of the wild type. Studies of the formation of CO_2 from glucose labelled in different positions, by wild type and mutant bacteria, show that only 20% of the glucose is metabolized normally in the pentose cycle. The cycle is proving to be important, in bacteria at least, for the provision of intermediates rather than energy.

TABLE VIIIA

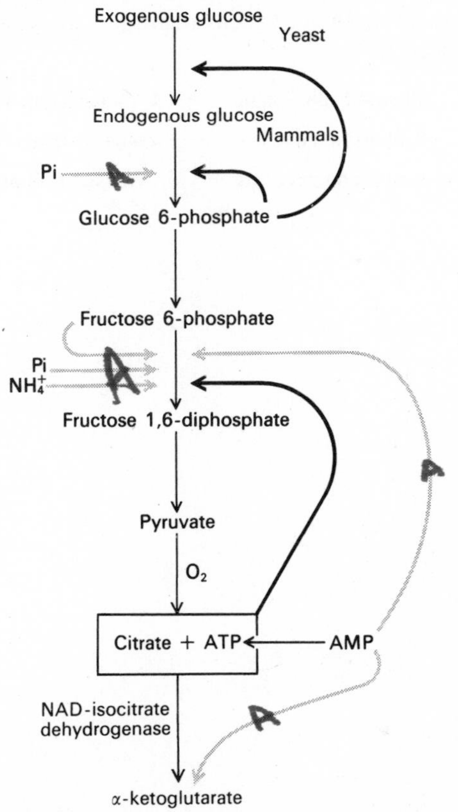

This table summarizes the main results in the regulation of glycolysis. Points of inhibition are shown by black arrows, activation by grey arrows. Excess ATP tends to slow down glycolysis and excess AMP and inorganic phosphate to accelerate it. The role of oxygen is indirect: the "Pasteur effect" is due to ATP formed during respiration. It is annulled by reagents which uncouple respiration and ATP synthesis, such as dinitrophenol.

The contribution which the pentose cycle makes to the degradation of glucose is difficult to evaluate in higher organisms; it seems to vary from one organ to another: the majority of oxidations in liver seem to pass through the pentose cycle, whereas degradation in muscle follows the glycolytic pathway solely.

In certain microorganisms, glucose is oxidized by a pathway which begins with the metabolism of certain non-phosphorylated compounds. Specific kinases then put on phosphoryl groups to later intermediates. Thus a glucose dehydrogenase has been described in mammalian liver and in certain molds. An interesting system has been described in the bacterium *Pseudomonas saccharophila*, which degrades glucose according to the following reactions (67):

Glucose 6-phosphate ⟶ 6-phosphogluconate

6-phosphogluconate ⟶ 2-keto-3-deoxy-6-phosphogluconate

2-keto-3-deoxy-6-phosphogluconate ⟶ Pyruvate + Phosphoglyceraldehyde

4

Tricarboxylic Acid Cycle

The tricarboxylic acid cycle comprises a series of reactions which carry out the complete oxidation of a molecule of acetate to CO_2 and H_2O. The acetate molecule can be considered to arise from pyruvate by a reaction which we shall analyze later.

Oxidation processes in the cycle are connected with electron transfer reactions to molecular oxygen by other reactions which lie outside the scope of this work. It is enough to say here that the latter involve the esterification of inorganic phosphate during substrate oxidation and electron transport. The cycle and the subsequent electron transport constitute a very efficient mechanism for the production of energy in the form of ATP. In many organisms, the tricarboxylic acid cycle is the main or only pathway for oxidation. The tricarboxylic acid cycle, citric acid cycle, or Krebs cycle (named after the learned scientist who has done most to elucidate the mechanism) is an example of a biochemical cycle in which a compound is regenerated after a series of reactions and so acts as a catalyst for the metabolism of other compounds. The regenerated molecule is not necessarily reconstituted from the same carbon atoms during successive turns of the cycle. In the tricarboxylic acid cycle, the reaction which introduces new carbon atoms is the condensation of oxaloacetate and acetyl coenzyme A, giving rise to citrate. We shall see below how acetyl CoA and oxaloacetate, indispensable for the start of the cycle, are obtained from pyruvate.

SYNTHESIS OF ACETYL CoA. PYRUVATE OXIDASE SYSTEM

In aerobiosis, the NADH formed in glycolysis is oxidized by the cytochrome chain and is not available for the reactions leading in yeast and muscle respectively to ethanol and lactic acid. Under these conditions pyruvate is converted to acetyl CoA (which will feed into the Krebs cycle) by a series of reactions catalyzed by an enzyme complex which has been named pyruvate oxidase:

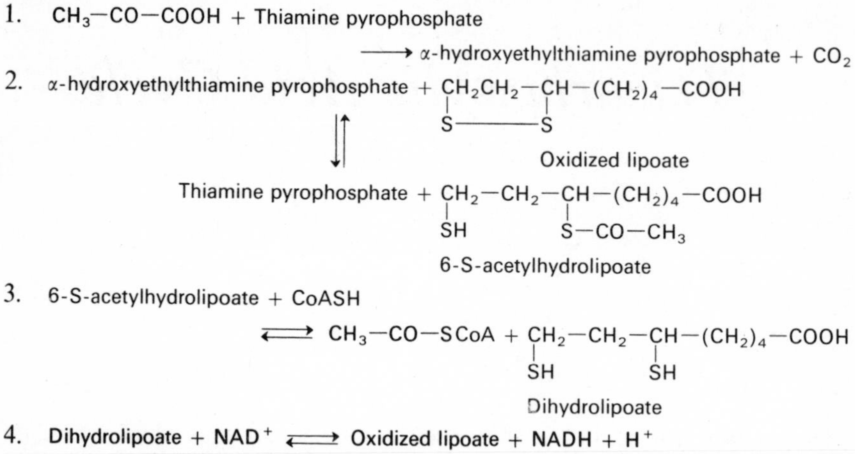

The sum of these four reactions can be written:

$$\text{Pyruvate} + \text{CoASH} + \text{NAD}^+ \longrightarrow \text{acetyl CoA} + CO_2 + \text{NADH} + H^+$$

The multienzyme complex which catalyzes this overall reaction has been obtained in a highly purified state from pigeon muscle (68) and *Escherichia coli* (69), with respective molecular weights of 4×10^6 and $4{\cdot}8 \times 10^6$.
The intermediates, hydroxyethylthiamine pyrophosphate, thiamine pyrophosphate, acetylhydrolipoate, and reduced and oxidized lipoate, exist only as complexes with the enzyme and never as free intermediates. In the *E. coli* system, it is possible to separate fractions which catalyze only some of the above reactions: *a*) a fraction catalyzing reaction 4 (dihydrolipoate dehydrogenase, formerly called diaphorase) which is a flavoprotein containing FAD; *b*) a fraction containing all the lipoic acid in the bound state and catalyzing reactions 2 and 3; this fraction can provisionally be called lipoate-reductase-transacetylase; *c*) a fraction catalyzing reaction 1 (pyruvate decarboxylase). It is possible to cause these separate fractions to reassociate to form a complex of molecular weight identical with that of the original, with the same composition and overall enzymatic activity (69*a*). The molecular weight of pyruvate decarboxylase isolated from the complex is 183,000 and of dihydrolipoate dehydrogenase 112,000 (with two molecules of FAD per molecule of enzyme). The complex nature of lipoate-reductase-transacetylase has not yet been elucidated; in particular, the question of whether different sub-units are responsible for reactions 2 and 3 is not resolved. Whatever the case, the complex represents about 34% of the whole. Its "molecular weight" can thus be estimated at $1{\cdot}6 \times 10^6$ (assuming one molecule of lipoate per

sub-unit, the hypothetical sub-units would then be 30,000). From data on the composition of the complex and the known molecular weights, the number of molecules of each enzyme in the complex can be estimated:

TABLE IX

Activity	Molecular weight	No. of sub-units	Total molecular weight
Decarboxylase	183,000	12–14	$2{\cdot}2 - 2{\cdot}6 \times 10^6$
Reductase-transacetylase	$1{\cdot}6 \times 10^6$	1	$1{\cdot}6 \times 10^6$
Dehydrogenase	112,000	6–8	$0{\cdot}7 - 0{\cdot}9 \times 10^6$
			$4{\cdot}5 - 5{\cdot}1 \times 10^6$

The advantage of molecular associations such as the pyruvate oxidase system cannot be overlooked. The efficiency of a system of sequential reactions is increased considerably by the organization of the enzymes into an integrated structure which does not dissociate under physiological conditions. The molecules of lipoate are bound by covalent bonds to the ε-amino groups of lysine residues in the enzyme protein.

SYNTHESIS OF OXALOACETATE

Two distinct enzymatic systems are capable of accomplishing the carboxylation of pyruvate to form oxaloacetate.

The first is pyruvate carboxylase which carries out the following reaction in the presence of ATP:

$$ATP + CH_3CO{-}COOH + CO_2 + H_2O \rightleftharpoons ADP + P_i + COOH{-}CH_2{-}CO{-}COOH$$

The enzyme contains biotin as a complex and requires Mg^{++}. It is found in bacteria and in animal tissues. The animal enzyme also requires catalytic amounts of acetyl CoA for its activity (70); reasons for this requirement will be discussed in the chapter on gluconeogenesis.

The second enzyme has phosphoenolpyruvate as substrate: this is phosphoenolpyruvate carboxykinase (71):

$$COOH{-}\underset{\displaystyle OPO_3H_2}{\underset{|}{C}}{=}CH_2 + CO_2 + GDP \longrightarrow COOH{-}CO{-}CH_2{-}COOH + GTP$$

The requirement for GDP is not satisfied by ADP. A kinase catalyzing the synthesis of oxaloacetate from phosphoenolpyruvate has been prepared from several plant tissues and shows no nucleotide requirement.

THE TRICARBOXYLIC ACID CYCLE

The cycle involves dehydration, hydration, oxidation and decarboxylation reactions, and with each turn gives more oxaloacetate, CO_2 and water. The carbon atoms of the oxaloacetate molecule produced are not the same as those which initiate the cycle. There are seven reactions in the cycle:

1. Condensation of acetyl CoA and oxaloacetate to give citrate;
2. Intramolecular rearrangement of citrate to isocitrate;
3. Oxidative decarboxylation of isocitrate to α-ketoglutarate;
4. Oxidative decarboxylation of α-ketoglutarate to succinate;
5. Oxidation of succinate to fumarate;
6. Hydration of fumarate to malate;
7. Oxidation of malate to oxaloacetate, completing the cycle. Figure 18 is a diagram of the Krebs cycle.

Condensation 3.1.

The keto group of oxaloacetate reacts with acetyl CoA in an aldol condensation:

$$\begin{array}{c} \text{COOH} \quad \text{COOH} \\ | \qquad\quad | \\ \text{CH}_2-\text{C}=\text{O} + \text{HCH}_2-\underset{\underset{\text{O}}{\|}}{\text{C}}\sim\text{SCoA} + \text{H}_2\text{O} \end{array}$$

$$\updownarrow$$

$$\begin{array}{c} \text{COOH} \quad \text{COOH} \quad \text{COOH} \\ | \qquad\quad | \qquad\quad | \\ \text{CH}_2-\text{C}-\!\!-\!\!-\!\!-\text{CH}_2 \qquad + \text{ CoASH} + \text{H}^+ \\ | \\ \text{OH} \end{array}$$

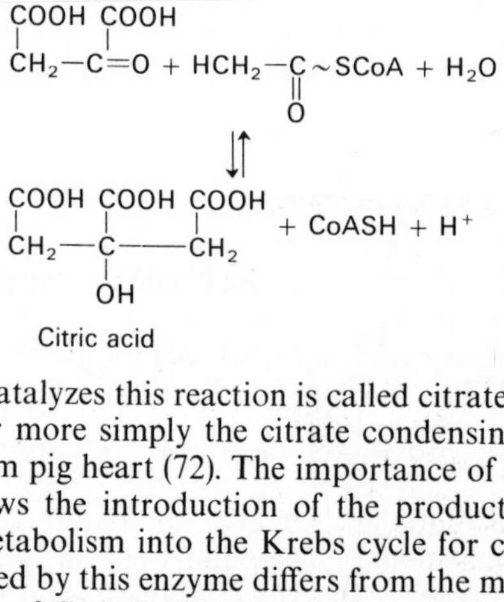

Citric acid

The enzyme which catalyzes this reaction is called citrate-oxaloacetate lyase (CoA acetylating) or more simply the citrate condensing enzyme, and has been crystallized from pig heart (72). The importance of this reaction lies in the fact that it allows the introduction of the products of carbohydrate, lipid and protein metabolism into the Krebs cycle for complete oxidation. The reaction catalyzed by this enzyme differs from the majority of reactions involving derivatives of CoA, in that it uses the methyl group of acetate in the condensation and not the carboxyl group. Two phenomena occur during the reaction: the true condensation and the thioester hydrolysis; the same enzyme is responsible for both reactions. The overall reaction is practically irreversible ($\Delta F = -8$ kcal).

Aconitase 3.2.

This enzyme catalyzes the reactions leading to equilibrium among the three tricarboxylic acids, citric, isocitric and cis-aconitic. The relative amounts at equilibrium are:

Citrate	89·5%
Isocitrate	6–7%
cis-aconitate	3–4%

The interconversions pass through an intermediate of unknown structure.

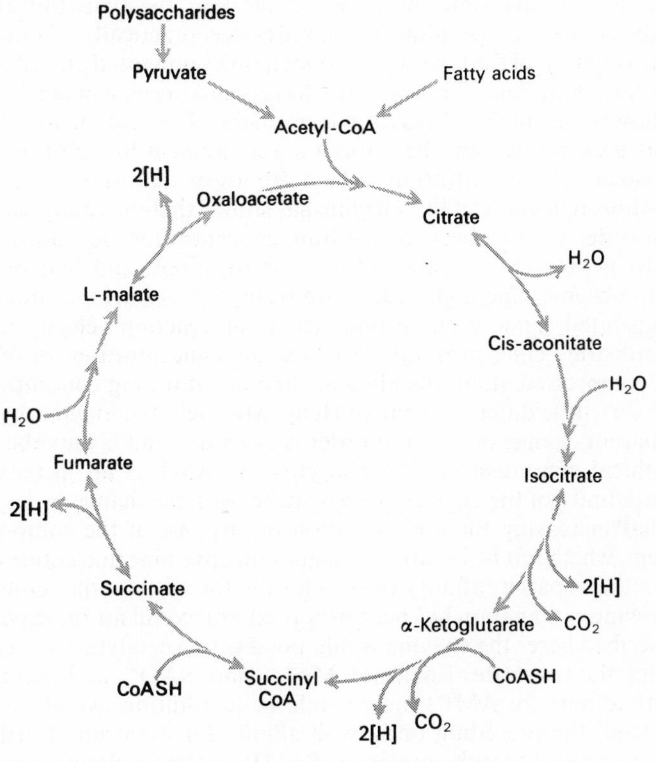

FIGURE 18
The tricarboxylic acid cycle.

Isocitrate dehydrogenase 3.3.

Many animal tissues, plants and yeast contain two isocitrate dehydrogenases which differ essentially in the nature of the pyridine nucleotide involved in the reaction (73). Early studies showed that NAD-specific isocitrate dehydrogenase in yeast was different from the NADP-specific enzyme in pig heart in two further ways: the NAD-dependent enzyme had an absolute requirement for AMP and did not seem to be reversible (73).

As the reaction catalyzed is the same in both cases,

$$\mathrm{COOH{-}CHOH{-}\underset{\displaystyle COOH}{\underset{|}{CH}}{-}CH_2{-}COOH + NAD(P)^+}$$

$$\longrightarrow \mathrm{COOH{-}CO{-}CH_2{-}CH_2{-}COOH + NAD(P)H + H^+ + CO_2}$$

there is no apparent reason for the surprising result that one of the two reactions is not reversible, when we know that the oxidation-reduction potentials of the two pyridine nucleotides are practically identical. This apparent violation of the laws of thermodynamics presented an embarrassing paradox for a long time. This paradox has recently been explained (74, 74*a*). It was shown that the NAD reaction is reversible if carried out at a pH lower than that used earlier; and here too, the requirement for AMP is manifest only at isocitrate concentrations which are lower than those in the earlier work. A thorough study of this enzyme has shown that the catalyzed reaction is fourth order with respect to isocitrate concentration, second order with respect to NAD^+, Mg^{++} and AMP concentrations, and first order with respect to enzyme. The high order with respect to isocitrate is indicated by the exaggerated sigmoid curve obtained when reaction velocity is plotted against substrate concentration. At increasing concentrations of AMP, this curve is compressed along the abscissa, and at saturating concentrations of AMP, is very little different from an Henri-Michaelis rectangular hyperbola. This apparent change of reaction order is deceptive and is only the result of the graphical compression. The real effect of AMP is an increase in the apparent affinity of the enzyme for isocitrate, with no change in V_{max}. It was found that increasing the concentration of any one of the components of the system, whether it be isocitrate, magnesium, pyridine nucleotide or AMP, increases the apparent affinity of the enzyme for all the other constituents. The following explanation has been proposed to account for the experimental facts described here: the enzyme would possess two catalytic sites, each with affinity for the substrates isocitrate, Mg^{++}, and NAD^+, and two allosteric sites, with affinity for AMP; there would be in addition two allosteric sites distinct from the preceding ones, with affinity for isocitrate. Furthermore, it must be assumed that the presence of AMP on the regulatory sites induces conformational changes which increase the affinity for isocitrate at all its binding sites, and for NAD^+ and Mg^{++} at their catalytic sites. Another inference is that the binding of NAD^+ and Mg^{++} increases the affinity for isocitrate of the catalytic sites only. Furthermore, it is necessary to postulate a co-operative effect for isocitrate molecules such that the binding of each molecule leads progressively to greater affinities for isocitrate at the sites as yet unoccupied. With all these assumptions, the mathematical model constructed by Atkinson predicts all the kinetic properties of the enzyme: for example, dilution of the reaction mixture containing all the components of the system in which the initial velocity is about 1% of V_{max}, results in a decrease in activity which follows an eleventh order law, as predicted by the model.

3.3.1. ROLE OF THE TWO ISOCITRATE DEHYDROGENASES IN THE GENERAL CONTROL OF METABOLISM

We have already seen in glycolysis that citrate strongly inhibits the activity of phosphofructokinase. In the absence of AMP, i.e. in strongly aerobic conditions (favoring synthesis of ATP), NAD-specific isocitrate dehydrogenase cannot function and citrate accumulates (citrate rather than isocitrate, because of the position of equilibrium in the aconitase reaction). The lack of AMP and the increase in ATP concentration tend to inhibit phosphofructokinase and NAD-isocitrate dehydrogenase, and so to re-establish a situation in which the concentration of ATP diminishes. On the other hand, the accumulated citrate under these conditions has an activating effect on acetyl CoA carboxylase, the enzyme which introduces acetate into the fatty acid synthesis cycle.

Oxidation of isocitrate by the NAD-enzyme must therefore favor respiration with conversion of AMP and ADP to ATP, while oxidation of isocitrate by the NADP-enzyme must favor the synthesis of fatty acids. A balance between the two overlapping routes is assured by the activation of the NAD-enzyme by AMP at low concentrations of isocitrate and by the activation of acetyl CoA carboxylase by citrate (75). The oxidation of isocitrate by the NAD-enzyme is thus limited by the conversion of AMP to ATP, and is

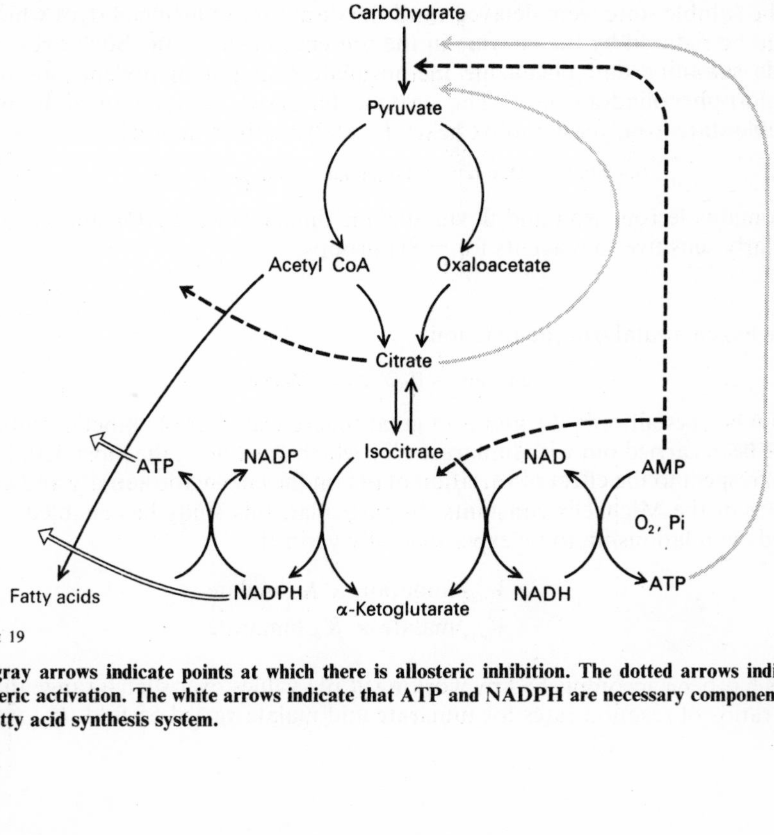

FIGURE 19

The gray arrows indicate points at which there is allosteric inhibition. The dotted arrows indicate allosteric activation. The white arrows indicate that ATP and NADPH are necessary components of the fatty acid synthesis system.

expressed as a disappearance of the activating effect of AMP. Accumulation of citrate favors the synthesis of fatty acids concurrent with the utilization of ATP and also of NADPH produced by the NADP-enzyme. The true physiological significance of these relationships *in vivo* remains to be determined. Figure 19 summarizes the regulating steps.

α-Ketoglutarate oxidase 3.4.

This enzymatic system is similar in many ways to the pyruvate oxidase system which was examined at the beginning of this chapter. The final product of the system is succinyl CoA instead of acetyl CoA. Succinyl CoA is then deacylated by a specific deacylase, and the succinate formed can then be used as substrate for succinate dehydrogenase. The molecular weight of the enzymatic complex prepared from *E. coli* is lower than that of the pyruvate oxidase complex from the same organism: $2{\cdot}4 \times 10^6$ instead of $4{\cdot}8 \times 10^6$.

Succinate dehydrogenase 3.5.

For a long time, the oxidation of succinate was studied with particulate systems (mitochondria) which could accomplish the true dehydrogenation and the resulting electron transfer to molecular oxygen. Studies of the enzyme in the soluble state were delayed until the discovery of artificial dyes which could be reduced by the enzyme in the presence of succinate. Such dyes include safranine and phenazine methosulfate (but not methylene blue or dichlorophenolindophenol). The enzyme has now been obtained in the soluble state from yeast and ox heart. It catalyzes the reaction:

$$\text{Succinate} + \text{Dye} \rightleftharpoons \text{Fumarate} + \text{Leuco-derivative}$$

It contains ferrous iron and flavin adenine dinucleotide (FAD), and is particularly sensitive to reagents for —SH groups.

Fumarase 3.6.

This enzyme catalyzes the reaction:

$$\text{Fumarate} + H_2O \rightleftharpoons \text{Malate}$$

It can be crystallized (76), and is of great theoretical interest: kinetic studies have been carried out with fumarase (77), which are among the most detailed with respect to the effect of variation of pH on the enzymatic activity and the values of the Michaelis constants. In particular, this study has enabled the Haldane relationship to be experimentally verified:

$$K_{eq} = \frac{V_{max}\,\text{fumarate} \times K_m\,\text{malate}}{V_{max}\,\text{malate} \times K_m\,\text{fumarate}}$$

This has been accomplished by working at pH values over such a range that the ratios of reaction rates for fumarate and malate varied 65-fold. K_{eq} was found to be remarkably constant throughout this range, at constant temperature.

Malate dehydrogenase 3.7.

This enzyme has been crystallized (MW 52,000) from ox heart. It catalyzes the reaction which completes the tricarboxylic acid cycle:

$$COOH{-}CHOH{-}CH_2{-}COOH + NAD^+ \longrightarrow COOH{-}CO{-}CH_2{-}COOH + NADH + H^+$$

It can use NADP in place of NAD, but the rate is only 5–7%. The position of equilibrium at physiological pH values favors the formation of malate, but the re-oxidation of NADH, or the condensation of oxaloacetate with acetyl CoA, to begin a new turn of the cycle, displaces the equilibrium in the physiological direction.

Two malate dehydrogenases which differ in their intracellular localization can be separated from rat liver (78). Although both these enzymes catalyze the same reaction, they can be distinguished by their specificity towards analogs of NAD and by the difference in their inhibition by oxaloacetate, the reaction product. One of the enzymes is of cytoplasmic origin, the other mitochondrial. Two malate dehydrogenases, with the same difference in location, have been isolated from peas and yeast.

ROLE OF THE TRICARBOXYLIC ACID CYCLE IN PROVIDING ENERGY AND CARBON ATOMS FOR BIOSYNTHESES

It might be thought that if the Krebs cycle is used only in consuming acetate derived from pyruvate to give CO_2 and water, the energy gained as ATP by the oxidation of reduced pyridine nucleotides would be of no use. The cell could then be compared with an expensive boiler!

Happily this is not so. Ketoglutaric acid, oxaloacetic acid, fumaric acid, and pyruvic acid are precursors of many essential metabolites which make up the framework of proteins and nucleic acids. In particular, if we consider organisms endowed with an enormous synthetic power, such as *E. coli* growing in aerobic conditions, about 30% of the glucose carbon atoms supplied are recovered as cellular material. Only 50% are lost as CO_2, and about 20% are recovered in the growth medium as various acids.

30% cellular apparatus!

When bacterial cells are adapted to grow on carbon sources such as pyruvate, acetate or succinate, they are no longer able to use glycolysis as a means of energy production. We expect to see a greater production of energy by the Krebs cycle, and this is indeed the case.

Although molecular oxygen is not directly involved in the enzymatic mechanism of the cycle, the functioning of the latter depends in most cases on a continuing supply of oxygen. The reason is that the four dehydrogenases of the system produce reduced pyridine nucleotides which must be re-oxidized if they are going to continue to participate in the cycle. Nevertheless, there exist many cases where oxygen can be replaced as the final electron acceptor by natural metabolites. *E. coli* can grow anaerobically with fumarate or nitrate as acceptor. Although these reactions are not accompanied by a normal liberation of energy, their existence has a more than theoretical interest when we remember that it provides the only means the organism has of synthesizing a large part of its essential metabolites.

THE GLYOXYLIC ACID CYCLE, A MODIFIED TRICARBOXYLIC CYCLE (79)

This cycle was discovered in the course of research to elucidate the way in which microorganisms such as yeast, molds and bacteria can draw their energy and substance from carbon sources like acetate or ethanol. Experiments using radioactive isotopes showed that in a few seconds, the radioactivity of acetate appeared in citrate and malate; the radioactivity of the malate was considerably higher than the theoretical value which would be expected if malate were synthesized from citrate through the conventional Krebs cycle. The latter cycle was quite functional, but in addition to the well-known condensation reaction with oxaloacetate to give citrate, acetate condenses with glyoxylate in a reaction of the same type to give malate, catalyzed by a malate synthetase:

$$CH_3{-}CO{-}SCoA + COOH{-}CHO + H_2O \longrightarrow COOH{-}CHOH{-}CH_2{-}COOH + CoASH$$

The origin of the glyoxylate was established by the discovery of the enzyme isocitratase which catalyzes the reaction:

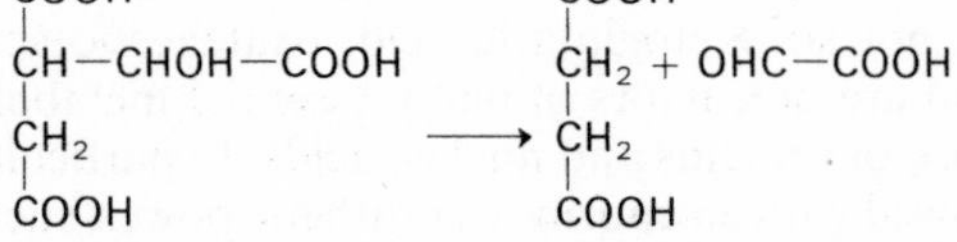

Isocitrate Succinate Glyoxylate

The cycle arising from these data can be written as on page 71.
The net result of one complete turn of the cycle is:

$$2\ \text{acetate} + \tfrac{1}{2}O_2 \longrightarrow \text{Succinate} + H_2O$$

The reaction which consumes oxygen is the re-oxidation of reduced pyridine nucleotide formed by the reaction malate → oxaloacetate, catalyzed by a malate dehydrogenase. The specific enzymes of the glyoxylic cycle, isocitratase and malate synthetase have been found in many microorganisms and plants, but never in the animal kingdom.

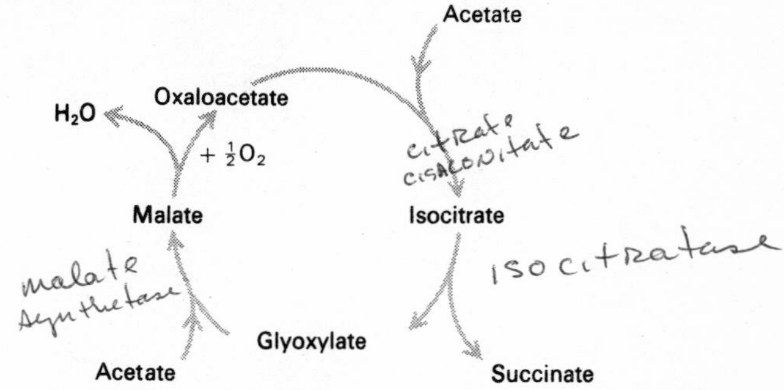

5

Gluconeogenesis
Synthesis of Glycogen and its Regulation

It has been known for more than forty years that the resynthesis of glucose from pyruvate and lactate is a process of physiological importance. Nevertheless, progress in understanding gluconeogenesis has been slow, because of the mistaken belief that every glycolytic reaction is reversible and that glucose is resynthesized by the same enzymes as those which degrade it. This concept, eminently respectable from a thermodynamic point of view, takes no account of the fact that three reactions in glycolysis are highly exothermic and constitute an energetically important barrier to the reverse working of the glycolytic cycle under physiological conditions. The reactions concerned are those catalyzed by hexokinase, phosphofructokinase and pyruvate kinase.

It is now known that gluconeogenesis uses all the glycolytic enzymes which are in actual fact reversible, together with three systems which substitute for the irreversible ones which are highly endergonic in the direction of resynthesis of glucose.

We shall be concerned with the synthesis of phosphoenolpyruvate from pyruvate (by a means other than pyruvate kinase) and with fructose diphosphatase and glucose 6-phosphatase.

SYNTHESIS OF PHOSPHOENOLPYRUVATE

The phosphorylation of pyruvate can be carried out in three ways, about each of which much information is available:

a) By pyruvate kinase. This enzyme, which we mentioned in discussing glycolysis, is of little or no importance in gluconeogenesis (80). Besides the energy barrier, its concentration in liver and kidney, the main organs for the resynthesis of glucose, is insufficient to account for the efficiency of gluconeogenesis. In addition, the affinity of pyruvate for pyruvate kinase is too weak for this enzyme to be effective at the likely intracellular substrate concentrations.

b) By the "malic" enzyme which catalyzes a reductive decarboxylation of pyruvate to malate:

$$\text{Pyruvate} + CO_2 + \text{NADPH} + H^+ \longrightarrow \text{Malate} + \text{NADP}^+$$

We can imagine that the malate formed can be oxidized to oxaloacetate by malate dehydrogenase, and the oxaloacetate transformed to phosphoenolpyruvate by phosphoenolpyruvate carboxykinase. This route is also ruled out by the low concentrations of the "malic" enzyme in liver and kidney. In this case too, the weak affinity of bicarbonate for the malic enzyme, considered in conjunction with its intracellular concentration, is incompatible with an effective functioning of the enzyme.

c) By the action of two successive enzymes, pyruvate carboxylase and phosphoenolpyruvate carboxykinase:

$$\text{Pyruvate} + \text{ATP} + CO_2 + H_2O \longrightarrow \text{Oxaloacetate} + \text{ADP} + P_i$$
(pyruvate carboxylase)

$$\text{Oxaloacetate} + \text{GTP} \longrightarrow \text{Phosphoenolpyruvate} + CO_2 + \text{GDP}$$
(PEP carboxykinase)

$$\text{Pyruvate} + \text{ATP} + \text{GTP} + H_2O \longrightarrow \text{Phosphoenolpyruvate} + \text{ADP} + \text{GDP} + P_i$$

Two equivalents of nucleoside triphosphate are required by this pathway, with the result that the reaction is exothermic and no longer presents an energy barrier (the free energy of hydrolysis of phosphoenolpyruvate is 12·8 kcal/mole, and of two equivalents of ATP is 14 kcal/mole).

In addition, the two enzymes, pyruvate carboxylase and phosphoenolpyruvate carboxykinase, occur in liver and kidney at high concentrations, and the K_m values for their respective substrates are considerably lower than the intracellular concentrations of the substrates (80). Pyruvate carboxylase is virtually absent in organs incapable of gluconeogenesis, such as brain, heart and striated muscle (80).

If pyruvate kinase were present in appreciable quantities in the same location as the two effective enzymes in gluconeogenesis, its reaction would be superimposed on theirs to give:

$$\text{Phosphoenolpyruvate} + \text{ADP} \longrightarrow \text{ATP} + \text{Pyruvate (pyruvate kinase)}$$

$$\text{Pyruvate} + \text{ATP} + \text{GTP} + H_2O \longrightarrow \text{Phosphoenolpyruvate} + \text{ADP} + \text{GDP} + P_i$$
(Pyruvate carboxylase + PEP carboxykinase)

Sum: $$\text{GTP} + H_2O \longrightarrow \text{GDP} + P_i$$

From this we can understand why pyruvate kinase and pyruvate carboxylase are not found in the same tissues or in the same subcellular fraction (81), as the result would be a hydrolysis of GTP!

Pyruvate carboxylase and its allosteric regulation (82, 83) 1.1.

This enzyme has been purified to a state of near homogeneity from chicken liver mitochondria. The enzyme contains four moles of biotin per mole of molecular weight 655,000. It is sensitive to low temperatures which dissociate it into sub-units with a sedimentation coefficient of 7 S (the native enzyme has a sedimentation coefficient of 14·8 S). The concomitant inactivation is partially reversed by restoring to ordinary temperatures. The phenomenon can be studied by ultracentrifugation and electron microscopy. Acetyl coenzyme A protects against inactivation. The reverse reaction, the decarboxylation of oxaloacetate, is possible with this enzyme, but the concentrations of phosphate required are so great that its physiological significance is doubtful.

The reaction obeys the usual rules for carboxylation reactions catalyzed by biotin-containing enzymes (84):

$$\text{Enzyme-biotin} + \text{ATP} + \text{HCO}_3^- \overset{\text{Mg}^{++}}{\rightleftarrows} \text{Enzyme-biotin} \sim \text{CO}_2 + \text{ADP} + \text{P}_i$$

(carboxylation of the enzyme)

$$\text{Enzyme-biotin} \sim \text{CO}_2 + \text{Acceptor} \rightleftarrows \text{Enzyme-biotin} + \text{Acceptor-COO}^-$$

(transcarboxylation)

Here the acceptor is pyruvate and the product oxaloacetate. The enzyme-biotin $\sim CO_2$ complex can be isolated and will carboxylate pyruvate in the absence of ATP. Acetyl CoA is necessary only for the carboxylation of the enzyme and is not involved in the transcarboxylation.

It is likely that the enzyme is made up of four sub-units of molecular weight about 150,000, each containing one molecule of biotin. Such sub-units would have a sedimentation coefficient of the order of 7 S and would be identical with the sub-unit obtained by cold dissociation. It should be noted that the activation of the enzyme by acetyl CoA at ordinary temperatures is not accompanied by a change in molecular weight; the activation does not involve an aggregation as has been described in other cases (effect of citrate on acetyl CoA carboxylase for example). A more likely explanation would be that the binding of acetyl CoA to the enzyme strengthens the degree of interaction between the sub-units while preventing the inactivation by cold. Whether this may cause the considerable increase in the catalytic activity remains open to investigation.

We have seen in the preceding chapter that oxaloacetate is a catalytic intermediate which is indispensable for the functioning of the tricarboxylic cycle, and therefore for the terminal oxidation of carbohydrates and fatty acids; in addition, the carboxylation of pyruvate to oxaloacetate is an indispensable step for the biosynthesis of every metabolite synthesized from intermediates from the cycle and from gluconeogenesis.

If the supply of oxaloacetate is low, acetyl CoA will tend to accumulate and will stimulate the synthesis of oxaloacetate through the activation of pyruvate carboxylase. This in turn will stimulate the production of citrate and other intermediates of the Krebs cycle. Gluconeogenesis will similarly be facilitated, as will fatty acid synthesis, an essential step of which is allosterically activated by citrate.

It has recently been shown that addition of acetoacetate, which brings about a notable increase in the intracellular concentration of acetyl CoA, causes gluconeogenesis from lactate to speed up greatly in kidney slices. The control of gluconeogenesis at the stage of pyruvate carboxylase activation seems therefore to be a physiological reality and not a figment of the imagination.

FRUCTOSE DIPHOSPHATASE AND ITS ALLOSTERIC REGULATION (88, 89, 90)

The existence of this enzyme avoids the difficulty presented by the highly exergonic nature of the phosphofructokinase reaction. Fructose diphosphatase hydrolyzes fructose 1,6-diphosphate to fructose 6-phosphate and inorganic phosphate. Its importance in gluconeogenesis is attested by its exclusive presence in tissues which are gluconeogenic or carry out an appreciable synthesis of glycogen (85). Some control of fructose diphosphatase activity is foreseeable, for in its absence, the simultaneous presence of phosphofructokinase and the diphosphatase would result in a hydrolysis of ATP by coupling of the two reactions:

$$\text{Fructose 1,6-diphosphate} \longrightarrow \text{Fructose 6-phosphate} + P_i$$

$$\text{Fructose 6-phosphate} + \text{ATP} \longrightarrow \text{Fructose 1,6-diphosphate} + \text{ADP}$$

Sum:

$$\text{ATP} \longrightarrow \text{ADP} + P_i$$

Different laboratories have discovered that mammalian fructose diphosphatase is strongly inhibited by AMP and is reversibly activated by ATP or ADP (86, 87). These effects are the opposite of those found with liver phosphofructokinase. This theoretically results in a fine control of the two enzymatic activities in a reciprocal fashion and avoids the eventual wastage mentioned above.

The reversible and highly specific inhibition of fructose diphosphatase by AMP is non-competitive with respect to substrate. The kinetics of the inhibition are complex: the enzyme activity decreases in a sigmoid fashion as a function of inhibitor concentration, and it seems, on a purely kinetic basis, that four AMP molecules complex with each enzyme molecule at saturation. The fact that the inhibition is non-competitive suggests that AMP binds at an allosteric site and causes a conformational change in the protein which affects its catalytic activity. The existence of distinct allosteric sites is attested by the following experimental observations:

a) Limited proteolysis by papain desensitizes the enzyme towards AMP without perceptibly affecting its catalytic activity.

b) The enzyme crystallized from rabbit liver contains about 39 tyrosyl residues per molecule. Ten of these can be acetylated by acetyl imidazole, a specific acetylating agent. The acetylation can be followed as a function of time. When only two tyrosines are acetylated, no change is found in the behaviour of the enzyme. When six are acetylated, an enzyme is obtained which is desensitized towards AMP. Acetylation of ten residues destroys the enzymatic activity. These acetylation reactions can be made selective by working in the presence of substrate or allosteric effector: in the presence of fructose 1,6-diphosphate, only six tyrosines are acetylated and the enzyme is desensitized; but in the presence of AMP, again six are acetylated, but the enzyme undergoes a heavy loss of activity, any activity remaining being sensitive to AMP. With the additional fact that AMP does not protect the enzyme which has been desensitized by papain from acetylation, it becomes clear that some of the tyrosine residues form part of the catalytic site and others of the allosteric site.

The enzyme crystallized from rabbit liver has a molecular weight of 127,000 (7·2 S). At pH 2, it dissociates into two sub-units with molecular weights about 75,000 (4·0 S). The two sub-units can be recombined to give a molecule with the original sedimentation properties (but only 70% of the specific activity) by treatment at pH 7 with 2-mercaptoethanol. Two N-terminal amino acids (serine and glycine) and two C-terminal ones (alanine and glycine) have been detected. The two sub-units would therefore appear to be different.

Fructose diphosphatase exists in two forms which can be interconverted by pre-incubation with different metabolites. One form is active with fructose 1,6-diphosphate and sedoheptulose 1,7-diphosphate, the other only with sedoheptulose 1,7-diphosphate (to date there is no physiological explanation for the activity with the C_7 compound). The transition from the inactive to the active state, which occurs rapidly at pH 7·5, is not associated with a change in sedimentation coefficient. This conversion is partially inhibited by fructose 1,6-diphosphate and fructose 6-phosphate and depends largely on pH and temperature. The reverse change is induced by ATP. At the present time, these effects have not received any physiological explanation.

Fructose diphosphatase in microorganisms 2.1.

Fructose diphosphatase has been crystallized from *Candida utilis* (91, 92). It is active only with fructose 1,6-diphosphate, unlike the rabbit liver enzyme. (This microorganism synthesizes a distinct sedoheptulose 1,7-diphosphatase as well). AMP exerts a sigmoid inhibition on the enzyme (total inhibition occurs at pH 7·5 at an AMP concentration of 4×10^{-4} M). The inhibitory effect of AMP can be completely abolished by treatment of the enzyme with fluorodinitrobenzene (FDNB) in the presence of the substrate, without loss of catalytic activity. In absence of the substrate, dinitrophenylation leads to complete inactivation. If the enzyme is desensitized with radioactive FDNB and hydrolyzed, and the radioactive dinitrophenylamino acids identified, equal amounts of O-DNP-tyrosine and ε-DNP-lysine are found exclusively. Quantitative measurement of dinitrophenylation in the presence and absence of substrate shows that two tyrosyl and two lysyl residues are involved in the sensitivity to AMP and that two other tyrosyl and two other lysyl residues are involved in the catalytic activity.

Mutants of *E. coli* deficient in fructose diphosphatase have been obtained (93, 94). They can not grow on acetate, glycerol or succinate, demonstrating the importance of diphosphatase for gluconeogenesis; these mutants have an absolute requirement for hexoses, for they have no other means of synthesizing ribose 5-phosphate, for example, which is indispensable in the synthesis of nucleic acids, histidine and tryptophan; or erythrose 4-phosphate required in the biosynthesis of the aromatic nucleus (see chapters dealing with these biosyntheses). Wild type organisms possess higher levels of diphosphatase when they are grown on glycerol than on glucose, for they must synthesize glucose (Table X).

TABLE X

Organism	Grown on: Glucose	Glycerol
	Specific activity of fructose diphosphatase (mμ moles/mg/min)	
Saccharomyces cerevisiae	1	25
Candida utilis	26	140

Glucose 6-phosphatase and its control 2.2.

The hydrolysis of glucose 6-phosphate is the final step in gluconeogenesis. Some sort of regulation of this enzyme is necessary, for if its action were unrestrained, in the presence of hexokinase (for example glucokinase), the end result would be a fruitless hydrolysis of ATP. Moreover, such a regulation is necessary to explain the constant blood glucose level, even in extreme conditions such as fasting; the importance of this enzyme in this regard is shown by the fact that diseases of liver glucose 6-phosphatase deficiency have relatively low blood glucose levels and increased amounts of muscle glycogen (95). The two products of glucose 6-phosphatase action, glucose and inorganic phosphate, are inhibitors of the enzyme and it was thought for a long time that this was sufficient for the physiological control of blood glucose concentration. However, recent discoveries have opened out new areas of research: glucose 6-phosphatase is a multifunctional enzyme (96, 97), able to carry out the reaction

$$\text{Glucose 6-phosphate} + H_2O \longrightarrow \text{Glucose} + P_i \quad (1)$$

and in addition,

$$\text{Pyrophosphate} + H_2O \longrightarrow 2\,P_i \quad (2)$$

$$\text{Glucose 6-phosphate} + {}^{14}\text{C-glucose} \rightleftharpoons {}^{14}\text{C-glucose 6-phosphate} + \text{Glucose} \quad (3)$$

$$\text{Pyrophosphate} + \text{Glucose} \longrightarrow \text{Glucose 6-phosphate} + P_i \quad (4)$$

A phosphorylated enzyme derivative is the common intermediate in all these reactions and it is evident that their relative importance depends on the relative glucose and pyrophosphate concentrations, which seem to bind to the same site. Pyrophosphate is a product of the reaction during which UDP-glucose, the precursor of glycogen, is synthesized, and glucose 6-phosphate is an activator of this synthesis. Pyrophosphate acts as an inhibitor for the hydrolysis of glucose 6-phosphate (reaction 4); furthermore it produces P_i, another inhibitor of the phosphatase. It can therefore act in conjunction with glucose 6-phosphate to divert the flow of glucose 6-phosphate into glycogen synthesis instead of leaving it to be simply hydrolyzed. Although these rationalizations are attractive, let us say at once that they have not yet received confirmation.

Glucose 6-phosphatase seems to be a lipoprotein and under certain conditions complex lipids seem to be able to activate or inhibit it. A systematic search for effectors able to influence the K_m and K_i values of this enzyme for its different substrates and effectors would be desirable. In fact, the K_m for glucose in reaction (4) is 8×10^{-2} M and the K_i for the inhibition of the hydrolysis of glucose 6-phosphate is of the same order. These values are considerably higher than the amounts of glucose in the blood.

GLYCOGEN SYNTHETASE

Even as recently as ten years ago, the concept that every enzymatic reaction was reversible so dominated the biochemical scene that everyone was certain that the synthesis of fatty acids, gluconeogenesis and glycogen synthesis used the reverse of the reactions which had been discovered in their degradation. This concept has happily been abandoned to make way for more rational considerations from the standpoint of thermodynamics.

Thus it is not phosphorylase which is responsible for the resynthesis of glycogen but UDP-glucose:glycogen glucosyl transferase or glycogen synthetase.

In glycogen synthesis, as with the two other natural polysaccharides, starch and cellulose, the same mechanism is used: the transfer of a glucosyl residue from a nucleoside diphosphate glucose to a primer whose length varies in each case, the primer being itself made up of a linear chain of glucosyl residues. The equation on page 80 shows the type of reaction common to the synthesis of the three polysaccharides. In the case of glycogen, the glucose donor is UDPG. For starch and bacterial glycogen, the donor is adenosine diphosphoglucose (98).

The acceptor, $(\text{glucose})_n$, can be an oligosaccharide, but the best acceptor is glycogen itself.

UDPG is synthesized from glucose 1-phosphate and uridine triphosphate by a specific enzyme, UDPG pyrophosphorylase (99):

$$\text{UTP} + \text{Glucose 1-phosphate} \longrightarrow \text{UDPG} + \text{Pyrophosphate}$$

In the last analysis, it is glucose 1-phosphate which is the origin of glycogen; now in gluconeogenesis the last reaction before glucose is glucose 6-phosphatase. We may remember that glucose 1-phosphate and glucose 6-phosphate are readily interconvertible by phosphoglucomutase.

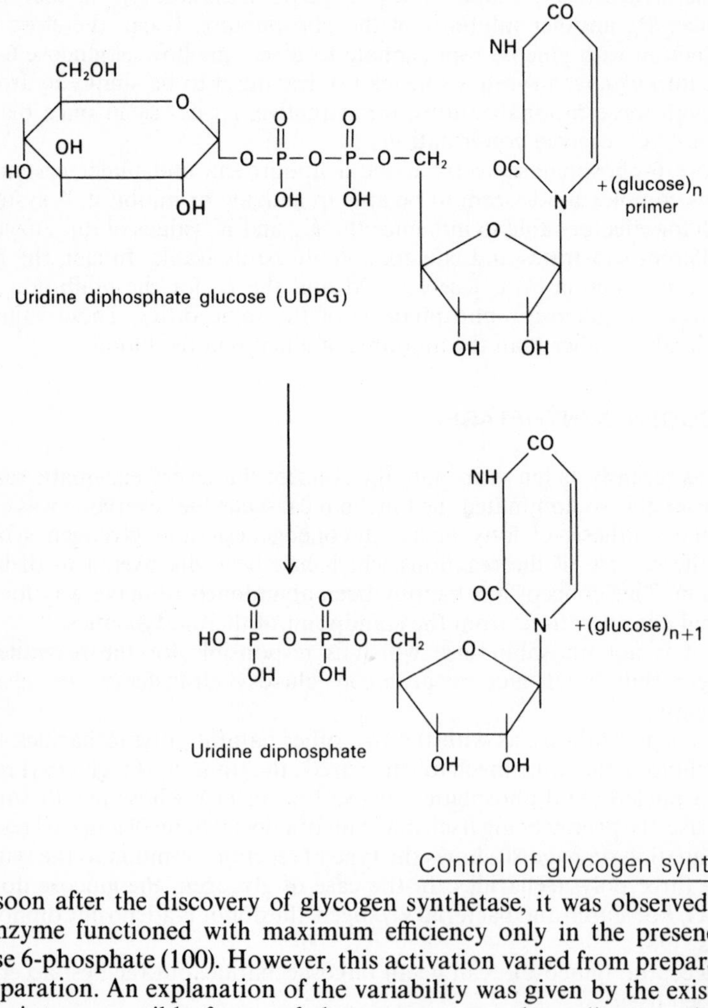

Control of glycogen synthesis 3.1.

Very soon after the discovery of glycogen synthetase, it was observed that this enzyme functioned with maximum efficiency only in the presence of glucose 6-phosphate (100). However, this activation varied from preparation to preparation. An explanation of the variability was given by the existence of two interconvertible forms of the enzyme, one depending on glucose 6-phosphate for its activity (form D) and a form independent of it (form I) (101). Conversion of form I to form D can be carried out in three different ways: 1) by phosphorylation of form I by ATP; 2) by an activation in the presence of Ca^{++} and a protein factor; 3) by a limited proteolysis by trypsin. The phosphorylation of form I by ATP requires the presence of Mg^{++} and is catalyzed by a specific kinase activated by 3′,5′-cyclic-AMP. The protein factor necessary for the activation by Ca^{++} may be identical with the one which we have already seen plays an analogous role in the activation of phosphorylase *b* kinase. The nature of the reactions occurring in the transformation I ⇌ D by methods (2) and (3) is not known, but the reactions depend on the presence of ATP or glucose 6-phosphate.

Conversely, form D can be transformed to form I by the action of a specific phosphatase.

Detailed analyses (102) of the mode of activation of form D by glucose 6-phosphate are available. All show a considerable increase in V_{max} and an increased affinity of the enzyme for UDP-glucose. In one case, lamb striated muscle, glucose 6-phosphate does not affect V_{max}, but has an influence on K_m. These facts, together with the protection given by glucose 6-phosphate against inactivation of the enzyme by *p*-mercuribenzoate, have been interpreted as follows: glucose 6-phosphate is an allosteric activator whose primary effect is a conformational change in the structure of the enzyme.

Glucose 6-phosphate has no influence on the V_{max} of form I, but causes a similar increase in the affinity for UDPG.

It is possible that glycogen itself may exert a feed-back control on the conversion I → D and so regulate its own biosynthesis (103). Studies *in vivo* with mouse muscles subjected to different physiological stimuli affecting their glycogen concentration show changes in this direction in the ratio of form I to form D. Generally, the relative concentration of form I increases when the concentration of glycogen decreases, and we conclude that the interconversion of forms I and D of glycogen synthetase provides an effective means of controlling its activity since it allows the transformation from a form intrinsically more active (I) to a form less active (D) which depends on the intracellular concentration of glucose 6-phosphate.

6

Biosynthesis of Lipids
and its Regulation

THE SYNTHESIS OF SHORT-CHAIN FATTY ACIDS (104)

A little more than thirty years ago, the anaerobic bacterium *Clostridium kluyveri* was isolated. This organism is able to grow in a mixture of ethanol and acetate as sole source of carbon, and produces butyrate and caproate as fermentation products. It was possible to obtain cell-free extracts of this organism which could reproduce all the enzymatic reactions involved in the biosynthesis of acids from C_4 to C_6.

Ethanol is first of all oxidized to acetic acid in two steps, catalyzed respectively by alcohol dehydrogenase and an acetaldehyde dehydrogenase whose action is dependent on the presence of coenzyme A:

$$CH_3{-}CH_2OH + NAD^+ \rightleftarrows CH_3CHO + NADH + H^+$$

$$CH_3{-}CHO + CoASH + NAD^+ \rightleftarrows CH_3CO{-}SCoA + NADH + H^+$$

We should note that it is not acetic acid, but the more reactive acetyl CoA which is formed. Other bacteria produce acetyl CoA by a much more complex reaction, called the phosphoroclastic decomposition of pyruvate. (1)

β-ketoacylthiolase carries out the condensation of two molecules of acetyl CoA by joining the methyl group of one to the carboxyl group of the other. The product is acetoacetyl CoA:

$$2\,CH_3{-}CO{-}SCoA \longrightarrow CH_3{-}CO{-}CH_2{-}CO{-}SCoA + CoASH$$

2 AcCoA ⟶ Acetoacetyl CoA (2)

β-hydroxybutyryl CoA dehydrogenase next reduces acetoacetyl CoA to β-hydroxybutyryl CoA:

$$CH_3{-}CO{-}CH_2{-}CO{-}SCoA + NADH + H^+ \rightleftarrows CH_3CHOH{-}CH_2{-}CO{-}SCoA + NAD^+$$

β-hydroxybutyryl CoA

This compound is dehydrated in a reaction catalyzed by a specific crotonase:

$$CH_3{-}CHOH{-}CH_2{-}CO{-}SCoA \rightleftarrows CH_3{-}CH{=}CH{-}CO{-}SCoA + H_2O$$

Crotonyl CoA

Crotonyl CoA is reduced to butyryl CoA by butyryl CoA dehydrogenase:

$$CH_3{-}CH{=}CH{-}CO{-}SCoA + 2H \rightleftarrows CH_3CH_2CH_2COSCoA$$

Butyryl CoA

A specific deacylase removes the CoA residue, and free butyric acid is formed. The synthesis of caproate takes place by an analogous series of reactions starting with a condensation of butyryl CoA with acetyl CoA to give β-ketocaproyl CoA. If *Cl. kluyveri* is grown on ethanol and propionate, the acids *n*-pentanoic and *n*-heptanoic are obtained, which have an odd number of carbon atoms. The synthesis of these acids occurs by the same kind of reaction sequence as outlined for butyric acid.

OXIDATION OF FATTY ACIDS

In brief, the degradation of fatty acids is carried out by means of reactions which are the reverse of those we have just examined in connection with the synthesis of butyric acid.

A long-chain fatty acid is esterified by coenzyme A in the presence of ATP by a fatty acid thiokinase:

$$R{-}CH_2{-}CH_2{-}COOH + CoASH + ATP \longrightarrow R{-}CH_2CH_2COSCoA + AMP + \text{pyrophosphate}$$

An acyl dehydrogenase transforms the acyl CoA derivative to the corresponding α,β-unsaturated compound:

$$R{-}CH_2{-}CH_2{-}COSCoA + X \rightleftarrows R{-}CH{=}CH{-}COSCoA + XH_2$$

An enoyl hydratase converts the unsaturated derivative to a β-hydroxyacyl CoA:

$$R{-}CH{=}CH{-}COSCoA + H_2O \rightleftarrows R{-}CHOH{-}CH_2{-}COSCoA$$

A β-hydroxyacyl dehydrogenase, which uses NAD as electron acceptor, then catalyzes the following reaction:

$$R{-}CHOH{-}CH_2{-}COSCoA + NAD^+ \rightleftarrows R{-}CO{-}CH_2{-}COSCoA + NADH + H^+$$

Finally, β-ketoacylthiolase converts this compound to acetyl CoA and an acyl CoA derivative with two carbon atoms fewer than the starting compound:

$$R{-}CO{-}CH_2{-}COSCoA + CoASH \rightleftarrows R{-}COSCoA + CH_3COSCoA$$

The acyl CoA derivative undergoes a new cycle of degradation and liberates a further molecule of acetyl CoA, and so on. The acetyl CoA formed condenses with oxaloacetate and is broken up by the enzymes of the citric cycle. The condensation reaction which gives rise to citrate can therefore be considered as making the connection between lipid and carbohydrate degradation.

SYNTHESIS OF LONG-CHAIN FATTY ACIDS

We have just seen how the biosynthesis of short-chain fatty acids uses the reverse of the scheme of reactions for the degradation of fatty acids. A second system is of much greater importance, for it is responsible for the synthesis of long-chain fatty acids which are permanent constituents of lipids. The first intermediate to be identified in the synthesis of long-chain fatty acids (C_{10} to C_{18}) was malonyl CoA (105). Its synthesis is catalyzed by a biotin-containing enzyme, acetyl CoA carboxylase, which brings about the carboxylation of acetyl CoA in the presence of ATP (106):

$$CH_3CO{-}SCoA + CO_2 + ATP \longrightarrow COOH{-}CH_2{-}COSCoA + ADP + P_i$$

Acetyl CoA carboxylase is under regulation by a mechanism to which we shall return later.

It is known that the main compound synthesized from acetate by extracts purified from pigeon liver is palmitic acid, the saturated fatty acid with a straight chain of 16 carbon atoms. The overall equation representing the stoichiometry of its synthesis is the following (107):

$$\underset{\text{Acetyl CoA}}{CH_3{-}COSCoA} + 7\,\underset{\text{Malonyl CoA}}{COOH{-}CH_2{-}COSCoA} + 14\,NADPH + 14\,H^+$$

$$\downarrow$$

$$\underset{\text{Palmitate}}{CH_3(CH_2)_{14}COOH} + 7\,CO_2 + 8\,CoASH + 14\,NADP^+ + 6\,H_2O$$

The carbon atoms of acetyl CoA are incorporated into the methyl group and the last methylene group of palmitic acid, whilst the carbon atoms of malonyl CoA appear as carbon atoms 1 to 14. Acetyl CoA can be substituted in this reaction by the butyryl, hexanoyl and tetradecanoyl CoA derivatives, a fact which led to the belief that these compounds were probable intermediates in the synthesis of palmitate. We shall see that this is not so.

Recent work on the system synthesizing palmitate from acetyl CoA and malonyl CoA has been carried out with three systems, isolated respectively from the bacterium *E. coli*, yeast and chicken liver.

It has been possible to show in *E. coli* (108, 109) that the product of the condensation of acetyl CoA and malonyl CoA is an acetoacetyl derivative bound to a heat-stable protein fraction; this protein has been called by the American authors *acyl carrier protein* (ACP). In the presence of NADPH and a crude *E. coli* fraction, acetoacetyl-ACP is reduced to butyryl-ACP. The latter then reacts with a new molecule of malonyl-ACP to form β-ketohexanoyl-ACP, which is reduced to hexanoyl-ACP. The process of elongation is repeated until palmityl-ACP is formed and palmitate finally liberated.

The *E. coli* fatty acid synthetase has been decomposed into several purified fractions. Studies with these fractions suggest the following series of reactions as the mechanism of palmitate synthesis in this bacterium:

$$\text{Malonyl—CoA} + \text{ACP—SH} \rightleftharpoons \text{Malonyl—S—ACP} + \text{CoASH}$$

$$\text{Acetyl—CoA} + \text{ACP—SH} \rightleftharpoons \text{Acetyl—S—ACP} + \text{CoASH}$$

$$\text{Acetyl—S—ACP} + \text{Malonyl—S—ACP} \rightleftharpoons \text{Acetoacetyl—S—ACP} + \text{ACP—SH} + CO_2$$

$$\text{Acetoacetyl—S—ACP} + \text{NADPH} + H^+ \rightleftharpoons \beta\text{-hydroxybutyryl—S—ACP} + \text{NADP}^+$$

$$\beta\text{-hydroxybutyryl—S—ACP} \rightleftharpoons \text{Crotonyl—S—ACP} + H_2O$$

$$\text{Crotonyl—S—ACP} + \text{NADPH} + H^+ \rightleftharpoons \text{Butyryl—S—ACP} + \text{NADP}^+$$

$$\text{Butyryl—S—ACP} + \text{Malonyl—S—ACP} \rightleftharpoons \text{Ketohexanoyl—S—ACP} + \text{ACP—SH} + CO_2 \text{ etc.}$$

Thus coenzyme A esters are not involved as intermediates in this synthesis after the first two steps which form the ACP derivatives of malonate and acetate. The next four reactions, previously demonstrated to occur with CoA, reflect a lack of absolute specificity in the enzymes whose normal substrates are the ACP-bound derivatives.

It was discovered quite recently (110, 111) that the substrate binding site of ACP is the sulfhydryl group of a prosthetic group, 4′-phosphopantetheine. Thus both ACP and coenzyme A have 4′-phosphopantetheine as their acyl-binding site. It has been shown very recently that this group is itself bound to ACP by a phosphodiester linkage with a serine hydroxyl group of ACP; a part of the sequence around the prosthetic group has been determined:

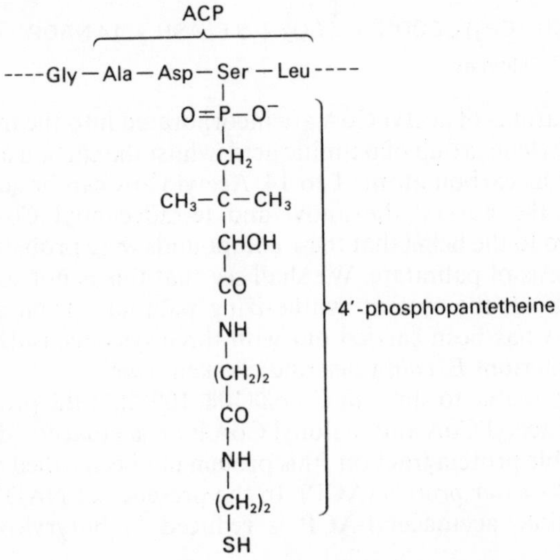

The ACP protein has a molecular weight of about 9,000 and an N-terminal serine (different from the serine binding the prosthetic group), and C-terminal alanine. It is to the —SH group of phosphopantetheine that the acetyl, malonyl and the intermediate acyl groups are covalently linked during the synthesis. ACP is characterized by the absence of cysteine and tryptophan. The same system as described in *E. coli* is present in chicken liver. Very recently, it has been shown that mammals and plants use the same pathway for the synthesis of fatty acids.

Unlike the *E. coli* system which can be fractionated into independent elements, the fatty acid synthetase in yeast (112) behaves as a multi-enzyme complex and can be purified until it becomes a homogeneous protein. The molecular weight of the complex is $2{\cdot}3 \times 10^6$. It contains four moles of flavin mononucleotide per mole of protein.

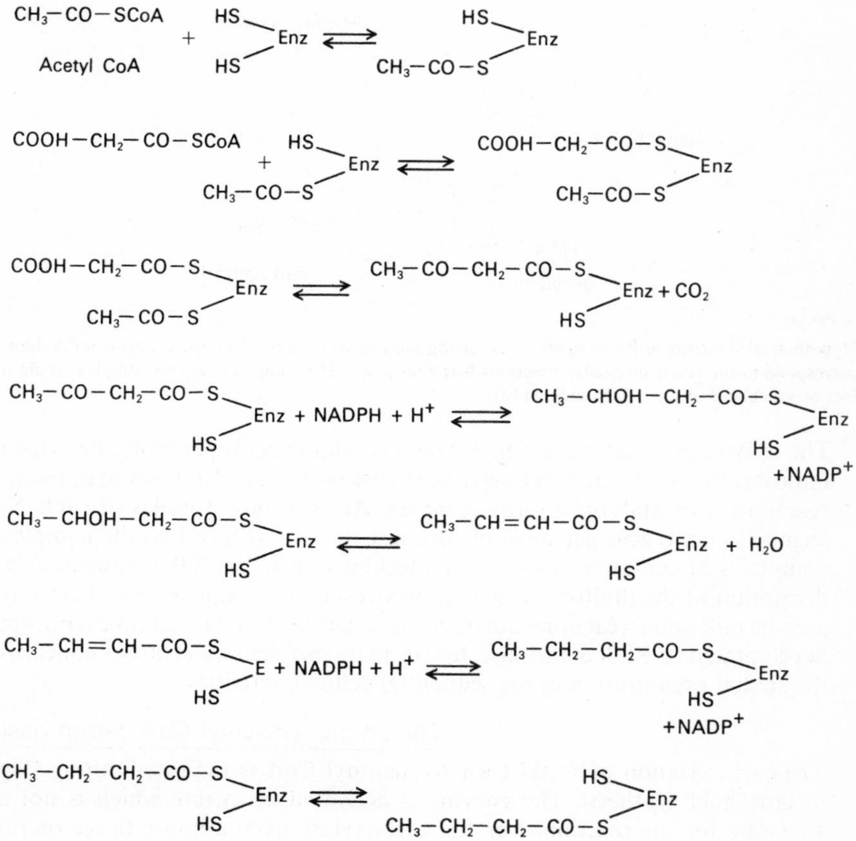

Electron micrographs of the synthetase show it as a particle of diameter 200 to 250 Å. The above scheme has been proposed for the synthesis of fatty acids by this particle. The last reaction involves the transfer of the butyryl group which has been synthesized by this scheme onto the —SH group to which the initial acetyl group attached itself, thus freeing the other —SH group which will accept a new malonyl group to continue the elongation. This scheme involves two sulfhydryl groups with different specificities, one for the acetyl group, the other for the malonyl group. The one associated with acetyl CoA (called the peripheral —SH) has been identified by its extreme sensitivity to alkylating agents and the power of acetyl CoA to protect it. It is part of a cysteinyl residue. The other group (central —SH) has little reactivity with alkylating agents, is associated with the malonyl residues, and has been identified as part of a 4′-phosphopantetheine residue presumably connected to the protein by a phosphodiester bond. Three peripheral —SH groups have been determined per mole of enzyme.

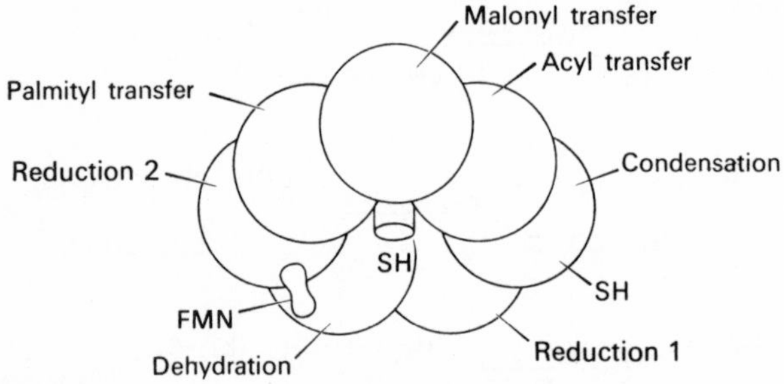

FIGURE 20

Hypothetical structure of the complex synthesizing fatty acids in yeast. The seven enzyme units shown correspond to the seven successive reactions listed on p. 87. The complete enzyme complex would in fact be composed of three such units (112).

The enzyme complex has seven N-terminal amino acids per molecule, which indicates that there are seven separate proteins (fig. 21). Now, seven different reactions are catalyzed by the complex. As there are 3 moles of each N-terminal amino acid per mole of complex, we can deduce that the complex comprises 21 sub-units of average molecular weight 100,000. Unfortunately, disruption of the multi-enzyme complex results in complete loss of activity and the individual reactions can only be studied in the intact complex. Future developments are full of promise, for the main problem which arises concerns the spatial organization of the sequential cellular activities.

The control of acetyl CoA carboxylase 3.1.

The carboxylation of acetyl CoA to malonyl CoA is the rate-limiting step in fatty acid synthesis. The enzyme is activated by citrate which is not a substrate for the reaction. For the carboxylase from adipose tissue or rat

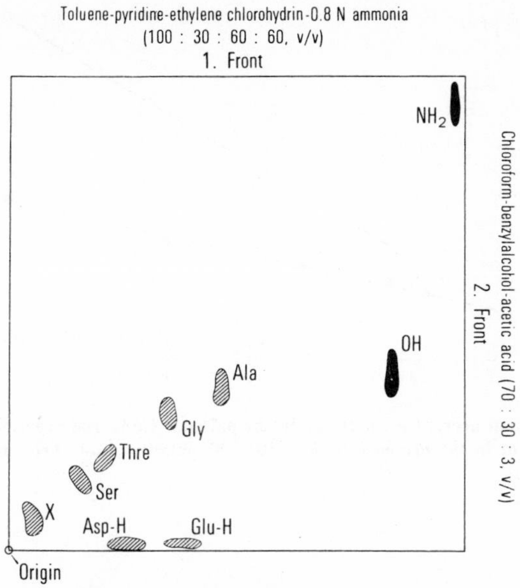

FIGURE 21

Two-dimensional thin layer chromatography of the dinitrophenylamino acids obtained by reaction of the pure synthetase with fluorodinitrobenzene. One of the seven amino acids has not been identified. Fluorodinitrobenzene reacts with the amino ends of proteins (112).

liver, this important activation is accompanied by a conformational change in the protein. By sucrose density gradient centrifugation, the sedimentation coefficient of the enzyme has been estimated to be 18·8 S. When the enzyme is incubated with citrate under the same conditions as are necessary for its activation, and centrifuged in the presence of citrate, its sedimentation coefficient becomes 43 S. The rate of activation of the enzyme is concentration-dependent. There are grounds for thinking that in this case, activation and aggregation are two expressions of the same fundamental phenomenon (113). Let us recall that citrate accumulates when NAD-dependent isocitrate dehydrogenase is non-functional due to lack of AMP; besides the effect of citrate on the carboxylase, the exclusive functioning of the other isocitrate dehydrogenase, the one requiring NADP, increases the amount of NADPH which becomes available for fatty acid synthesis.

In addition to its sensitivity to activation, acetyl CoA carboxylase is susceptible to feed-back inhibition by distant products resulting from its action, the long-chain acyl CoA derivatives (fig. 22). These derivatives are competitive inhibitors and are more effective the longer the aliphatic chain (114). We should also note that the addition of citrate to tissue slices causes an increase in fatty acid synthesis and a decrease in sterol synthesis, both of which start from acetyl CoA.

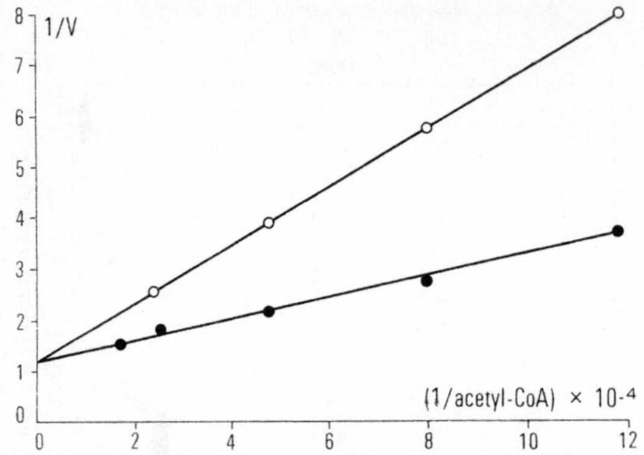

FIGURE 22

Competitive inhibition of acetyl CoA carboxylase by palmityl CoA. The experiment shown by white circles was carried out in the presence of 2×10^{-5} M palmityl CoA. Free palmitic acid has no inhibitory action (114).

SYNTHESIS OF TRIGLYCERIDES AND COMPLEX LIPIDS

The direct acylation of glycerol has never been observed.

From extracts of *Clostridium butyricum* (115) obtained by sonication, a soluble fraction and a particulate fraction can be prepared. In the presence of these two fractions plus ACP (obtained from *E. coli*), the acylation of glycerol 3-phosphate by palmityl CoA can be accomplished. The same acylation has been obtained directly by using palmityl-ACP. The reaction product is lysophosphatidic acid:

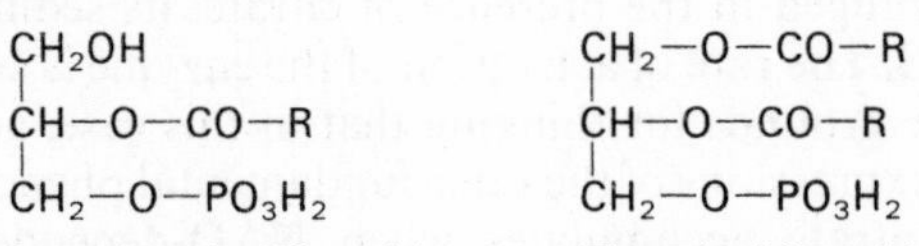

Lysophosphatidic acid — Phosphatidic acid

A membrane preparation from *E. coli* can carry out the same reactions. Besides lysophosphatidic acid, the synthesis of monopalmitin and phosphatidic acid have been demonstrated. It is very likely that monopalmitin comes from the dephosphorylation of lysophosphatidic acid. The dephosphorylation of phosphatidic acid, on the other hand, produces an α,β-diglyceride, the precursor of both triglycerides and lecithin.

An enzyme from chicken liver has been described, which synthesizes triglycerides from diglycerides and acyl CoA (116):

$$\text{R—COSCoA} + \alpha,\beta\text{-diglyceride} \longrightarrow \text{triglyceride} + \text{CoA—SH}$$

The other precursor of lecithin is choline:

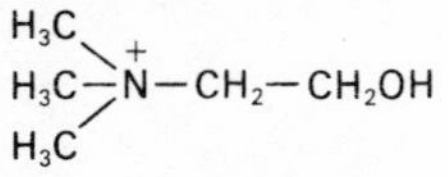

Choline

which is synthesized by successive methylation reactions, using S-adenosylmethionine, from ethanolamine, which arises from serine:

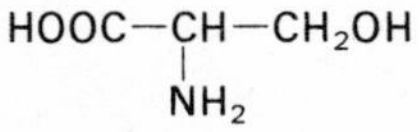

Serine

H_2N-CH_2-COOH

Ethanolamine

Choline is phosphorylated to become phosphorylcholine:

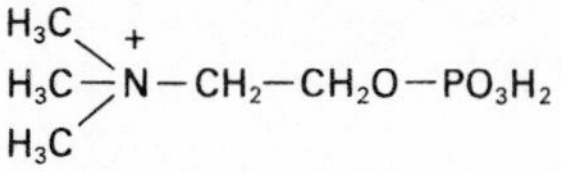

Phosphorylcholine

This reacts with CTP, with elimination of pyrophosphate, to give CDP-choline:

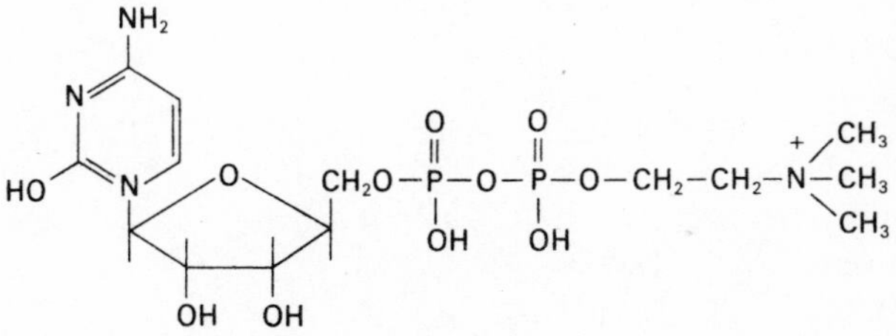

Cytidine diphosphate choline (CDP-choline)

CDP-choline reacts with an α,β-diglyceride, with the formation of CMP and lecithin:

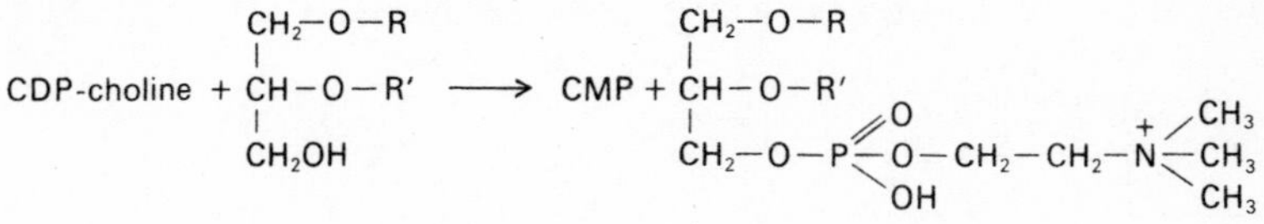

Lecithin

7

Biosynthetic Pathways

Methods of study, and outline of the control of enzyme biosynthesis

In order to determine the pathways of biosynthesis, it is preferable to use organisms which are growing actively. Newly synthesized material can be recognized by the increase in cell numbers in a bacterial culture or the increase in weight in a growing animal such as a rat. Animal and plant cells grow slowly in general: the cells of the mammalian central nervous system grow only during the early life of the animal and divide no further; muscle cells divide and grow slowly; liver cells divide about every three months; those of the intestinal mucosa have a division time easily measured in days. In contrast, bacterial cells can double their number and weight every twenty minutes. Newly synthesized material, in a bacterium such as *E. coli*, arises solely from a simple carbon source such as glucose or acetate, and ammonia, sulfate and inorganic phosphate. Such a bacterium is capable of intense chemical activity.

Nearly all the metabolic energy in the bacterium is used in biosyntheses. It is obvious that bacteria of this kind are the material of choice for the study of anabolic phenomena.

Several methods have been used to elucidate the pathways of biosynthesis for small molecules (amino acids, purines, pyrimidines), which make up the materials from which proteins and nucleic acids are synthesized. The most important, which we are going to survey, are the use of isotopes, the use of auxotrophic mutants (unable to synthesize a given essential metabolite), and finally the examination of the individual enzyme reactions.

USE OF ISOTOPES

Organisms can be grown on specific carbon sources, such as glucose labelled in the C_1 or C_6 position with ^{14}C, acetate labelled with radio-carbon, or acetate doubly labelled in the methyl group with ^{14}C and in the carboxyl group with the non-radioactive heavy isotope ^{13}C (see in particular reference 117). After growth, the organisms are collected, and the protein fraction (for example) is isolated and subjected to acid or alkaline hydrolysis; the individual amino acids are separated and the distribution of the individual carbon atoms is determined by laborious degradation methods. Such methods are generally very difficult, and seldom provide unambiguous answers to the question of the detailed chemical reactions by which the carbon atoms of the nutrient are incorporated into an amino acid. More often, they at best allow us to exclude a pathway which might have seemed possible. A much more useful method is isotope competition (24), which is described below.

The principle is as follows: if uniformly labelled glucose is provided as sole carbon source for the bacterium, all the essential metabolites will be uniformly labelled. If a suspected intermediate is added to the culture as an

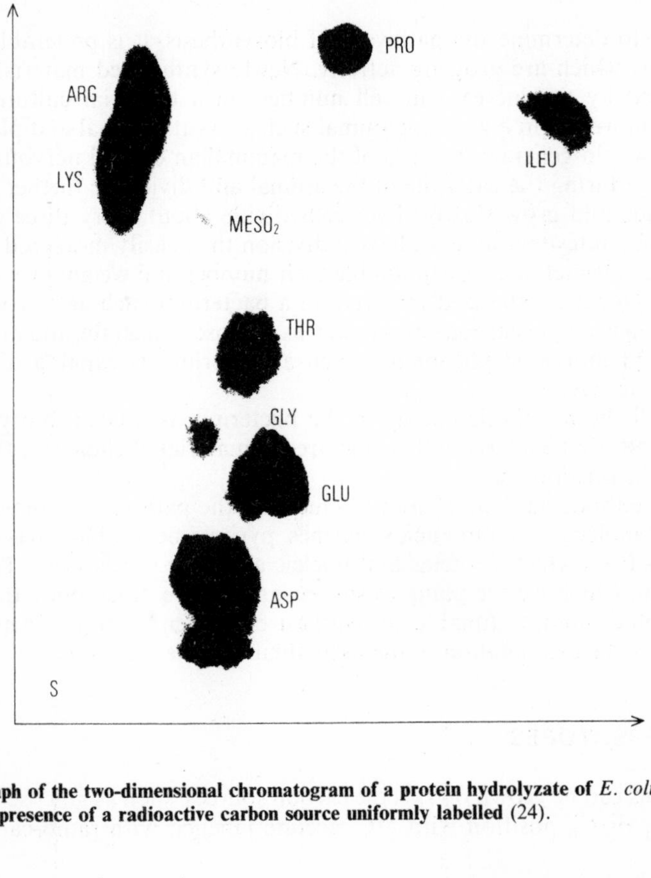

FIGURE 23

Radioautograph of the two-dimensional chromatogram of a protein hydrolyzate of *E. coli* which was grown in the presence of a radioactive carbon source uniformly labelled (24).

unlabelled compound, and if there is no permeability barrier, it will dilute the radioactivity of the labelled intermediate enormously. As a result, the final metabolite will be non-radioactive, or at least its specific activity will be greatly reduced. Let us look at some applications of this method.

a) A culture is grown in a synthetic medium containing uniformly labelled glucose and non-radioactive homoserine. After growth, the culture is centrifuged, washed, and the protein fraction isolated and hydrolyzed. The resulting amino acids are separated by paper chromatography. The chromatogram is placed on a film sensitive to radiation; the spots corresponding to radioactive amino acids will blacken the film. In addition, amino acids can be located on the chromatogram by ninhydrin. The amino acids threonine, methionine and isoleucine are found to have little or no radioactivity, while the specific activity of all the other amino acids is identical with that of the original glucose. The conclusion is reached that homoserine is probably an intermediate in the biosynthesis of threonine, isoleucine and methionine.

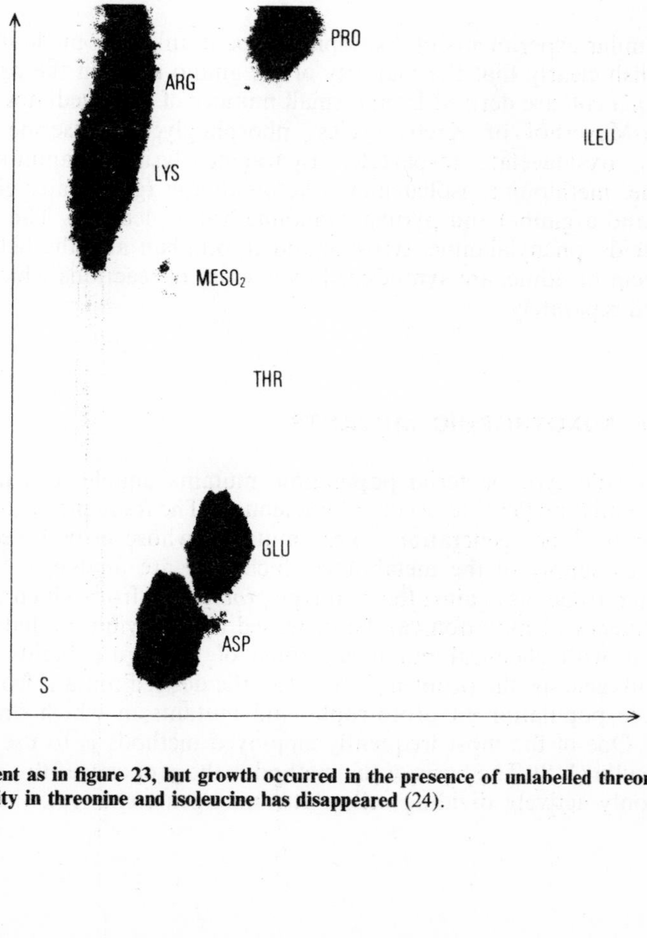

FIGURE 24

Same experiment as in figure 23, but growth occurred in the presence of unlabelled threonine. Note that radioactivity in threonine and isoleucine has disappeared (24).

b) If the same experiment is carried out, but this time adding non-radioactive aspartate, the radioactivity of the protein aspartate is found to be greatly reduced, and so also is that of diaminopimelic acid (a cell wall constituent in *E. coli*), lysine, and the same three amino acids of the previous experiment, threonine, methionine, and isoleucine.
c) On addition next of non-radioactive threonine as competitor, the radio-autograms of the protein hydrolyzate show that threonine and isoleucine from protein are not radioactive (figures 23 and 24).
d) When non-radioactive methionine and isoleucine are used as competitors, they affect only their own specific radioactivities.
The results of these experiments collectively suggest the following biosynthetic pathway:

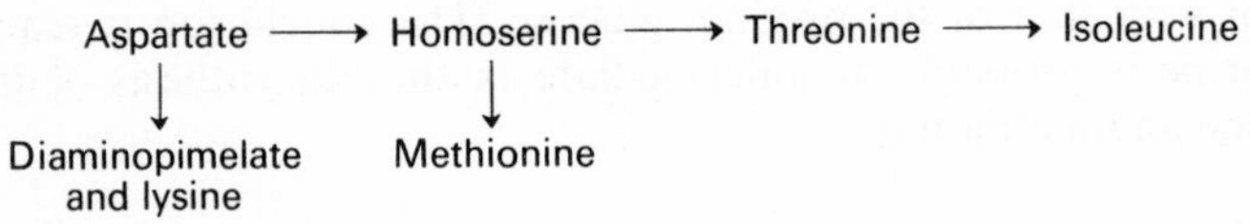

Many similar experiments of "isotopic competition" have made it possible to establish clearly that the majority of the amino acids in the proteins of *Escherichia coli* are derived from a small number of intermediates from the Embden-Meyerhof or Krebs cycles: phosphoglycerate (serine, glycine, cysteine), oxaloacetate (aspartate, asparagine, lysine, diaminopimelate, threonine, methionine, isoleucine), α-ketoglutarate (glutamate, glutamine, proline and arginine) and pyruvate (alanine, valine, leucine). The aromatic amino acids, phenylalanine, tyrosine and tryptophan and the heterocyclic amino acid histidine, are synthesized by a series of reactions which will be examined separately.

USE OF AUXOTROPHIC MUTANTS

In every wild type bacterial population, mutants unable to synthesize a given essential metabolite occur spontaneously. The frequency is low, of the order of 10^{-8} per generation. These mutants, whose growth requires an exogenous supply of the metabolite which they are unable to make, are called *auxotrophs* as against the wild type *prototrophs* from which they arise. The frequency of mutation can be increased by ultraviolet radiation or by treatment with chemical mutagens, some of which are highly effective. After mutagenesis, the problem is to select the desired mutant from amidst the whole population of prototrophs and mutants in which one has no interest. One of the most frequently employed methods is to use selection by penicillin (118). The basis of the method is the property of this antibiotic to kill only actively dividing cells. After mutagen treatment, the bacteria are allowed to divide a number of times in the presence of the growth factor for which auxotrophs are desired. The reasoning is as follows: bacteria have several nuclei, and therefore several identical chromosomes; the mutagen has acted on only one of these chromosomes and the unaffected ones have still all the information required for synthesis of the growth factor. After a few divisions, the nuclei have become segregated among the different daughter cells, and the bacteria have become arranged into groups with a homogeneous chromosome make-up. Excess growth factor is eliminated by washing several times, and the culture is resuspended in a medium containing every growth factor (amino acids, purines, pyrimidines, vitamins) except the one for which auxotrophic mutants are being sought. The new medium also contains penicillin. Bacteria which have not been killed by the mutagen make up a population comprising prototrophic bacteria, mutants which are of no interest, and the mutants desired. The first two classes can divide and will be killed by penicillin. The third class cannot grow and so will escape being killed. After removal of penicillin, plating on a suitable medium will in principle give colonies which will be very largely those of the mutant desired.

Let us consider a group of mutants obtained independently by this method, all of which are unable to synthesize an amino acid: for example, tryptophan. None of the mutants will grow in a synthetic medium which contains only glucose as sole carbon source, but all will be able to grow if tryptophan is added. A class of mutants may be found, which under certain conditions secretes into the growth medium a substance not found in the growth medium of the parental type. This substance has been identified as indole; it allows the growth of a second class of mutants. This class, like the first, comprises individuals unable to synthesize tryptophan, but unlike the first class, also unable to synthesize indole. Mutants of this second kind can also accumulate a substance, anthranilic acid, which allows a third class to grow. Thus the third class is unable to carry out a reaction in the synthesis of tryptophan earlier than anthranilate production, and can only grow in the presence of anthranilic acid, indole, or tryptophan. The biosynthesis of tryptophan can therefore be written schematically in the following provisional way:

$$\text{Glucose} + NH_4^+ \xrightarrow[(3)]{} \text{Anthranilate} \xrightarrow[(2)]{} \text{Indole} \xrightarrow[(1)]{} \text{Tryptophan}$$

The numbers in parentheses indicate "genetic blocks" of different kinds, i.e. reactions which cannot be carried out. Auxotrophic mutants have been obtained for practically every pathway in amino acid, purine, pyrimidine and vitamin biosynthesis, and have proved to be of immense use for elucidating the pathways. However, it remains to show, in each case, that the accumulated products are truly direct intermediates and not metabolic products of the actual intermediates.

ENZYMATIC ANALYSIS

The interpretation of the results obtained by the above methods is not always as easy and unequivocal as the concise summary just given would lead us to believe. The results must be considered as a point of departure for more detailed studies, and not as a definite proof of the existence of the reactions postulated. As a result, it is necessary to confirm them independently by using cell suspensions or cell-free extracts to show that every postulated reaction does indeed take place and is missing in the mutants which are suspected to be unable to carry it out. For example, a mutant requiring homoserine (or threonine + methionine) for growth has been shown to lack the enzyme homoserine dehydrogenase which catalyzes the reduction of aspartic semialdehyde to homoserine. This result confirms the evidence from the methods of isotopic competition and nutrition, and makes it virtually certain that homoserine is an intermediate in the synthesis of threonine and methionine.

THE REGULATION OF ENZYME BIOSYNTHESIS

Enzymes themselves must be synthesized by the cell. If we consider only their primary structure as proteins, it is possible to represent them as a linear sequence of amino acids linked together by peptide bonds. The sequence of amino acids in a given protein is fixed and is determined by the sequence of bases in the messenger RNA specific for that protein. This messenger RNA is itself a transcription of the sequence of bases in a particular segment of DNA. We say that this DNA sequence codes for the protein in question, or that it is the *structural gene* containing the information necessary for synthesizing the protein.

Protein synthesis cannot be governed solely by structural genes. A living cell is an integrated and complex system of thousands of degradative and synthetic processes which can exist together in an orderly fashion only by the mechanisms of *cellular regulation.*

We have already on several occasions studied one means of control: the regulation of the catalytic *activity* of enzymes, which mostly involves a conformational change in the tertiary or quaternary structure of an enzyme, by transitions which we have termed *allosteric.* There is a second kind of control available to cells which acts not on the activity of enzymes but on their *synthesis.*

Some years ago, an observation was made at the Pasteur Institute: when *E. coli* was grown in the presence of an amino acid, cell suspensions or extracts of the bacterium had much lower amounts of one of the enzymes involved in the biosynthesis of this amino acid (25, 26). Later it was shown that this *repression* of enzyme synthesis affected several enzymes in the same biosynthetic pathway (119). The terminal metabolite appeared to be the repressor, and intermediates lacked this ability only because they were converted to the end-product. It was readily understood that repression provided not only an economic response to the presence of exogenous essential metabolites, but was also able to cause a control of the synthesis which depended on the size of the intracellular "pool" of the final metabolite. The size of this intracellular "pool" is determined by the differences in the rates of synthesis of the metabolite and its incorporation into macromolecules, such as proteins or nucleic acids. By artificially maintaining the size at a very low level by using auxotrophic mutants and different ingenious devices (27), it has been possible to increase considerably the amount of certain enzymes in the cells, allowing the genetic potential to be completely expressed (derepression).

On the other hand, mutants have been isolated which are not subject to regulation by repression, that is, they contain high levels of the enzymes for a particular biosynthetic pathway and are insensitive to endogenous or exogenous fluctuations of the final metabolite of the pathway (120).

The mechanistic and genetic implications of repression are discussed in many other texts. We have had to devote some space to it here in order to be able to understand the study of individual biosynthetic pathways and their control mechanisms.

8

Biosynthesis of Aspartate

and Amino Acids derived from it

THE BIOSYNTHESIS OF ASPARTATE

Aspartic acid can be synthesized by two different reactions, both of which involve a substrate that is a participant in the tricarboxylic cycle. It can be obtained either by the direct amination of fumaric acid:

$$\mathrm{COOH{-}CH{=}CH{-}COOH} + \mathrm{NH_3} \rightleftarrows \mathrm{COOH{-}CH_2{-}\underset{\displaystyle NH_2}{\underset{|}{CH}}{-}COOH}$$

or by transamination of oxaloacetic acid with glutamic acid, which in turn is the direct product of the amination of α-ketoglutaric acid:

$$\mathrm{COOH{-}CH_2{-}CO{-}COOH} + \mathrm{COOH{-}CH_2{-}CH_2{-}\underset{\displaystyle NH_2}{\underset{|}{CH}}{-}COOH}$$
$$\updownarrow$$
$$\mathrm{COOH{-}CH_2{-}\underset{\displaystyle NH_2}{\underset{|}{CH}}{-}COOH} + \mathrm{COOH{-}CH_2{-}CH_2{-}CO{-}COOH}$$

At the end of this chapter, the reader will find a paragraph on the mechanism of transamination reactions and other enzyme reactions with pyridoxal phosphate as coenzyme.

SYNTHESIS OF ASPARAGINE

Pig liver and heart, bakers' yeast, peas and lupins contain an enzyme which can accomplish an outright synthesis of asparagine from L-aspartate and ammonia in the presence of ATP and Mg^{++} ions (121). The formation of asparagine is accompanied by the stoichiometric formation of ADP and inorganic phosphate:

$$COOH-CH_2-\underset{NH_2}{\underset{|}{C}}H-COOH + ATP + NH_3$$

$$\longrightarrow H_2N-CO-CH_2-\underset{NH_2}{\underset{|}{C}}H-COOH + APD + P_i$$

L-asparagine

In *Lactobacillus arabinosus*, another system is found, which leads to the formation of asparagine, AMP and pyrophosphate from the same substrates (122):

$$\text{L-aspartate} + ATP + NH_3 \longrightarrow \text{L-asparagine} + AMP + PP$$

THE BIOSYNTHESIS OF ASPARTATE SEMIALDEHYDE, THE COMMON INTERMEDIATE IN THE BIOSYNTHESIS OF LYSINE, METHIONINE, THREONINE AND ISOLEUCINE

A specific β-aspartokinase catalyzes the phosphorylation of aspartate in the β-position:

$$COOH-CH_2-\underset{NH_2}{\underset{|}{C}}H-COOH + ATP \rightleftarrows PO_3H_2\sim OOC-CH_2-\underset{NH_2}{\underset{|}{C}}H-COOH + ADP$$

β-aspartyl phosphate thus formed is an unstable compound, and when aspartokinase is to be studied, the reaction is performed in the presence of hydroxylamine, the product being a hydroxamate for which a good assay method exists. The reaction can also be carried out with an excess of aspartate semialdehyde dehydrogenase and the reoxidation of NADPH measured spectrophotometrically (123, 124, 125).

The following step is the reduction, just mentioned, of β-aspartyl phosphate to aspartate semialdehyde (126):

$$PO_3H_2\sim OOC-CH_2-\underset{NH_2}{\underset{|}{C}}H-COOH + NADPH + H^+$$

$$\rightleftarrows CHO-CH_2-\underset{NH_2}{\underset{|}{C}}H-COOH + P_i + NADP^+$$

This reaction is reminiscent of that catalyzed by triose phosphate dehydrogenase, which similarly involves the reduction of an acyl phosphate group to an aldehyde. The equilibrium constants for the two reactions are also of the same order.

BIOSYNTHESIS OF LYSINE IN BACTERIA

Aspartate semialdehyde condenses with one molecule of pyruvic acid to eliminate two molecules of water. The reaction product is dihydrodipicolinic acid and the enzyme catalyzing this reaction is dihydrodipicolinate synthetase (127):

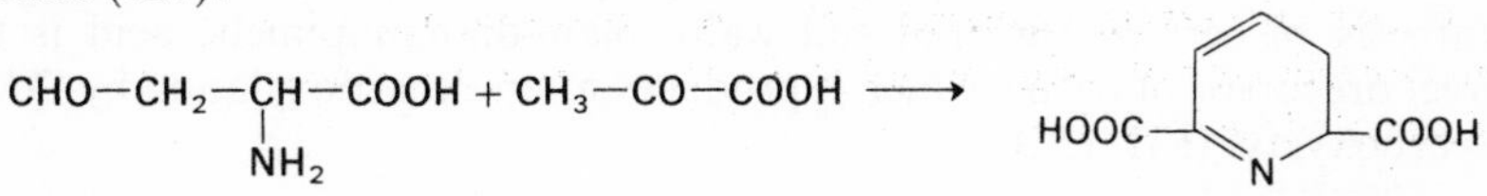

Dihydrodipicolinate

A dihydrodipicolinate reductase reduces this product with NADPH to form tetrahydrodipicolinic acid (127):

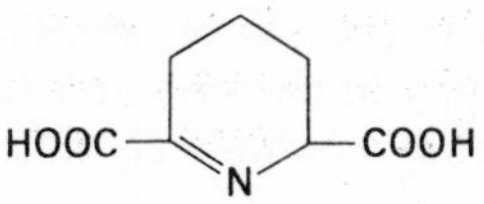

Tetrahydrodipicolinate

The heterocyclic ring is then opened with a concomitant succinylation to form N-succinyl-ε-keto-L-α-aminopimelic acid:

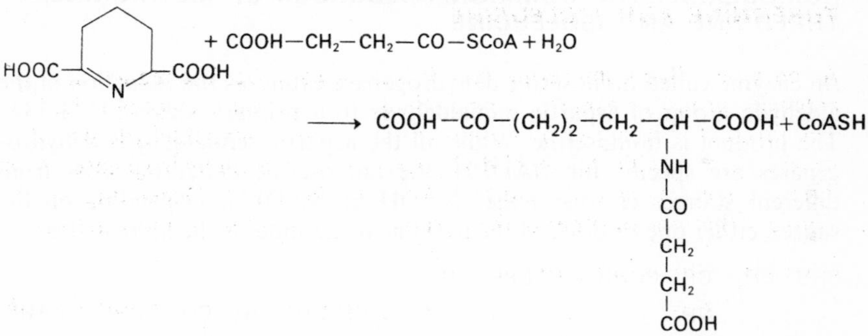

N-succinyl-ε-keto-L-α-aminopimelate

A specific transaminase (128) leads to the synthesis of N-succinyl-LL-diaminopimelic acid, which is then desuccinylated by a specific deacylase to give LL-diaminopimelic acid (129):

$$\text{COOH}-\underset{\displaystyle NH_2}{\underset{|}{\text{CH}}}-(\text{CH}_2)_3-\underset{\displaystyle NH_2}{\underset{|}{\text{CH}}}-\text{COOH}$$

Diaminopimelate (DAP)

It is interesting to note that the succinylation step which protects the amino group is the kind of device an organic chemist would use to avoid the spontaneous ring closure of the ε-keto-L-α-aminopimelic acid, which would render impossible the synthesis of the desired compound.

A specific epimerase (130) converts LL-diaminopimelic acid to *meso*-diaminopimelic acid, the optical isomer present in the cell wall of *E. coli* (in other bacterial species, it is the LL-acid which is present in the complex wall structure). Besides the property of being an essential metabolite for the synthesis of certain bacterial cell walls, *meso*-diaminopimelic acid is the direct precursor of lysine, which it produces upon decarboxylation by DAP-decarboxylase (131, 132):

$$\mathrm{COOH-\underset{\underset{NH_2}{|}}{CH}-(CH_2)_3-\underset{\underset{NH_2}{|}}{CH}-COOH \longrightarrow NH_2-(CH_2)_4-\underset{\underset{NH_2}{|}}{CH}-COOH + CO_2}$$

L-lysine

It is important to note that the above series of reactions leading to the formation of lysine exists only in bacteria and vascular plants. Yeasts, fungi and certain other forms utilize a completely different pathway starting from glutamic acid.

THE REDUCTION OF ASPARTATE SEMIALDEHYDE TO HOMOSERINE, THE COMMON PRECURSOR OF METHIONINE, THREONINE AND ISOLEUCINE

An enzyme called homoserine dehydrogenase catalyzes the reduction of the aldehyde group of aspartic semialdehyde to a primary alcohol (133, 134). The product is homoserine. While all the aspartic semialdehyde dehydrogenases are specific for NADPH, the homoserine dehydrogenases from different sources can use either NADH or NADPH. Depending on the source, either one or other of the pyridine nucleotides is the more active:

$$\mathrm{CHO-CH_2-\underset{\underset{NH_2}{|}}{CH}-COOH + NADPH + H^+ \rightleftharpoons CH_2OH-CH_2-\underset{\underset{NH_2}{|}}{CH}-COOH + NADP^+}$$

L-homoserine

BIOSYNTHESIS OF METHIONINE

The primary alcohol group of homoserine is acylated in *E. coli* with succinyl CoA and in *Neurospora crassa* with acetyl CoA to give either O-succinyl- or O-acetylhomoserine (135):

$$\mathrm{COOH-CH_2-CH_2-CO-O-CH_2-CH_2-\underset{\underset{NH_2}{|}}{CH}-COOH}$$

O-succinylhomoserine

In both cases, the acylated derivative reacts with cysteine in a manner still not completely understood, to produce cystathionine (136), which is a thioether:

$$\mathrm{COOH{-}\underset{NH_2}{\underset{|}{CH}}{-}CH_2{-}S{-}CH_2{-}CH_2{-}\underset{NH_2}{\underset{|}{CH}}{-}COOH}$$

Cystathionine is then hydrolyzed to homocysteine, pyruvate and ammonia:

$$\mathrm{COOH{-}\underset{NH_2}{\underset{|}{CH}}{-}CH_2{-}S{-}CH_2{-}CH_2{-}\underset{NH_2}{\underset{|}{CH}}{-}COOH + H_2O}$$

$$\longrightarrow \mathrm{\underset{L\text{-}homocysteine}{HS{-}CH_2{-}CH_2{-}\underset{NH_2}{\underset{|}{CH}}{-}COOH} + CH_3{-}CO{-}COOH + NH_3}$$

The homocysteine is methylated on the sulfhydryl group, the product of the reaction being methionine. The methyl donor is serine, or more specifically the β carbon atom of serine[1]:

$$\mathrm{CH_3{-}S{-}CH_2{-}CH_2{-}\underset{NH_2}{\underset{|}{CH}}{-}COOH}$$

L-methionine

BIOSYNTHESIS OF THREONINE FROM HOMOSERINE

Threonine is an isomer of homoserine in which the alcohol group is a secondary alcohol. The conversion is brought about in two steps (137, 138). First of all, a homoserine kinase phosphorylates the primary alcohol group of homoserine, to give homoserine phosphate (139). The bond so formed is not energy-rich, unlike aspartyl phosphate where the phosphorylated group was a carboxyl:

$$\mathrm{CH_2OH{-}CH_2{-}\underset{NH_2}{\underset{|}{CH}}{-}COOH + ATP}$$

$$\longrightarrow \mathrm{H_2O_3P{-}OH_2C{-}CH_2{-}\underset{NH_2}{\underset{|}{CH}}{-}COOH + ADP + P_i}$$

An enzyme called homoserine phosphate mutaphosphatase, or O-phosphohomoserine lyase, causes the migration of the alcohol group (140). Pyridoxal phosphate is an obligatory participant in this reaction (138):

$$\mathrm{H_2O_3P{-}OH_2C{-}CH_2{-}\underset{NH_2}{\underset{|}{CH}}{-}COOH \xrightarrow[H_2O]{B_6al\ P} CH_3{-}CHOH{-}\underset{NH_2}{\underset{|}{CH}}{-}COOH + P_i}$$

1. This reaction will be discussed in greater detail in Chapter XIX.

BIOSYNTHESIS OF ISOLEUCINE FROM THREONINE

Besides its function as a constituent of proteins, threonine is also a precursor of isoleucine.

Threonine is first deaminated by biosynthetic threonine deaminase (141) (distinct from another enzyme called degradative threonine deaminase, which performs the same catalytic function, but is not involved in isoleucine biosynthesis), the product formed being α-ketobutyrate:

$$CH_3-CHOH-\underset{\underset{NH_2}{|}}{CH}-COOH \xrightarrow{B_6al\ P} CH_3-CH_2-CO-COOH + NH_3$$

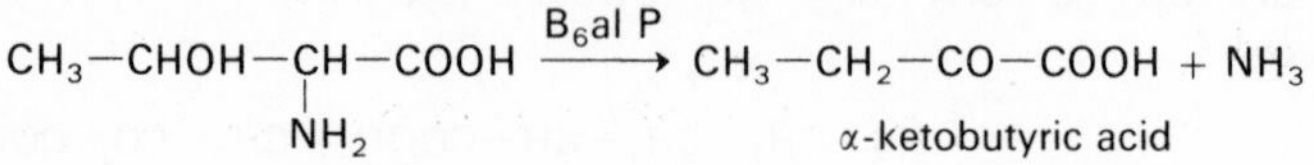

$$\alpha\text{-ketobutyric acid}$$

Biosynthetic threonine deaminase is a pyridoxal phosphate enzyme. α-ketobutyrate condenses with a molecule of acetaldehyde derived from pyruvate to give a α-aceto-α-hydroxybutyric acid (142)[1]:

$$CH_3-CO-\underset{\underset{\underset{CH_3}{|}}{\overset{\overset{OH}{|}}{\underset{CH_2}{|}}}}{C}-COOH$$

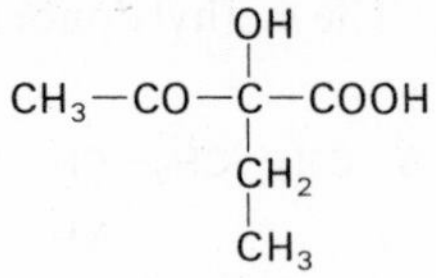

α-aceto-α-hydroxybutyric acid

A pinacol rearrangement together with reduction of the carbonyl group leads to α,β-dihydroxy-β-methylvaleric acid (143):

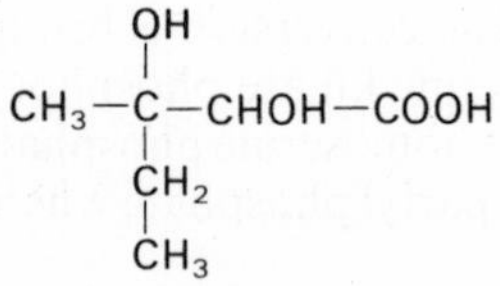

$$CH_3-\underset{\underset{\underset{CH_3}{|}}{\overset{\overset{OH}{|}}{\underset{CH_2}{|}}}}{C}-CHOH-COOH$$

α,β-dihydroxy-β-methylvaleric acid
(dihydroxyisoleucine)

A specific dehydrase catalyzes the loss of a molecule of water and the result is the keto acid corresponding to isoleucine (144):

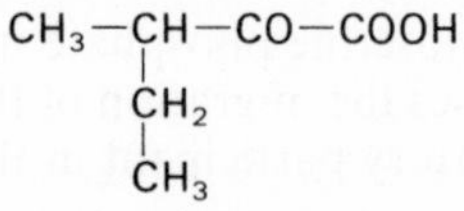

$$CH_3-\underset{\underset{\underset{CH_3}{|}}{\underset{CH_2}{|}}}{CH}-CO-COOH$$

α-keto-β-methylvaleric acid
(α-ketoisoleucine)

---

1. The enzyme catalyzing this reaction. α-aceto-α-hydroxyacid synthetase. will be examined in connection with the biosynthesis of valine.

This acid is the substrate for a transaminase which produces isoleucine.

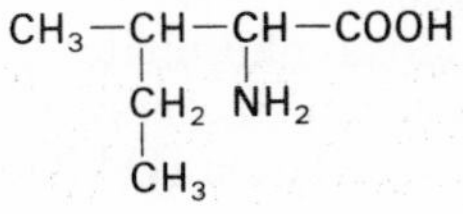

L-isoleucine

The following scheme summarizes our knowledge of the biosynthesis of the amino acids which derive all or part of their carbon atoms from the four carbons of aspartic acid.

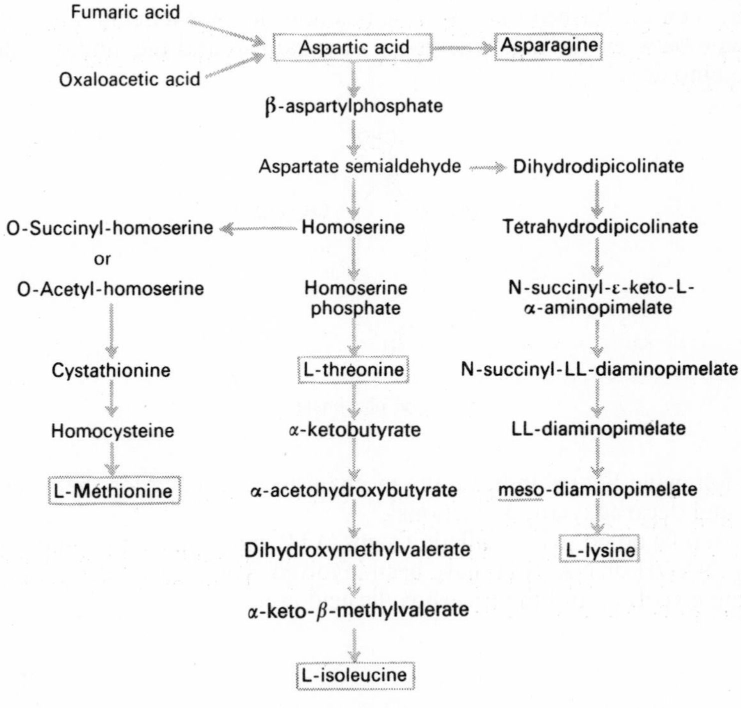

SOME REMARKS ON THE BIOSYNTHESES STUDIED IN THIS CHAPTER

We have met some interesting reactions during this study:

1) The phosphorylation of a carboxyl group, catalyzed by aspartokinase; this produces an energy-rich phosphate ester, whose reduction to an aldehyde is thus greatly facilitated.

2) The formation of intermediate heterocyclic compounds, the dihydro- and tetrahydro- dipicolinic acids.

3) The protection of an amino group by succinylation to avoid an inopportune spontaneous cyclization.
4) Reactions requiring pyridoxal phosphate: transaminations (formation of N-succinyl-DAP and isoleucine), racemization (formation of *meso*-DAP from the LL-isomer), decarboxylation (DAP-decarboxylase) and deamination (threonine deaminase).
5) A pinacol rearrangement associated with a reduction, during the synthesis of isoleucine.
It may be of interest at this stage to have a glance at some of these reactions, those which involve pyridoxal phosphate as cofactor and whose mechanism is now known.
It has been established that all these reactions involve a Schiff's base intermediate between the aldehyde group of pyridoxal and the amino group of the amino acid:

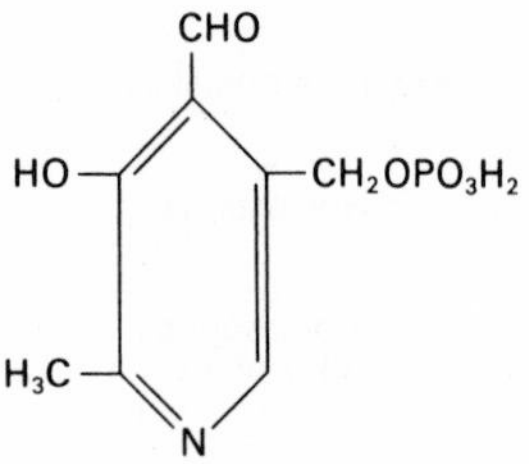

Pyridoxal phosphate

The following figures indicate the mechanism postulated for the racemization and decarboxylation reactions[1].
It should be noted that at different steps, ATP and reduced pyridine nucleotides (NADH or NADPH) have been involved. These molecules are formed during glycolysis and the tricarboxylic acid cycle.

1. These mechanisms are examined in detail in the book by Meister (145).

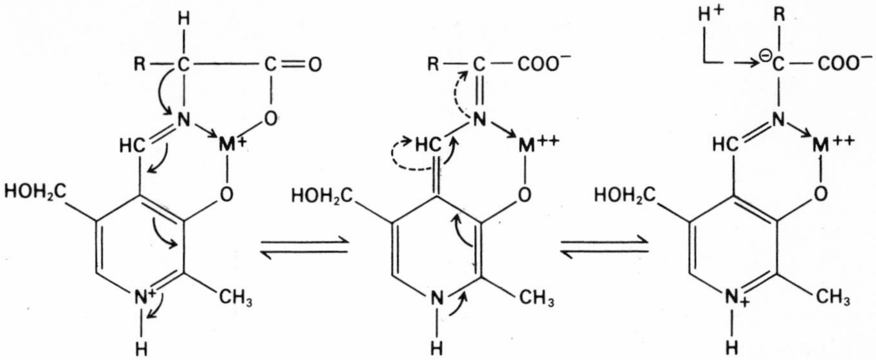

FIGURE 25

Proposed mechanism for the pyridoxal phosphate and metal ion (M) catalyzed racemization of amino acids. In the second formula it can be seen that the α-carbon atom of the amino acid has lost its asymmetry.

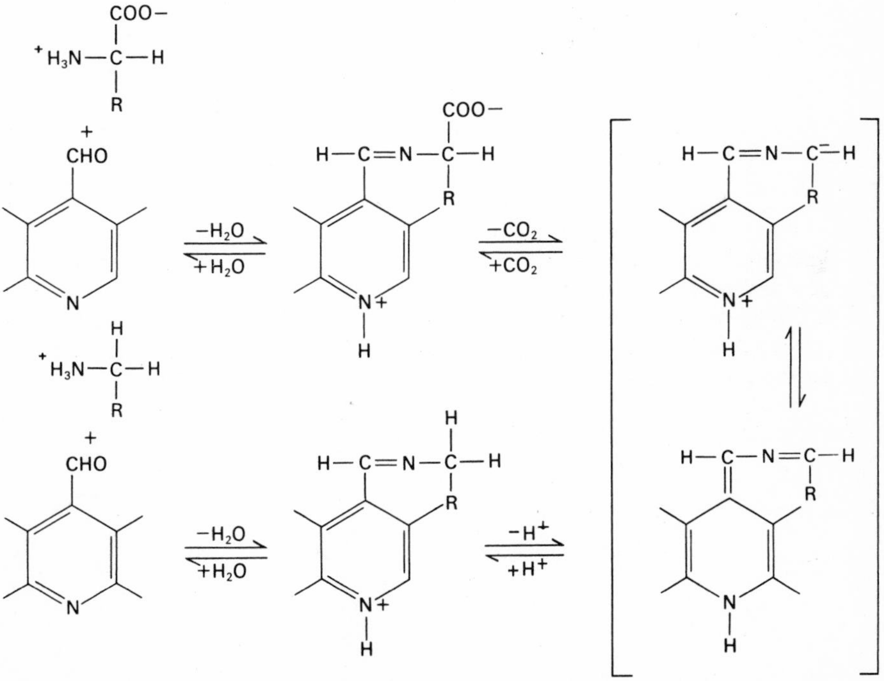

FIGURE 26

Proposed mechanism for amino acid decarboxylation catalyzed by pyridoxal.

9

Regulation of Biosynthesis
of Amino Acids derived from aspartic acid in Escherichia coli

In chapters 2 and 7 we have seen that cells have two main means at their disposal for regulating their metabolic reaction rates:

1) They can use small molecules with affinity for certain target-enzymes, which as a rule belong to a special class of protein, the allosteric enzymes. These ligands bring about conformational changes which result sometimes in a lower enzyme activity and sometimes in a higher.

2) The presence of essential metabolites in the cytoplasm at a high enough concentration causes the *repression* of the biosynthesis of enzymes leading to the formation of such metabolites.

We have also seen in the preceding chapter that the biosynthetic pathway leading from aspartic acid to diaminopimelic acid and lysine on the one hand, and to methionine, threonine and isoleucine on the other, is not a linear sequence of reactions, but a highly branched chain. Let us look at the implications of this fact for growing bacterial cells.

a) Consider a linear sequence of reactions:

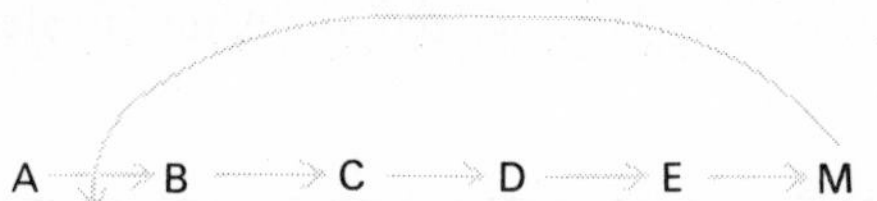

leading to the synthesis of the essential metabolite M. In the presence of excess M in the intracellular pool, the enzyme carrying out the conversion $A \rightarrow B$ will be inhibited by M, if, as is generally the case, this enzyme is an allosteric protein. The presence of M will also repress the synthesis of the enzymes of the whole chain. These control phenomena are not detrimental to the cell, because the final product M is in excess; when production of M falls sufficiently, the activity of the first enzyme will increase and the synthesis of the enzymes of the chain will take place at a rate which is greater than under the conditions of repression. This new state will hold until M again reaches a concentration high enough to cause inhibition and repression. Oscillations in the size of the pool are therefore expected, and have been observed experimentally in several instances.

b) Now consider a branched reaction sequence:

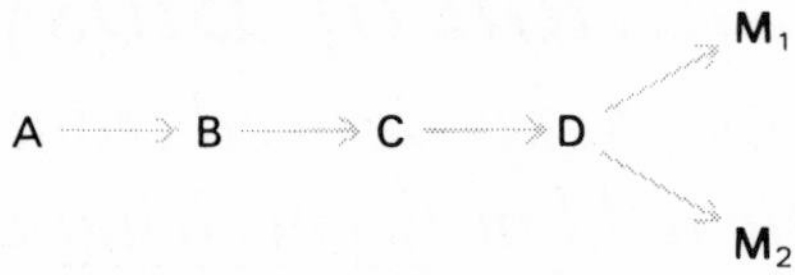

In this chain, the sequence of reactions leading from A to D is a metabolic pathway which is common to the biosynthesis of the two essential metabolites M_1 and M_2. It is obvious that in these circumstances an effective control of the reactions leading from A to D by an excess of one of the end products can cause serious disorder: if accumulation of M_1 effectively inhibits or represses any one of the enzymes of the common pathway, the production of D will be reduced to the point where there is a deficiency of M_2.

In order to solve such a problem, we must look at the chain leading from aspartate to the amino acids whose biosynthesis has been studied in the preceding chapters.

Examination of the diagram of the reaction sequence (p. 107) shows that accumulation of any one of the end products will reduce the production of aspartyl phosphate or aspartate semialdehyde and create a deficiency in the other end products.

The solution of this problem differs according to the organism studied.

THE THREE ASPARTOKINASES OF E. COLI

Three aspartokinase species co-exist in the same cells. For clarity, we shall call them aspartokinase I, II and III.

The table below describes the control of the three activities, which have been separated physically and characterized as distinct protein species (125, 146, 147, 148):

Enzyme	Repressor	Allosteric inhibitor
Aspartokinase I	Threonine + isoleucine (149)	Threonine
Aspartokinase II	Methionine (147)	None
Aspartokinase III	Lysine (125, 146, 149)	Lysine

Figures 27 and 28 clearly indicate the co-operativity between inhibitor molecules for aspartokinases I and III (see chapter II).

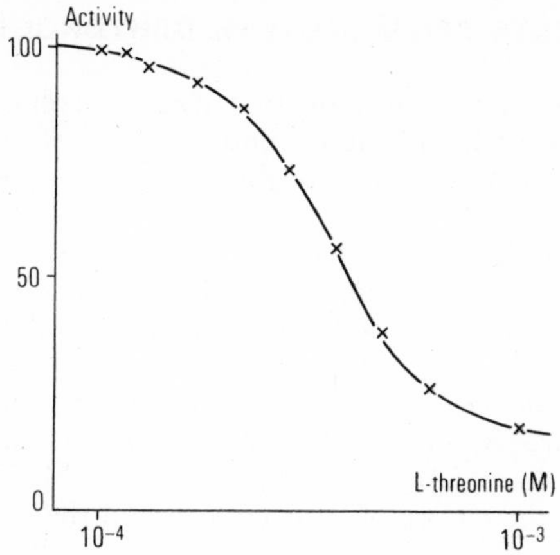

FIGURE 27

Co-operativity between threonine molecules for aspartokinase I (148).

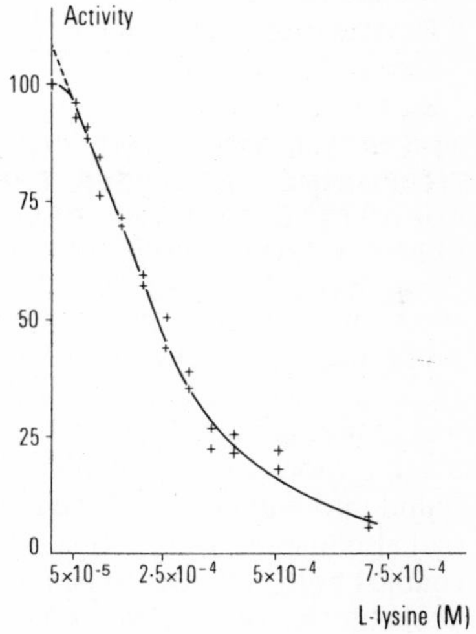

FIGURE 28

Co-operativity between molecules of lysine for aspartokinase III (150).

A well-regulated flow of the common intermediates is thus ensured in the cells of *E. coli* by the existence of these three "isofunctional" enzymes, each of which is subject to separate control by repression, and two of which are in addition allosterically regulated. This pattern of control is reinforced by supplementary mechanisms at other critical points in the biosynthetic chain (see later).

E. COLI ASPARTATE SEMIALDEHYDE DEHYDROGENASE

This enzyme which catalyzes the reduction of aspartyl phosphate to aspartate semialdehyde is not under allosteric control by any of the end products of the chain, but its synthesis is specifically but not completely repressed by lysine (149).

From aspartate semialdehyde to diaminopimelic acid and lysine. This branch is made up of at least seven enzymes (see the diagram in the preceding chapter). The first, dihydrodipicolinate synthetase, is inhibited allosterically by L-lysine (151).

The two E. coli *homoserine dehydrogenases.* This organism possesses two homoserine dehydrogenases side by side which we shall call homoserine dehydrogenase I (134, 147) and II. Inspection of Table XI reveals striking analogies between the nature of their control and that of aspartokinases I and II of the same species.

TABLE XI

Enzyme	Repressor	Allosteric inhibitor
Homoserine dehydrogenase I	Threonine + isoleucine (149)	Threonine (125, 148)
Homoserine dehydrogenase II	Methionine (147)	None

IN E. COLI, THE SAME PROTEIN COMPLEX INHIBITED BY THREONINE CATALYZES THE PHOSPHORYLATION OF ASPARTATE AND THE REDUCTION OF ASPARTATE SEMIALDEHYDE (148, 152, 153, 154)

After mutation, it is possible to select organisms with modified allosteric properties, either of aspartokinase I or homoserine dehydrogenase I. Invariably, it is found that the other activity is modified in the same way. It was at first thought that the two enzymes possessed a common polypeptide chain responsible for the allosteric properties of both enzymes. It was then found that mutants which had lost the homoserine dehydrogenase I activity had also lost the aspartokinase I activity. Mutations which caused reversion enabled both activities to be recovered simultaneously. From this it seemed probable that both activities resided in the same protein complex. A considerable purification of the wild-type enzyme failed to result in any separation of the two activities, the ratio of which remained constant throughout (table XII). There are additional arguments to support the identity of the two enzymes:
a) As well as the two activities being protected against heat inactivation by their allosteric inhibitor, L-threonine, homoserine dehydrogenase I is also protected by NADPH, one of its substrates. Aspartokinase I is protected to an equal extent against thermal inactivation by NADPH which in no way is involved in the enzyme reaction (fig. 29). Support for this result is

TABLE XII

Purification scheme for homoserine dehydrogenase I and aspartokinase I of E. coli

Fraction	Homoserine dehydrogenase I		Aspartokinase I		Ratio A/B
	Total units	Specific activity A	Total units	Specific activity B	
	μmole/min	μmole/min/mg	μmole/min	μmole/min/mg	
I	1,193	0·109	226	0·021	5·2
II	1,129	0·242	208	0·044	5·5
III	1,032	0·533	206	0·107	5·0
IV	971	4·032	194	0·809	5·0
V	729	6·452	143	1·257	5·1
VI	451	67·7	90	13·5	5·0

I. Fraction obtained after nucleic acid precipitation with streptomycin.
II. Fraction after ammonium sulfate precipitation.
III. Fraction after heat treatment in the presence of threonine.
IV. Preceding fraction purified on a hydroxylapatite column.
V. Preceding fraction purified by filtration on Sephadex G-200.
VI. Preceding fraction purified on DEAE-cellulose.

provided by the fact that aspartokinase III, which catalyzes exactly the same reaction as aspartokinase I, is completely protected against thermal inactivation by its allosteric effector, L-lysine, but NADPH has no effect on the rate of this inactivation.

b) The aspartokinase I activity is inhibited by homoserine and NADPH, substrates of the associated activity; D-homoserine and higher and lower homologs of L-homoserine have no effect. In an analogous way, the homoserine dehydrogenase I activity is inhibited by aspartate and ATP, substrates of aspartokinase I; D-aspartate and L-glutamate have no effect. The following hypothesis is derived directly from these observations: the protein complex is composed of two forms in equilibrium:

$$\text{Dehydrogenase I} \rightleftharpoons \text{Kinase I}$$

the equilibrium being displaced in favour of each of the two forms by their respective substrates: for example, we can assume that ATP displaces the equilibrium in favour of the kinase form, and decreases the proportion of molecules in the dehydrogenase form, with the result that the latter activity is inhibited.

c) Homoserine dehydrogenase I is inactivated in two stages by *p*-mercuribenzoate. The first stage corresponds to a desensitization of the enzyme towards its allosteric effector, L-threonine (fig. 30). The desensitized activity is protected against further action of *p*-mercuribenzoate by its own substrates (L-homoserine and NADPH) and by the substrates of aspartokinase, ATP and L-aspartate, which induce conformational changes in the part of the molecule carrying the homoserine dehydrogenase activity (fig. 31).

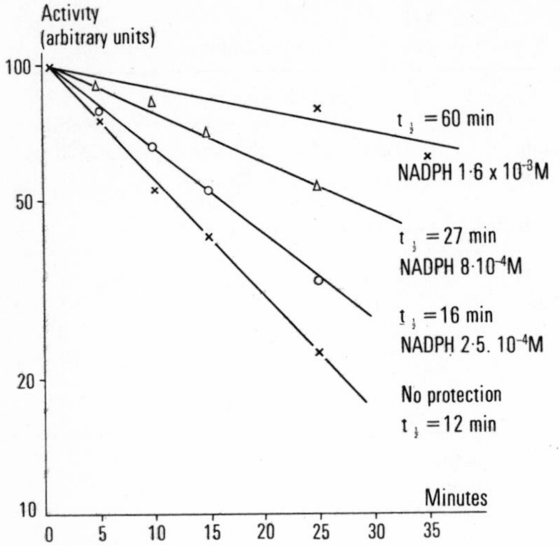

FIGURE 29

Heat inactivation of aspartokinase I. NADPH gives protection at different concentrations. Abscissa is the time of heating at 44°C (148).

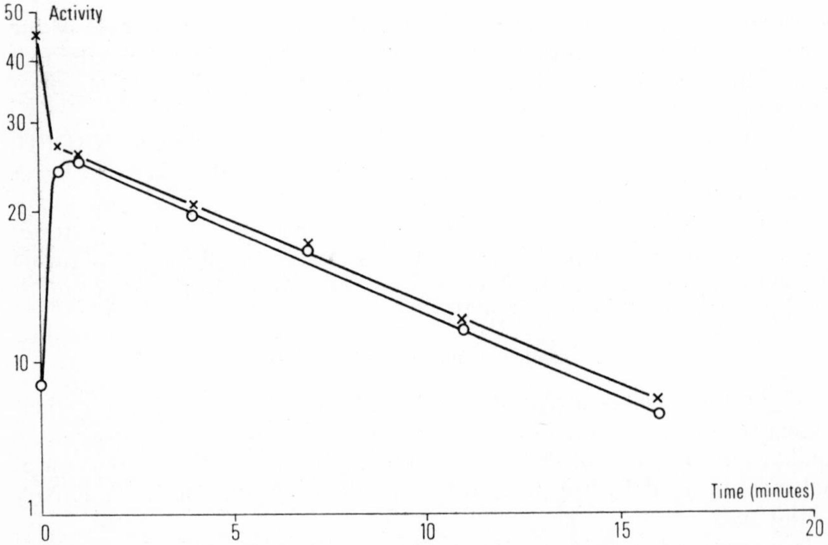

FIGURE 30

Kinetics of the inactivation of homoserine dehydrogenase I by *p*-mercuribenzoate. The activity is expressed as mμmole NADPH oxidized per minute per ml (substrates are aspartate semialdehyde and NADPH). The curve through the crosses shows the two phases of the inactivation. The curve through the circles represents enzyme activity measurements in the presence of a high (2×10^{-2} M) concentration of L-threonine. The first phase of the inactivation is clearly a desensitization of the enzyme (153).

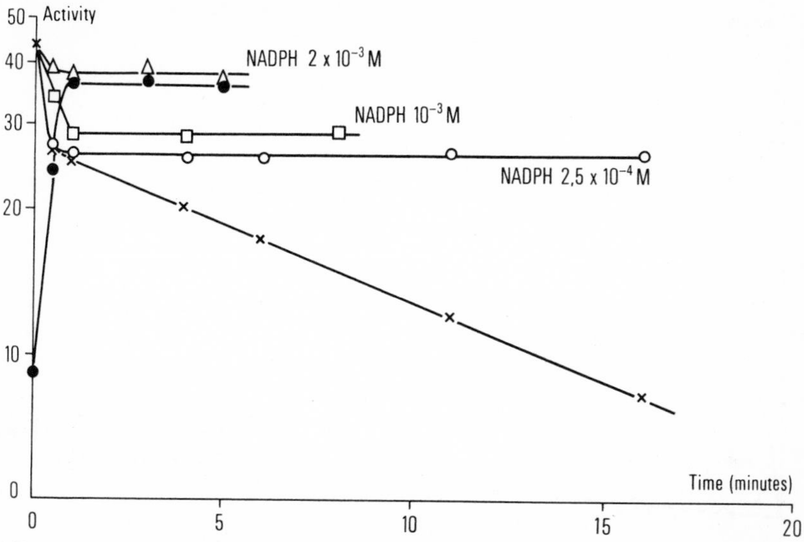

FIGURE 31

Protection against *p*-MB inactivation of homoserine dehydrogenase I by the presence of different concentrations of NADPH. The full circles are enzyme activity measurements in the presence of 2×10^{-2} M L-threonine. The protection afforded by NADPH evidently does not prevent desensitization of the enzyme to its allosteric effector. The enzyme activities are expressed in the same units as in fig. 30 (153).

d) The same two-stage phenomenon is found on exposure of homoserine dehydrogenase to pH 9 under certain conditions. Here the correlation between the two activities is again clear-cut: L-aspartate protects the homoserine dehydrogenase activity not only against inactivation, but also against desensitization towards its allosteric effector (fig. 32).

Although the average molecular weight of the wild-type enzyme complex is greater than 3×10^5, it has been possible to obtain by mutation 1) complexes possessing both enzyme activities, but with molecular weight $1{\cdot}8 \times 10^5$, and modified in their allosteric properties; 2) complexes possessing both enzyme activities and an apparently unchanged molecular weight, but with modified allosteric properties; 3) complexes which have lost the dehydrogenase activity, either with an apparently unchanged molecular weight, or molecular weight of $1{\cdot}8 \times 10^5$; and finally molecules with only the aspartokinase activity, completely insensitive to inhibition, with apparent molecular weight 4×10^4 (determined by gel filtration) (155).

This shows how effective genetic methods are in analyzing the quaternary structure of proteins, successfully complementing the results of treatment with urea, cold, or different chemical reagents.

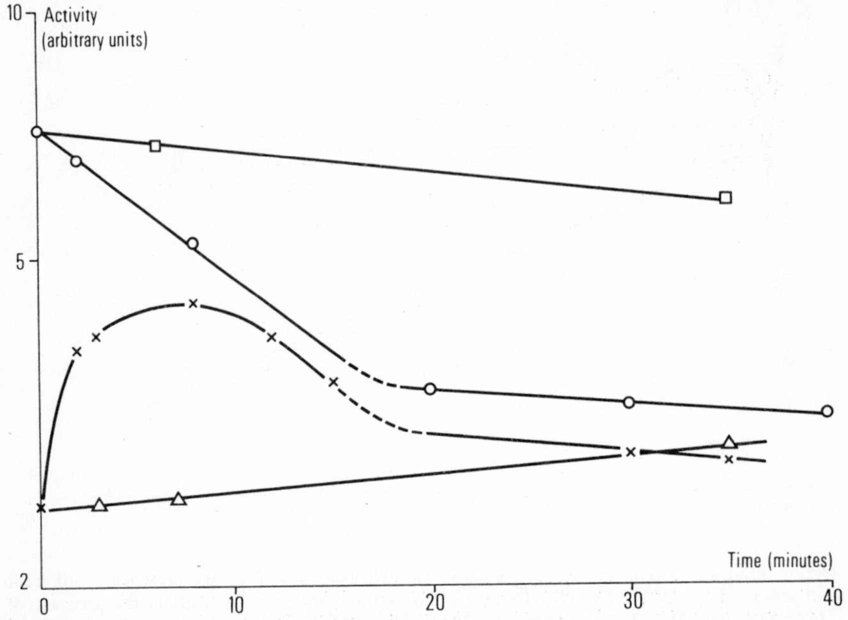

FIGURE 32

The circles represent the kinetics of the inactivation of homoserine dehydrogenase I subjected to alkaline pH. The crosses are the same measurements made in the presence of 2×10^{-2} M L-threonine. We find a desensitization of the enzyme analogous to that obtained with *p*-MB. The squares represent protection of the enzyme by aspartate; the triangles are the same measurements but in the presence of the allosteric inhibitor: aspartate not only protects against inactivation but also against desensitization (154).

MULTIVALENT REPRESSION

In the tables earlier in the chapter showing the different controls to which the enzymes in this biosynthetic pathway are subject, we saw that aspartokinase I and homoserine dehydrogenase I are repressed by threonine + isoleucine. How can the simultaneous requirement for these two effectors be demonstrated? The simplest method is to use a double mutant, deficient in both homoserine dehydrogenase and threonine deaminase. This mutant has an absolute requirement for threonine and isoleucine in order to grow. It can be grown in a chemostat (one of the devices referred to in chapter 7), with limiting threonine and excess isoleucine, or with limiting isoleucine and excess threonine. In both cases, the synthesis of the two enzymes under consideration is derepressed (Table XIII). We have here an example of bivalent repression. We shall see later a case of quadrivalent repression.

TABLE XIII
Multivalent repression and derepression of aspartokinase I and homoserine dehydrogenase I

Strain	Conditions of growth	Aspartokinase I	Homoserine dehydrogenase I
		Specific activity	
Wild type	*a*) No additions	11·0	160
	b) +L-isoleucine 5×10^{-2} M	1·0	45
Double mutant (Thr^-Ileu^-)	*a*) Excess of both growth factors	Not detectable	29
	b) Excess of threonine and limiting isoleucine	30·0	254
	c) Excess of isoleucine and limiting threonine	32·0	242

IN E. COLI, ASPARTOKINASE II AND HOMOSERINE DEHYDROGENASE II ARE PART OF ANOTHER PROTEIN COMPLEX WHOSE SYNTHESIS IS REPRESSED BY METHIONINE (147)

Genetic and biochemical arguments, the details of which it is impossible to examine here, show that aspartokinase II and homoserine dehydrogenase II form a multienzyme complex, with an apparent molecular weight of $1{\cdot}5 \times 10^5$ in the wild type, and with kinetic properties totally different from those of the preceding complex.

It has been possible to obtain mutants in which the synthesis of these activities is derepressed so as to facilitate the preparation and study of the complex.

THE BRANCH LEADING TO HOMOSERINE AND METHIONINE

The first enzyme of this branch, which catalyzes the succinylation of homoserine, is allosterically inhibited by methionine (156). Moreover, every enzyme in the pathway is repressed by L-methionine. The same mutation results in derepression of these enzymes and of aspartokinase II and homoserine dehydrogenase II (147).

BIOSYNTHETIC THREONINE DEAMINASE

This is one of the best studied microbial allosteric enzymes from the kinetic point of view, although as a protein its investigation has been delayed by reason of its extreme instability. The enzyme is of historic interest since it was during its study that Umbarger described the first case of feed-back inhibition in a micro-organism and drew attention to the fact that its kinetics as a function of substrate concentration did not obey the Henri-Michaelis law (29).

The allosteric inhibitor of this enzyme is L-isoleucine, the end-product of the branch of the chain coming from L-threonine. Umbarger in his first paper described this inhibition as competitive. To quote his own words: "when the double reciprocal plot of Lineweaver and Burk is employed, it is necessary to square the substrate [or inhibitor] concentration. This property of the data would be expected if the enzyme combined with 2 molecules of substrate or inhibitor" (fig. 33 and fig. 11, chapter 2). Later it was confirmed that this enzyme does not follow the simple Michaelis-Henri law, but neither does it obey a purely bimolecular law with respect to substrate or inhibitor concentration. The results obtained have been interpreted as showing that several substrate or inhibitor molecules can react with a molecule of enzyme and that under these conditions, co-operative interactions exist between several molecules of ligand or several of the specific receptors (157). This research, together with the work on *E. coli* aspartate transcarbamylase, is one of the foundations on which the theory of allosteric transitions in its present state has been built. It is impossible to deal here with all the kinetic arguments. We shall confine ourselves to some of the outstanding facts which are characteristic of many allosteric enzymes.

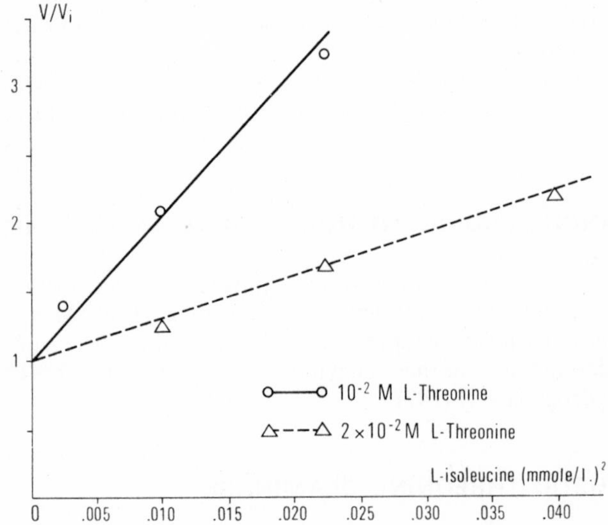

FIGURE 33

"Bimolecular" relationship between the inhibition of biosynthetic threonine deaminase by isoleucine and the concentration of this allosteric effector (29).

Threonine deaminase is very unstable. The inhibitor, L-isoleucine, provides considerable stability. During inactivation (thermal or spontaneous), the enzyme becomes desensitized, i.e. it is converted to a protein species insensitive to inhibition by isoleucine (fig. 34). This desensitization can also be obtained by treatment with mercurials, by incorporation of amino acid analogs into the enzyme molecule, or by mutation. Thus we meet again the desensitization phenomenon which we have encountered several times

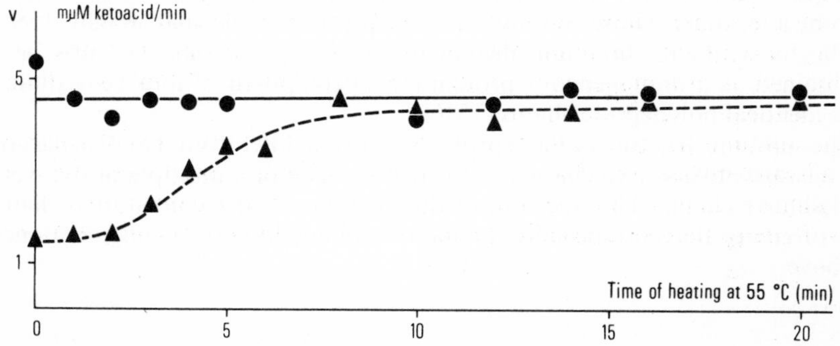

FIGURE 34

Desensitization of biosynthetic L-threonine deaminase by heat treatment. The solid line represents the enzyme activity in the absence of inhibitor; the dotted line the activity in the presence of L-isoleucine 10^{-2} M (157).

already in this book, but which was originally demonstrated for threonine deaminase. An important property of the desensitized preparations is that they no longer exhibit co-operative interactions between substrate molecules, the kinetics adhering closely to the Michaelis law. In several other cases, we have seen that desensitization and dissociation of an oligomeric molecule to its constitutive protomers occur together. In this particular case, desensitization does not seem to be accompanied by a change in the apparent molecular weight of the enzyme.

FROM THREONINE TO ISOLEUCINE

Besides the allosteric inhibition of threonine deaminase, the enzymes leading from threonine to isoleucine are subject to multivalent repression by valine, leucine, isoleucine and pantothenate (158). The selective advantage of the development of such a multivalent repression will become apparent during the study of the biosynthesis of valine and leucine.

The scheme below shows clearly the metabolic controls (repressive or allosteric) of the synthesis and activities of the enzymes involved in the biosynthesis of lysine (and DAP), methionine, threonine and isoleucine in *E. coli.*

Recent developments. Aspartokinase I-homoserine dehydrogenase I has been obtained in the homogeneous form from *E. coli.* Its molecular weight has been determined to be 360,000. The rôle of its sulfhydryl groups has been quantitated (158*a*). It is composed of six sub-units of MW = 60,000. The sub-units contain an intra-chain disulfide bond each and are very similar, if not identical (158*b*). The protein exhibits six L-threonine binding sites per molecule (158*c*). Aspartokinase II-homoserine dehydrogenase II has also been obtained in the pure state from the same organism and appears to be a tetramer whose sub-units are of equivalent molecular weight (158*d*). The biosynthetic threonine deaminase of *S. typhimurium* has also been obtained as a homogeneous protein (158*e*) composed of four very similar or identical polypeptide chains (158*f*).
The sub-unit structure of these proteins seems to differ from that of aspartate transcarbamylase (see chapter 15) which is made of a multiple of two very dissimilar chains. The question of the identity of their constitutive chains is of great interest, especially for the two bifunctional proteins mentioned above.

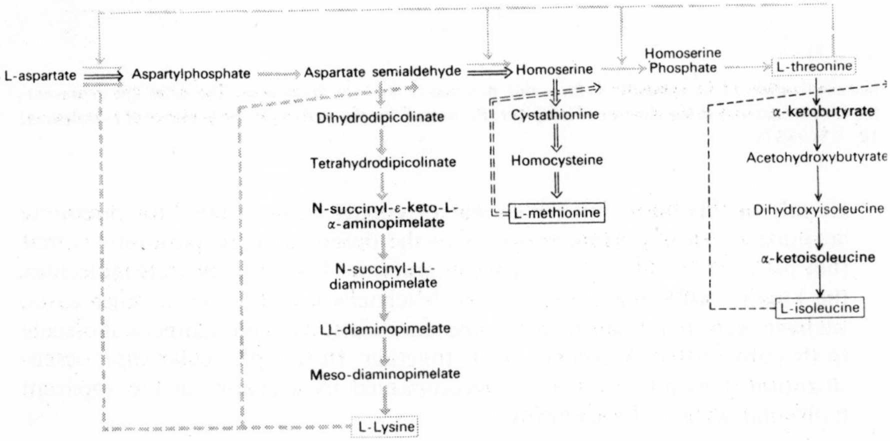

The dotted arrows interrupting the biosynthetic pathways indicate points of feedback inhibition. The hollow arrows indicate repression by methionine; the heavy arrows trivalent repression by leucine, valine and isoleucine. All the reactions shown with gray arrows leading from aspartate to threonine, except the second, are subject to bivalent repression by threonine and isoleucine. The enzymes in the branch leading from aspartate semialdehyde to lysine which are repressed are still not fully known from the point of view of their regulation.

10

Regulation of Biosynthesis
of Amino Acids derived from Aspartic Acid in other microbial species

In contrast to *Escherichia coli* which makes use of several "isofunctional" enzymes to accomplish a differential control of the aspartokinase activity, other species have different regulatory systems.

CONCERTED FEEDBACK INHIBITION OF ASPARTOKINASE ACTIVITY IN RHODOPSEUDOMONAS CAPSULATUS AND BACILLUS POLYMYXA

These species seem to possess only a single aspartokinase which is insensitive to feedback inhibition by excess of any one of the essential metabolites, L-lysine, L-threonine or L-isoleucine. However, if L-lysine and L-threonine are simultaneously present in excess, a considerable inhibition of the enzymatic activity is found (159, 160). This absolute requirement for two or more of the end products to accomplish inhibition has been called concerted feedback inhibition or multivalent feedback inhibition. This mechanism seems to be a less delicate control than the one using "isofunctional" enzymes, since it does not allow the independent regulation of the first reaction in branched pathways. Rather, it presents an alternative solution to the difficulty raised by the existence of such branched pathways. Figure 35 shows a typical experiment carried out with an extract of *Rps. capsulatus*. The concerted inhibition by threonine and lysine is never 100 %, a fact which would seem to be important to enable the synthesis of methionine to proceed even in the presence of an excess of both allosteric effectors.

The synthesis of the single aspartokinase of *Rps. capsulatus* is repressed by the presence of methionine in the culture medium (161). As a result, the growth of this organism, a prototroph in the wild type, is partially inhibited by excess methionine, or by an excess of the combination of threonine plus lysine, growth being re-established in the presence of all three amino acids (fig. 36).

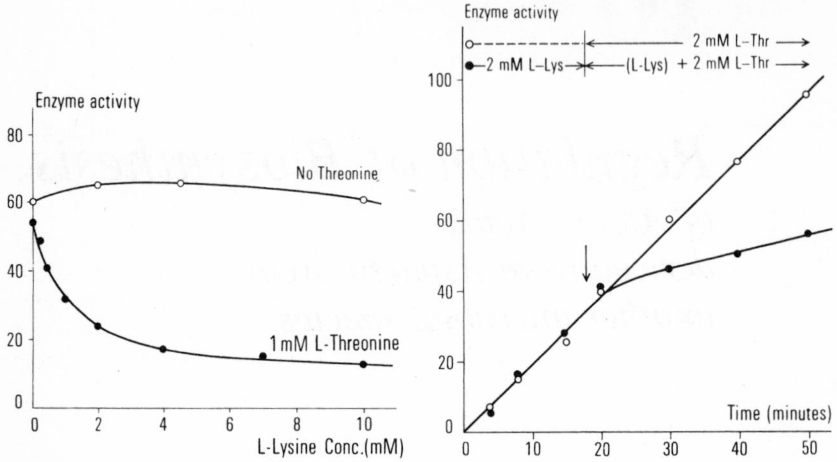

FIGURE 35

Two experiments showing the concerted feedback inhibition of the single aspartokinase of *Rhodopseudomonas capsulatus*. The first experiment shows the absence of any effect with lysine alone, and the progressive inhibition on increasing the lysine concentration in the presence of threonine. In the right-hand figure, white circles represent the enzyme activity measured in the absence of the allosteric effector, black circles the same in the presence of lysine. At time T = 18 minutes, threonine is added to the two incubation mixtures. Inhibition occurs only where lysine is present (159).

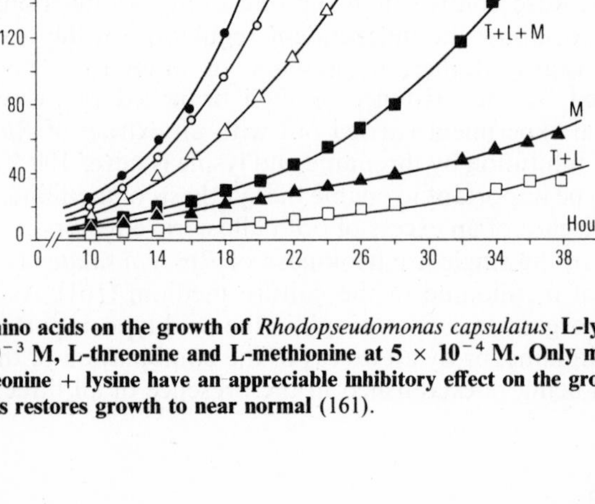

FIGURE 36

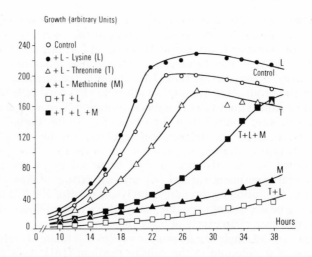

Effect of adding amino acids on the growth of *Rhodopseudomonas capsulatus*. L-lysine is added at a concentration of 10^{-3} M, L-threonine and L-methionine at 5×10^{-4} M. Only methionine and the combination of threonine + lysine have an appreciable inhibitory effect on the growth. The mixture of three amino acids restores growth to near normal (161).

SPECIFIC REVERSAL OF A PARTICULAR FEEDBACK INHIBITION BY OTHER ESSENTIAL METABOLITES. CASE OF RHODOSPIRILLUM RUBRUM (162)

This organism, like *Rps. capsulatus*, possesses only one aspartokinase and apparently only a single homoserine dehydrogenase. A study of the repression of the synthesis of these enzymes has not been made, but the feedback inhibition by L-threonine has been examined in detail.

Both enzymes are inhibited by L-threonine, the inhibition being reversed by the addition to the reaction mixture of isoleucine in the case of aspartokinase, or of methionine or isoleucine in the case of the dehydrogenase. Inspection of table XIV shows that in the absence of inhibitor, isoleucine and methionine have an activating effect on aspartokinase. Lysine is completely without effect.

TABLE XIV
Effect of certain amino acids on the aspartokinase activity of Rhodospirillum rubrum

Additions (10^{-4}M)	Enzyme activity (arbitrary units)
None	41
L-isoleucine	74
L-methionine	70
L-threonine	0
L-threonine + L-isoleucine	47
L-threonine + L-methionine	4
L-isoleucine + L-methionine	69

The effect of different ligands on homoserine dehydrogenase has been studied with regard to the state of aggregation of the enzyme (163). Centrifugation experiments in sucrose gradients show that L-threonine stimulates an aggregation of the enzyme to an inactive form, presumably a dimer. This aggregation by threonine is reversed by the allosteric modifiers, isoleucine or methionine. As can be seen in figure 37, both forms of the enzyme can also be distinguished by gel filtration on Sephadex G 200 in buffer containing the different effectors. These observations are interpreted as reflections of the importance in this organism of monomer $\rightleftharpoons$ polymer interconversions in controlling the activity of homoserine dehydrogenase.

In this organism which possesses only one aspartokinase, an increase in the size of the intracellular pool of threonine above a critical level must produce a decrease in the concentrations of common intermediates, due to allosteric inhibition of the kinase and the dehydrogenase. Now, it is found that the threonine deaminase of *R. rubrum*, unlike that of *E. coli*, is practically insensitive to isoleucine; it is therefore probable that the synthesis of isoleucine

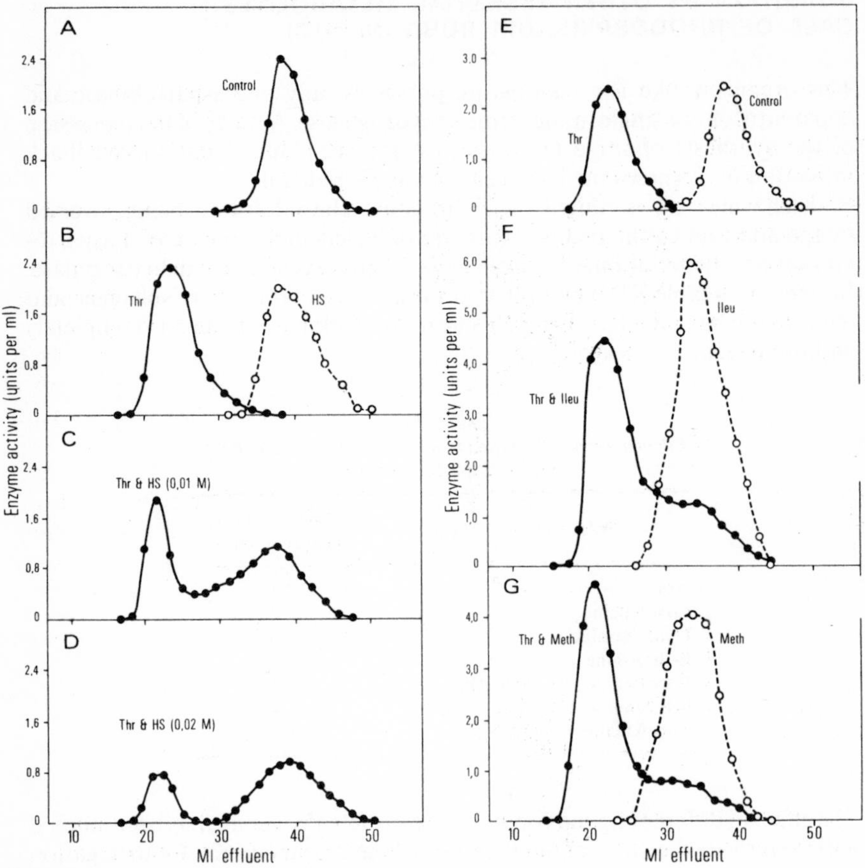

FIGURE 37

Elution patterns of *Rhodospirillum rubrum* homoserine dehydrogenase on Sephadex G-200 in the presence and absence of substrate and/or allosteric modifiers.
A: enzyme filtered in buffer with no additions.
B: enzyme filtered in the presence of threonine.
C and D: enzyme filtered in the presence of different concentrations of threonine and homoserine.
E: enzyme filtered in the presence of threonine.
F and G: enzyme filtered in the presence of threonine and modifiers. The dotted curves come from different experiments and are included for comparison. Threonine evidently causes the enzyme to aggregate, the effect being reversed in the presence of sufficient substrate (C and D). In F and G, the high molecular weight peak characteristic of the threonine-treated enzyme is always present, but a considerable trailing is observed which extends into the region where species of lower molecular weight are expected.

continues in these circumstances, but the problem of achieving a normal synthesis of DAP, lysine and methionine remains. The specific reversal of the allosteric inhibition (caused by threonine) of aspartokinase and homoserine dehydrogenase provides the answer: it thus appears that it is an increase in the isoleucine/threonine ratio which is the signal for an accelerated production of common intermediates required in the synthesis of DAP, lysine and methionine.

THE HOMOSERINE DEHYDROGENASES OF SACCHAROMYCES CEREVISIAE AND MICROCOCCUS GLUTAMICUS (164, 165)

In these two species, homoserine dehydrogenase is specifically repressed by methionine. As in *E. coli*, it is threonine which is the allosteric inhibitor in *M. glutamicus*, while in *S. cerevisiae* the activity is inhibited by threonine and methionine, the latter effector being by far the more active.

The above examples have been chosen to illustrate the very marked variations which are met with in different organisms in regard to the means of reaching the same goal, i.e. the harmonious integration of the rates of synthesis of the different cellular constituents (see ref. 162 for a discussion).

11

Biosynthesis of Glutamate

and the Amino Acids derived from it, and its Regulation

SYNTHESIS OF GLUTAMATE

This amino acid can result from the transamination reaction between α-ketoglutaric acid and aspartic acid or several other amino acids:

$$\mathrm{COOH{-}CH_2{-}CH_2{-}CO{-}COOH + R{-}\underset{\displaystyle NH_2}{\underset{|}{C}H}{-}COOH \rightleftharpoons COOH{-}CH_2{-}CH_2{-}\underset{\displaystyle NH_2}{\underset{|}{C}H}{-}COOH + R{-}CO{-}COOH}$$

We recall that α-ketoglutaric acid is an intermediate in the tricarboxylic acid cycle. The principal pathway for the introduction of amino nitrogen into proteins is through the reductive amination of α-ketoglutaric acid to glutamate, catalyzed by glutamic dehydrogenase:

$$\mathrm{COOH{-}CH_2{-}CH_2{-}CO{-}COOH + NH_3 + NADPH + H^+ \rightleftharpoons COOH{-}CH_2{-}CH_2{-}\underset{\displaystyle NH_2}{\underset{|}{C}H}{-}COOH + NADP^+ + H_2O}$$

The central role of glutamic dehydrogenase is demonstrated by the fact that mutants of *Neurospora crassa* which are deficient in it can only grow if they are provided with an amino acid capable of transferring its α-amino group by transamination (166). Such mutants can grow after a considerable lag period on minimal medium, without a reverse mutation being involved: *Neurospora crassa* also produces a glutamic dehydrogenase, using NAD and not NADP, which is not affected by the mutation in question and can function as an auxiliary mechanism for the utilization of ammonia.

While *Neurospora crassa* glutamic dehydrogenase has been the object of many genetic studies, forming the basis of our knowledge of the mechanisms of intra-allelic complementation (167), the enzyme from ox liver is the object of many studies on the quaternary structure of oligomeric proteins (168).
Glutamate, besides being one of the constituents of proteins, is also the source of all or part of the carbon atoms of glutamine, proline and arginine, and in some organisms at least, of lysine.

BIOSYNTHESIS OF GLUTAMINE

This reaction is carried out by an enzyme, glutamine synthetase, whose occurrence is not restricted to microorganisms. The enzyme has been obtained in a purified condition from different sources, and in the pure state from *Escherichia coli* (169). It catalyzes the following reactions:

$$\text{L-glutamate} + NH_3 + \text{ATP} \longrightarrow \text{L-glutamine} + \text{ADP} + P_i$$

$$\text{L-glutamate} + NH_2OH + \text{ATP} \longrightarrow \text{L-glutamylhydroxamate} + \text{ADP} + P_i$$

Regulation of glutamine synthetase activity in *E. coli* 2.1.

This allosteric control deserves a detailed examination, for it differs from the schemes which we have seen before for branched biosynthetic pathways. Firstly, we should note that the glutamine amide group supplies the nitrogen atoms of the following molecules by means of reactions which we shall study in due course: tryptophan, adenylic acid, cytidylic acid, glucosamine 6-phosphate, histidine, and carbamyl phosphate. In addition, it can be shown in *E. coli* that glutamine is used as a substrate for transaminases which respectively convert pyruvate to alanine and glyoxylate to glycine.
It is very interesting to note that the eight compounds listed are inhibitors of the glutamine synthetase of *E. coli* (170), and also of organisms as different as *Salmonella typhimurium*, *Pseudomonas fluorescens*, *Neurospora crassa*, *Bacillus licheniformis*, and *Chlorella pyrenoidosa*. Many other compounds containing nitrogen not derived from glutamine are not inhibitors. None of the organisms studied possesses isofunctional glutamine synthetases (as found for *E. coli* aspartokinase and homoserine dehydrogenase) and no glutamine synthetase shows the phenomenon of concerted inhibition (as found for *Rps. capsulatus* aspartokinase). The best known enzyme, that of *E. coli*, presents the first known case of what is called cumulative allosteric inhibition (169). This phenomenon is as follows: each of the allosteric inhibitors tested individually produces only a partial inhibition, even at near-saturation. Studies with varying combinations of different possible inhibitors show that each acts independently of the others and the presence of one inhibitor has no effect on the activity of another. As a result, when two or more of the end-products are present together at saturating concentrations, the residual activity is equal to the product of the residual activities observed

with each of the inhibitors at saturating concentration. For example, the residual activities of the enzyme tested with saturating concentrations of the inhibitors tryptophan, cytidylic acid, carbamyl phosphate and adenylic acid are respectively 84 %, 86 %, 87 % and 59 %. When the four inhibitors are present simultaneously, the residual activity is $0{\cdot}84 \times 0{\cdot}86 \times 0{\cdot}87 \times 0{\cdot}59 = 0{\cdot}37$. Thus although any one compound alone is incapable of strong inhibition, collectively they give 63 % inhibition. In the presence of all eight inhibitors, the cumulative inhibition is of the order of 93 %.
This mechanism leads to a partial reduction of the total activity by each of the end products, and like the other branched systems which we have examined, would be of no advantage, and indeed might prove disastrous for the economy of the cell, if there did not exist individual control mechanisms for each branch. We shall see later that such mechanisms are known for adenylic acid, cytidylic acid, tryptophan, histidine and carbamyl phosphate.

Glutamine synthetase of *E. coli* as a protein (170) 2.2.

This enzyme has been obtained as a homogeneous protein of molecular weight $6{\cdot}8 \times 10^5$. It is dissociated by guanidine hydrochloride into twelve to fourteen sub-units which are probably identical (on the basis of analysis of fragments obtained by tryptic hydrolysis) and of molecular weight $5{\cdot}3 \times 10^4$. Electron micrographs of the native enzyme show that it is made up of twelve sub-units arranged in two layers of six. In the presence of 1 M urea and a chelating agent for heavy metals, the native enzyme is dissociated at pH 8·0 into inactive sub-units which can reassociate in the presence of Mn^{++} ions to reform an active enzyme with the same physical properties as the native enzyme, provided that the reassociation is carried out at 4°. At 25°, Mn^{++} ions also cause a reassociation but the aggregate obtained has no enzymatic activity.
The fundamental mechanism underlying the cumulative inhibition is not yet clear; in fact, it is difficult to visualize a simple model which accounts for the experimental observations. Every model must explain the restricted inhibition by each of the effectors, together with the absence of synergistic effects or antagonism at saturating concentrations. This last phenomenon implies that the enzyme must possess distinct allosteric sites for each of the eight inhibitors. The existence of distinct sites is shown by the fact that inhibition by glycine, cytidylic acid or tryptophan is competititive with respect to glutamate, inhibition by glucosamine 6-phosphate or histidine is competitive with respect to ammonia, while inhibition by alanine, adenylic acid or carbamyl phosphate is not competitive with respect to either of the two substrates. This result implies at least three binding sites. 1 M urea (in the absence of chelating agents) desensitizes the enzyme with respect to tryptophan, histidine and glucosamine 6-phosphate; there must therefore be at least one additional site. Treatment of the enzyme with 30 % acetone does not cause any loss of enzyme activity, but produces an increased

inhibition by alanine and glycine: we thus have six sites. Another difference arises from the observation that adenylic acid and histidine protect the enzyme against mercaptide formation with *p*-chloromercuriphenylsulfonate, while carbamyl phosphate and cytidylic acid accelerate the rate of inactivation by this reagent.

After examining all these results together, we reach the conclusion that there are eight independent binding sites. Direct measurements of the number of binding sites are absolutely necessary to construct a model for this enzyme and other allosteric enzymes to account for the observed facts.

Reversible enzyme modification induced by substrates of *E. coli* glutamine synthetase (171, 172, 172*a*) 2.3.

The synthesis of glutamine synthetase in this organism is repressed when growth takes place in the presence of NH_4^+ ions. Addition of these ions *in vivo* to derepressed cells causes not only a repression of the synthesis of new enzyme, but also a rapid "inactivation" of the enzyme already present. This inactivation can be obtained *in vitro* in the presence of glutamine, ATP and Mg^{++} ions, and a specific inactivating enzyme. It is presumed that the effect observed *in vivo* is due to a synthesis of glutamine from NH_4^+ ions, followed by an inactivation of glutamine synthetase by the inactivating enzyme.

The modifying enzyme adenylylates the glutamine synthetase, a maximum of twelve adenylyl groups being covalently linked to the dodecamer. Due consideration has been recently given to this phenomenon in a general review (172*a*). The adenylyl group forms an ester bond with the hydroxyl of a unique tyrosyl residue of the constitutive polypeptide chain (172*b*).

Since *E. coli* contains in addition a glutamine synthetase deadenylylating enzyme stimulated by α-ketoglutarate and inhibited by glutamine (172*c*), this organism appears to regulate its nitrogen metabolism by altering the structure of glutamine synthetase, a principal enzyme in organic nitrogen fixation.

BIOSYNTHESIS OF L-PROLINE (173, 174)

The γ-carboxyl group of glutamate is reduced to an aldehyde:

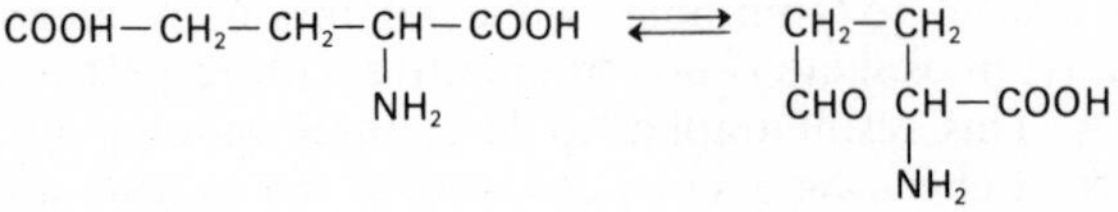

Glutamate-γ-semi-aldehyde

This compound undergoes a cyclization to form Δ^1-pyrroline 5-carboxylic acid. This reaction occurs spontaneously in aqueous solution, and the compound is then reduced to form L-proline:

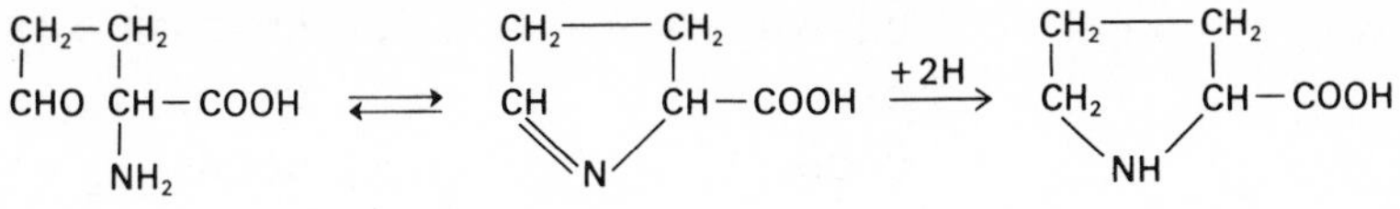

Δ¹-pyrroline carboxylate L-proline

BIOSYNTHESIS OF ARGININE (175, 176, 177)

In the course of evolution, microorganisms have developed a mechanism analogous to the one we have already seen in lysine biosynthesis to protect an amine group from involvement in spontaneous cyclization. But in this case, it is acetylation rather than succinylation which we find.

A specific acetylase (subject to feedback inhibition by arginine in *E. coli*) produces N-acetylglutamic acid:

$$COOH-CH_2-CH_2-CH(NH-CO-CH_3)-COOH$$

which is reduced to N-acetylglutamate semialdehyde; this is the acetylated form of the intermediate occurring in proline biosynthesis, and were it not for the acetylation, all the semialdehyde would be converted to proline. N-acetylglutamate semialdehyde undergoes a transamination reaction to form N-α-acetylornithine:

$$CHO-CH_2-CH_2-CH(NH-CO-CH_3)-COOH + R-CH(NH_2)-COOH \rightleftharpoons NH_2-CH_2-CH_2-CH_2-CH(NH-CO-CH_3)-COOH + R-CO-COOH$$

N-α-acetylornithine

In some organisms, the N-acetyl group is then removed by a specific deacylase, but in others it is transferred again to the amino group of glutamate. The ornithine produced in this way is then transformed to citrulline in a reaction catalyzed by ornithine transcarbamylase, which in addition to ornithine has carbamyl phosphate as substrate:

$$NH_2-(CH_2)_3-CH(NH_2)-COOH + NH_2-COO\sim PO_3H_2 \longrightarrow NH(CO-NH_2)-(CH_2)_3-CH(NH_2)-COOH + P_i$$

L-citrulline

Citrulline participates in a reaction with ATP and aspartate:

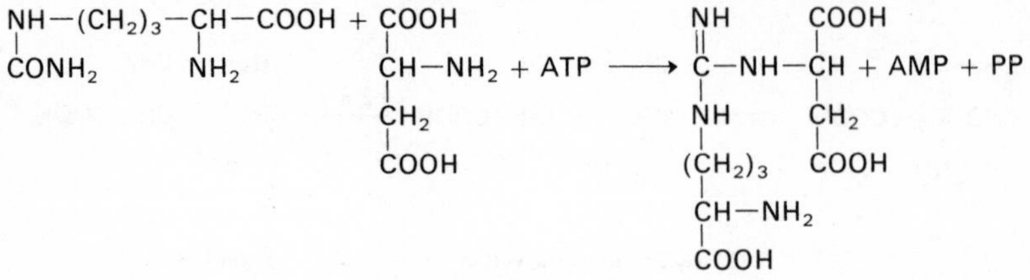

Argininosuccinate

The argininosuccinate so formed is then hydrolyzed to arginine and fumaric acid by the enzyme argininosuccinase:

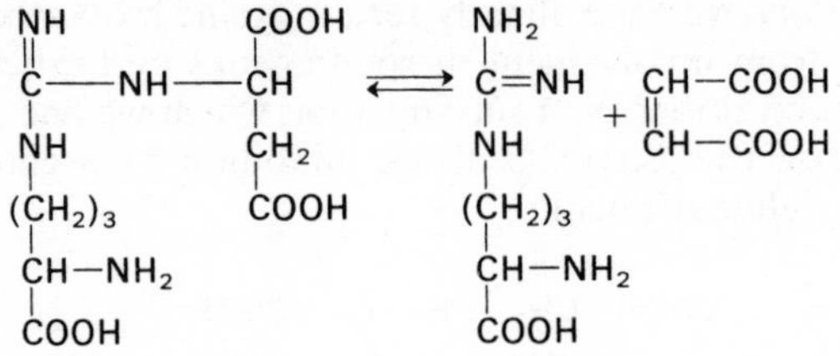

Argininosuccinate L-arginine

Control of arginine, putrescine and proline synthesis 4.1.

We have seen how the acetylation of glutamate, the first reaction specific to the synthesis of arginine, is allosterically inhibited by this amino acid. In addition, in *E. coli*, the presence of excess arginine represses the synthesis of all the enzymes involved in its biosynthesis (178).

However, the synthesis of arginine can not be considered as a perfectly linear sequence of reactions. In fact, one of the intermediates, ornithine, is the precursor of a diamine, putrescine:

$$H_2N-CH_2-CH_2-CH_2-CH(NH_2)-COOH \longrightarrow H_2N-(CH_2)_4-NH_2 + CO_2$$

This reaction is catalyzed by ornithine decarboxylase.

Putrescine has been found in Gram-negative bacteria and molds. Spermine and spermidine which are derived from it are universal constituents of bacteria, fungi and animals. In the presence of excess arginine, the synthesis of ornithine would be reduced to a rate unsuitable for the synthesis of these polyamines, the level of which is about 15 mg/g of protein in *E. coli*. A new means of production of putrescine from arginine, less direct than the decarboxylation of ornithine, has therefore been evolved. It is a decarboxylation of arginine:

$$\underset{\text{Arginine}}{H_2N-\underset{\underset{NH}{\|}}{C}-NH-(CH_2)_3-\underset{\underset{NH_2}{|}}{CH}-COOH} \longrightarrow \underset{\text{Agmatine}}{H_2N-\underset{\underset{NH}{\|}}{C}-NH-(CH_2)_4-NH_2} + CO_2$$

Agmatine amidinohydrolase hydrolyzes the product of this decarboxylation to putrescine and urea:

$$H_2N-\underset{\underset{NH}{\|}}{C}-NH-(CH_2)_4-NH_2 + H_2O \longrightarrow \underset{\text{Putrescine}}{H_2N-(CH_2)_4-NH_2} \qquad \underset{\text{Urea}}{H_2N-\underset{\underset{O}{\|}}{C}-NH_2}$$

This scheme of control is a new example of the diversity of the solutions arising in the course of evolution to the problem posed by the existence of branched pathways. As can be seen in the scheme below:

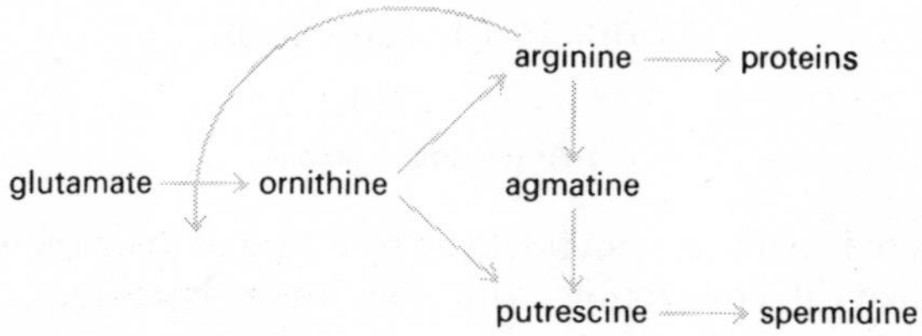

the synthesis of arginine is effectively part of a branched system, the branch point being situated at ornithine. The most economical pathway for production of putrescine is evidently the decarboxylation of ornithine. However, when repressible strains of *E. coli* are grown in the presence of excess arginine, the synthesis of the biosynthetic enzymes leading to arginine is inhibited. Under these conditions, the conversion of arginine to putrescine is the only alternative for the biosynthesis of polyamines (179).

One of the important compounds in the biosynthesis of arginine is carbamyl phosphate, a precursor, as we shall see later, of the pyrimidines.

L-proline and its analogs inhibit the formation of Δ^1-pyrroline carboxylate from glutamate in cell suspensions of *E. coli* (180).

SYNTHESIS OF L-LYSINE IN YEASTS AND MOLDS

In these organisms, the carbonyl group of α-ketoglutaric acid condenses with the methyl group of acetate to give homocitric acid. This reaction is similar to the formation of citrate from acetyl CoA and oxaloacetate, or to the formation of α-isopropylmalate (β-carboxy-β-hydroxyisocaproate) which we shall meet in the study of L-leucine biosynthesis in the next chapter:

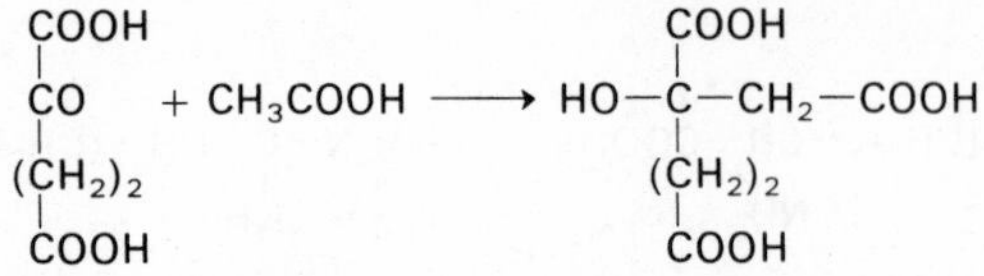

α-ketoglutarate Homocitrate

Homocitrate is then isomerized to homoisocitrate in two enzymatic steps with homoaconitate as a free intermediate in the reaction, which calls to mind the catalysis by aconitase which we met in the tricarboxylic cycle. Homoisocitrate is then oxidized and decarboxylated with the formation of α-ketoadipic acid, the immediate higher homolog of α-ketoglutaric acid:

$$COOH-(CH_2)_3-CO-COOH$$

α-ketoadipic acid

Transamination leads to α-aminoadipic acid:

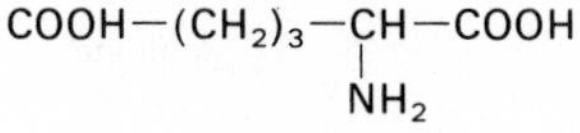

α-Aminoadipic acid

This diacid is reduced to a semialdehyde by a type of reaction which we have already studied in connection with the lower homologs, aspartic and glutamic acids:

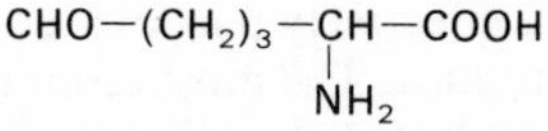

α-Aminoadipate semialdehyde

This condenses with a new molecule of glutamate to produce a molecule of saccharopine:

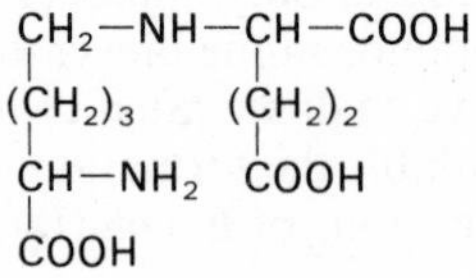

Saccharopine

which is the substrate for an enzyme producing L-lysine:

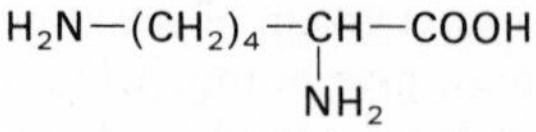

The biosynthesis of L-lysine is an interesting exception to the extraordinary identity of biosynthetic pathways from one organism to another. In bacteria and vascular plants, this amino acid is synthesized by the pathway through diaminopimelic acid, whereas in yeasts and molds, it is synthesized via α-aminoadipic acid. Diaminopimelic acid is itself an essential constituent of many species of bacteria, being an integral part of the complex cell-wall structure. So far, in spite of urgent research, no organism has been found in which both pathways exist together. It is tempting to think that the amino-adipic pathway may be more economical than the diaminopimelic acid pathway and has therefore been selected during evolution in yeasts and molds. Bacteria, in which diaminopimelic acid is a necessary compound for the cell wall, have only had to acquire an additional decarboxylase to obtain their lysine, thus saving the necessity to synthesize the enzymes of the α-aminoadipic pathway.

The following scheme summarizes the biosynthesis of the amino acids of the glutamic acid family:

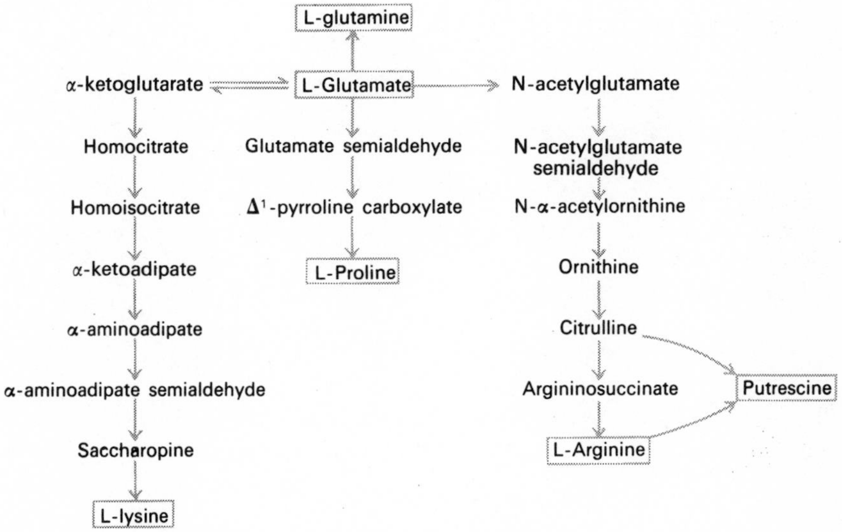

12

Biosynthesis of Amino Acids derived from Phosphoglyceric Acid and Pyruvic Acid

BIOSYNTHESIS OF GLYCINE AND SERINE

It is only recently that the use of appropriate mutants and an adequate enzyme analysis has enabled it to be decided which of these amino acids is synthesized first (181).

A specific enzyme oxidizes 3-phosphoglycerate, an intermediate in glycolysis, to 3-phosphohydroxypyruvate:

$$H_2O_3P{-}O{-}CH_2{-}CHOH{-}COOH + NAD^+ \rightleftharpoons H_2O_3P{-}O{-}CH_2{-}CO{-}COOH + NADH + H^+$$

3-phosphoglycerate → 3-phosphohydroxypyruvate

The 3-phosphohydroxypyruvate is the substrate for a transamination reaction which produces phosphoserine:

$$H_2O_3P{-}O{-}CH_2{-}\underset{\displaystyle NH_2}{\underset{|}{CH}}{-}COOH$$

Phosphoserine

A specific serine phosphate phosphatase hydrolyzes this compound to L-serine:

$$CH_2OH{-}\underset{\displaystyle NH_2}{\underset{|}{CH}}{-}COOH$$

L-serine

The conversion serine $\rightleftharpoons$ glycine takes place under the influence of serine hydroxymethyltransferase (182):

$$\text{Serine} \rightleftharpoons \text{Glycine} + \text{Formaldehyde}$$

The mechanism of this reaction, which can be considered as a model for transfers of one-carbon residues, is worth attention: it has been shown that (1) the C_1 fragment obtained from serine is a derivative of formaldehyde, (2) that this derivative is a tetrahydrofolate compound, (3) that pyridoxal phosphate is also necessary for the reaction.
The structural formulas of tetrahydrofolic acid and its "formaldehyde" derivative, N^5,N^{10}-methylene tetrahydrofolic acid, are given below:

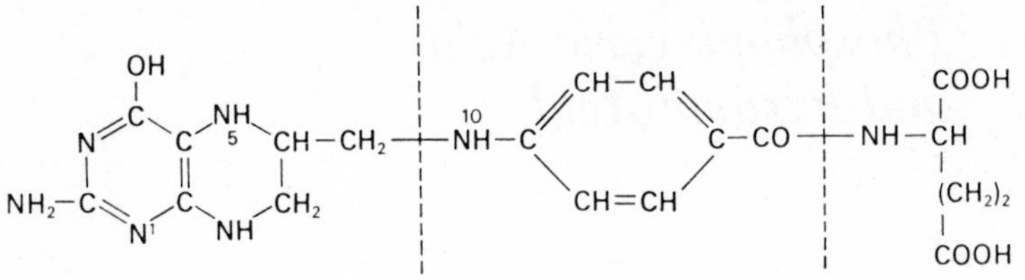

Pteridine moiety p-aminobenzoic acid moiety Glutamic acid moiety

Tetrahydrofolic acid (FH_4)

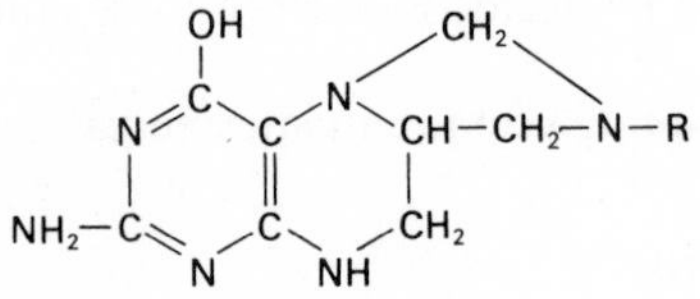

N^5,N^{10}-methylene tetrahydrofolic acid (CH_2OH-FH_4)

The interconversion can now be written:

$$\text{Serine} + FH_4 \rightleftarrows \text{Glycine} + CH_2OH-FH_4$$
$$CH_2OH-FH_4 \rightleftarrows HCHO + FH_4$$

Sum:

$$\text{Serine} \rightleftarrows \text{Glycine} + HCHO$$

It is thought that pyridoxal phosphate participates in this reaction through the formation of a Schiff's base between the amino group of the amino acid and the formyl group of pyridoxal phosphate. The resulting system of conjugated double bonds extends from the α-carbon of the amino acid to the nitrogen of the pyridine ring, thus labilizing the hydroxymethyl group of serine and facilitating its cleavage.
Experiments carried out using isotopes show that under certain conditions of growth, *E. coli* and *Clostridium pasteurianum* are able to obtain glycine

from threonine by the action of an enzyme called threonine aldolase:

$$\underset{\text{L-threonine}}{CH_3{-}CHOH{-}\underset{\displaystyle NH_2}{\underset{|}{C}H}{-}COOH} \longrightarrow \underset{\text{Glycine}}{H_2N{-}CH_2{-}COOH} + \underset{\text{Acetaldehyde}}{CH_3{-}CHO}$$

Control of serine and glycine synthesis 1.1.

In animal tissues, the inhibition of serine phosphate phosphatase by serine has been observed. Since the oxidation of phosphoglyceric acid and the transamination reaction are reversible, the practically irreversible hydrolysis of phosphoserine could be considered a likely site for the action of a control mechanism. In enterobacteriaceae on the other hand, the phosphatase is insensitive to serine, which instead inhibits the oxidation of phosphoglycerate, the first reaction in its pathway of biosynthesis (183).

No detailed study of the control of glycine and serine biosynthesis by repression has been carried out to date (1966).

BIOSYNTHESIS OF CYSTEINE (184, 185)

Auxotrophic mutants of *E. coli* which cannot utilize sulfate as a sulfur source, but can grow on sulfite, have been known for some time. Other mutants cannot utilize either sulfate or sulfite but can grow on thiosulfate. A recent series of publications presents evidence that the sole pathway of sulfate assimilation in bacteria and fungi involves an activation of sulfate with ATP, catalyzed by sulfate adenylyltransferase (or ATP sulfurylase):

$$\text{ATP} + \text{sulfate} \longrightarrow \text{adenosine-5}'\text{-phosphosulfate} + \text{pyrophosphate}$$

A specific kinase, adenylylsulfate kinase, produces a derivative phosphorylated at the 3′ position:

$$\text{adenosine-5}'\text{-phosphosulfate} + \text{ATP} \longrightarrow \text{3}'\text{-phosphoadenosine-5}'\text{-phosphosulfate} + \text{ADP}$$

The latter compound is the substrate of different enzymes which catalyze the formation of sulfate conjugates of phenols, arylamines, and steroids in the liver.

The reduction of phosphoadenosine phosphosulfate (PAPS) to sulfite has been studied in detail in yeast (186, 187). It involves the participation of two heat-labile proteins and a thermostable one, containing a disulfide group. One of the two labile proteins reduces this disulfide group with NADPH, and the other catalyzes the formation of sulfite in the presence of PAPS and the reduced heat-stable protein:

$$\text{PAPS} \longrightarrow \text{3}'\text{-phosphoadenosine-5}'\text{-phosphate} + SO_3^{--}$$

Sulfite reductase then reduces the sulfite ion to sulfide.
Thiosulfate was eliminated as an intermediate; its utilization by the mutants mentioned above is due to a reductive cleavage of the ion yielding sulfite and sulfide.
An enzyme, O-acetylserine sulfhydrylase, catalyzes the reaction of sulfide with a derivative of serine, O-acetylserine, to give L-cysteine in enterobacteriaceae (188):

$$HS-CH_2-\underset{\displaystyle NH_2}{\underset{|}{CH}}-COOH$$

L-cysteine

O-acetylserine is synthesized from acetyl coenzyme A and L-serine (188) by serine transacetylase.

Control of cysteine synthesis 2.1.

In yeast, controls occur at different levels. The synthesis of ATP sulfurylase is repressed by methionine, and its activity is inhibited allosterically by sulfide (189). The synthesis of sulfite reductase is also repressed by cysteine. In addition, as well as ATP sulfurylase, the synthesis of PAPS is inhibited by low concentrations of the reaction products. The most immediate control is therefore effected through inhibition by the reaction products. Furthermore, sulfide is a good inhibitor. It is therefore unlikely that cysteine is ever produced in excess. If, for physiological reasons, the regulatory barriers should no longer be functioning, methionine would repress the synthesis of ATP sulfurylase and cysteine would repress sulfite reductase.
In the enterobacteriaceae, addition of cysteine to the culture medium represses the synthesis of the proteins responsible for the reduction of PAPS and sulfite as well as O-acetylserine sulfhydrylase. We have also seen in chapter 1 that a very effective repression of sulfate permease by cysteine is observed in these organisms. Serine transacetylase is allosterically inhibited by L-cysteine, the inhibition being non-competitive with respect to L-serine and competitive with respect to acetyl CoA (188).

SYNTHESIS OF ALANINE

In several microorganisms, pyruvate can undergo a reductive amination to form alanine (190):

$$CH_3-CO-COOH + NH_3 + NADH + H^+ \rightleftarrows CH_3-\underset{\displaystyle NH_2}{\underset{|}{CH}}-COOH + NAD^+ + H_2O$$

However, the following process, involving a transamination between glutamate and pyruvate, is more widespread throughout living things:

$$CH_3{-}CO{-}COOH + COOH{-}CH_2{-}CH_2{-}\underset{\displaystyle NH_2}{\underset{|}{CH}}{-}COOH$$

$$\rightleftarrows CH_3{-}\underset{\displaystyle NH_2}{\underset{|}{CH}}{-}COOH + COOH{-}CH_2{-}CH_2{-}CO{-}COOH$$

SYNTHESIS OF VALINE

This biosynthetic route is exactly parallel to that of isoleucine and uses the same enzymes. α-aceto-α-hydroxyacid synthetase, which we have seen catalyzes the condensation of a molecule of acetaldehyde arising from pyruvate with a molecule of α-ketobutyrate, is also able to carry out the condensation of a molecule of acetaldehyde with a second molecule of pyruvate. This enzyme requires the presence of Mg^{++} and thiamine pyrophosphate for its activity. The reaction takes place in two steps: a molecule of hydroxyethylthiamine pyrophosphate or active acetaldehyde is first formed (see p. 55), and condenses with a second molecule of pyruvate to produce α-acetolactate. The reaction can be summarized as follows:

$$2\,CH_3{-}CO{-}COOH \longrightarrow CH_3{-}CO{-}\overset{\displaystyle OH}{\overset{|}{\underset{\displaystyle CH_3}{\underset{|}{C}}}}{-}COOH + CO_2$$

α-acetolactate

A rearrangement similar to the one already seen in isoleucine biosynthesis occurs under the influence of the reductoisomerase. It involves a reduction of the carbonyl group of α-acetolactate and the production of α,β-dihydroxy-β-methylbutyrate:

$$CH_3{-}CO{-}\overset{\displaystyle OH}{\overset{|}{\underset{\displaystyle CH_3}{\underset{|}{C}}}}{-}COOH \longrightarrow CH_3{-}\overset{\displaystyle OH}{\overset{|}{\underset{\displaystyle CH_3}{\underset{|}{C}}}}{-}CHOH{-}COOH$$

α,β-dihydroxy-β-methylbutyrate

The dehydratase specific for α,β-dihydroxyacids catalyzes loss of a molecule of water to yield α-keto-β-methylbutyric acid:

$$\begin{matrix} CH_3 \searrow \\ \quad\quad CH{-}CO{-}COOH \\ CH_3 \nearrow \end{matrix}$$

The same transaminase as was involved with isoleucine acts on this α-keto acid to give L-valine:

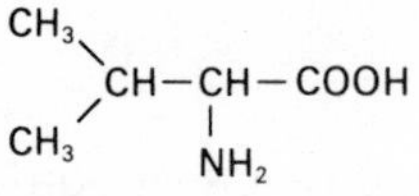

L-valine

The implications of the existence of a series of enzymes common to the biosynthesis of valine and isoleucine in microorganisms become obvious when we examine the following scheme:

L-threonine		
↓ (threonine deaminase)		
α-ketobutyrate		Pyruvate
↓	A	↓
α-aceto-α-hydroxybutyrate		α-acetolactate
↓	B	↓
α,β-dihydroxy-β-methylvalerate		α,β-dihydroxy-β-methylbutyrate
↓	C	↓
α-keto-β-methylvalerate		α-keto-β-methylbutyrate
↓	D	↓
L-isoleucine		L-valine

Every mutant deficient in threonine deaminase will be an isoleucine auxotroph; every mutant deficient in α-aceto-α-hydroxyacid synthetase, reductoisomerase, dehydratase or transaminase (reactions A, B, C and D) will show a double requirement for growth: valine plus isoleucine. We have seen that isoleucine causes allosteric feedback inhibition of threonine deaminase; this creates no problems for growth since the end-product, isoleucine, is in excess. But in contrast, an effective feedback inhibition of α-aceto-α-hydroxyacid synthetase by valine will present difficulties, since it automatically produces a deficiency in isoleucine. This is in fact the case in many organisms when their growth is inhibited by valine, the inhibition being removed by the addition of isoleucine.

SYNTHESIS OF LEUCINE (191, 192, 193)

α-keto-β-methylbutyric acid, the keto acid corresponding to valine, is the direct precursor of leucine. It is acetylated by a molecule of acetyl CoA to yield α-isopropylmalate:

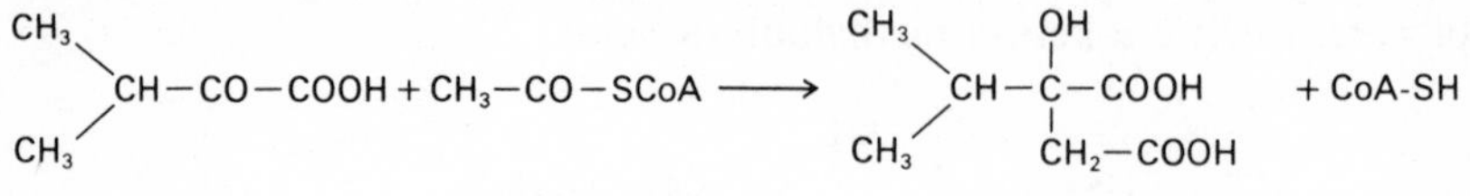

α-isopropylmalate

This compound is dehydrated and then rehydrated to β-isopropylmalate:

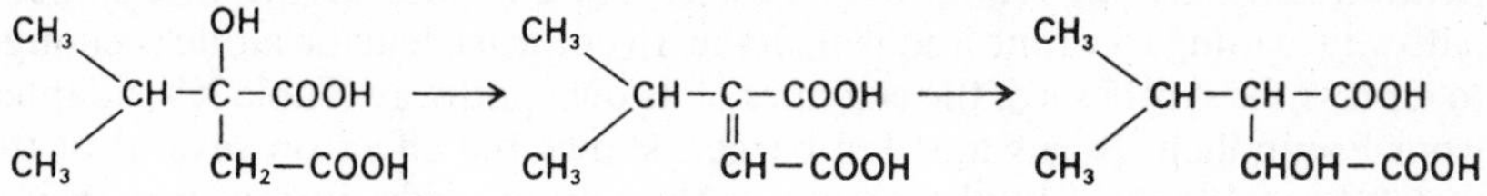

β-isopropylmalate

An oxidative decarboxylation of the latter leads to the formation of α-ketoisocaproic acid:

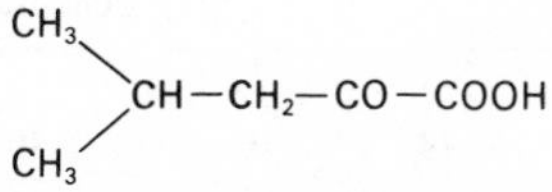

α-ketoisocaproate

Finally, a transamination reaction produces L-leucine:

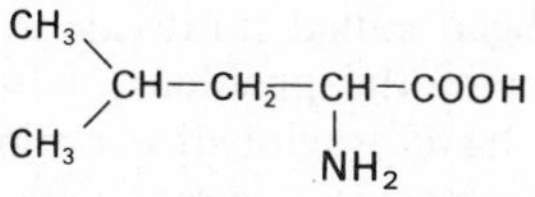

L-leucine

In a later chapter, we shall see that α-keto-β-methylbutyric acid is also the precursor of a vitamin, pantothenic acid.

CONTROL OF VALINE, LEUCINE AND ISOLEUCINE SYNTHESIS

We have already seen that threonine deaminase is subject to feedback inhibition by isoleucine, and α-aceto-α-hydroxyacid synthetase by valine. In both cases, the site of the allosteric inhibition is the first enzyme specific to the synthesis of the particular amino acid; the branch leading to leucine does not deviate from this rule: α-isopropylmalate synthetase is subject to allosteric feedback inhibition by L-leucine.

The controls by repression are more complex. It is necessary to remember that each of the last four steps in the biosynthesis of valine and isoleucine are catalyzed by the same enzymes. Repression of their synthesis presents a delicate problem since they bring about the production of two essential metabolites. In addition, the first reaction leading to the biosynthesis of leucine uses an intermediate in the synthesis of valine as a substrate. The solution of this problem is the following: valine, leucine, isoleucine and pantothenate are all required to repress the enzymes in the biosynthetic pathway leading to valine and isoleucine. In contrast, leucine alone is enough to repress the synthesis of the enzymes of its own pathway. Table XV, adapted from Freundlich, Burns and Umbarger, shows the effect on several of the enzymes involved of limiting each of the amino acids during growth in a chemostat.

TABLE XV

Limiting amino acid	Threonine deaminase	Dihydroxyacid dehydratase	α-isopropylmalate synthetase
None	4	5·8	1·2
Isoleucine	74	30	3·6
Valine	77	37	2·4
Leucine	58	24	12

The results are expressed as specific activities, μmoles of product formed per mg of protein per hour.

This phenomenon has been called multivalent repression by the authors; it adds another solution of the problem of branched-chain pathways in biosynthesis to those we have previously examined (158).
The following scheme summarizes the reactions involved in the biosynthesis of the amino acids derived from phosphoglyceric acid and pyruvic acid.

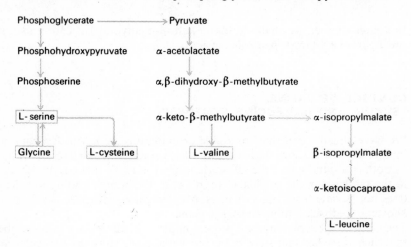

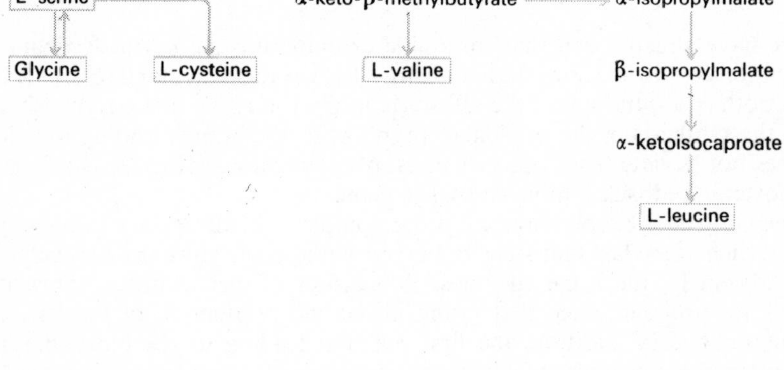

13

Biosynthesis of Aromatic Amino Acids and its Regulation

Glucose is an aliphatic substance, and so the synthesis from it of phenylalanine, tyrosine and tryptophan presents the biochemist with the problem of the biosynthesis of the aromatic nucleus.

The key to this problem was given some fifteen years ago by the isolation of polyauxotrophic mutants which required the presence of the three aromatic amino acids in the medium for growth, and in addition *p*-aminobenzoic acid (a precursor of folic acid). The existence of this multiple requirement as a result of a single mutation, immediately suggested that the block consisted in the inability to synthesize a precursor common to all four essential metabolites. After trying 55 cyclic derivatives, without success, B. D. Davis discovered that shikimic acid could replace the four growth factors. Moreover, growth was proportional to the amount of shikimate added. Other bacterial mutants, in which the lesion lies in a later step in aromatic biosynthesis, accumulate shikimic acid in the medium. It was therefore concluded that shikimic acid was the precursor sought; however its identification relied only on chromatographic analysis and on the response given by mutants. Later, the compound was isolated and characterized by the classical methods of organic chemistry.

Shikimic acid has been known since the nineteenth century as a rare constituent of certain plants. We shall first examine how this compound is formed in *Escherichia coli*.

FORMATION OF SHIKIMIC ACID (194, 195, 196, 197)

Erythrose 4-phosphate and phosphoenolpyruvate are known compounds in glucose degradation; they undergo a condensation catalyzed by a specific aldolase to produce a seven-carbon compound, 7-phospho-3-deoxy-Darabino-heptulosonic acid (PDAH):

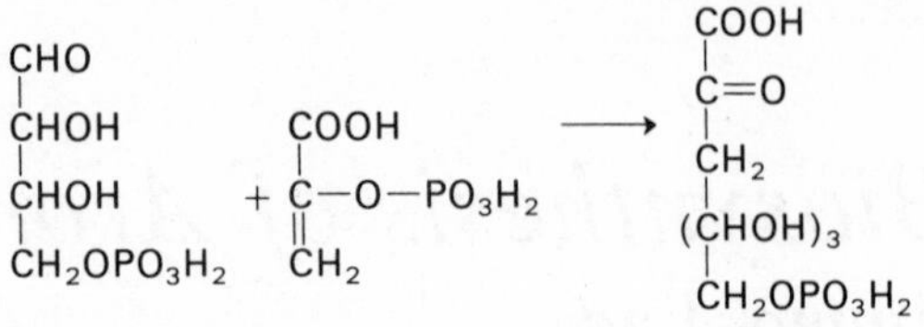

Erythrose 4-phosphate PDAH

One or more enzymes are necessary to transform this sugar derivative into 5-dehydroquinic acid. The transformation requires the presence of NAD^+ and cobaltous ions. The need for NAD^+ remains unexplained, since the reaction does not seem to involve a net transfer of electrons.

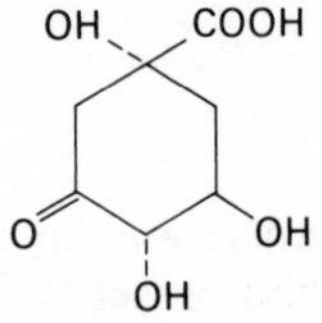

5-dehydroquinic acid

Although dehydroquinic acid is a cyclic compound, it has as yet no aromatic properties, since it is devoid of the characteristic system of conjugated double bonds. The enzyme dehydroquinase, with no known cofactor requirement, catalyzes the elimination of a water molecule to form dehydroshikimic acid, a compound which shows the beginnings of aromatization:

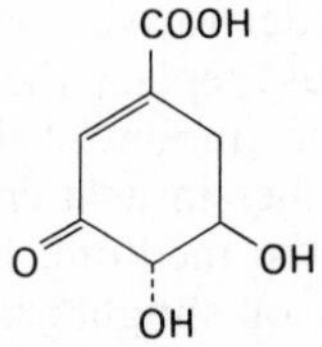

5-dehydroshikimic acid

5-dehydroshikimate reductase reduces this compound with NADPH to yield the intermediate mentioned at the beginning of the chapter, shikimic acid (3,4,5-trihydroxycyclohexene-1-carboxylic acid):

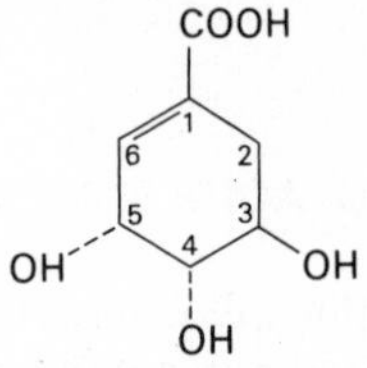

Shikimic acid

The first experimenters in the field of aromatic biosynthesis studied the distribution of radioactivity in tyrosine and phenylalanine isolated from organisms which were grown in the presence of glucose, acetate or pyruvate. These methods could not distinguish between the two sides of the aromatic ring. A series of experiments was then devoted to the study of the distribution of radioactivity in the different carbon atoms of shikimic acid accumulated by an *E. coli* mutant with glucose labelled in specific positions as sole carbon source (198). The results showed that the carboxyl group and carbon atoms 1 and 2 of shikimic acid were derived from a three-carbon intermediate of glycolysis, and that the four remaining carbon atoms could come from a tetrose. This suggested that a seven-carbon intermediate might be formed by the condensation of a C_3 derivative with a C_4. We have seen that these predictions are confirmed in every detail by enzymatic analysis. This example is typical of the result obtained by using the complementary methods of attack provided by biochemical mutants, the skilled use of isotopes, and enzymological techniques.

FORMATION OF CHORISMIC ACID (199, 200, 201)

Shikimic acid is not the compound from which the four pathways diverge, leading to the three amino acids and *p*-aminobenzoic acid. It is phosphorylated first of all:

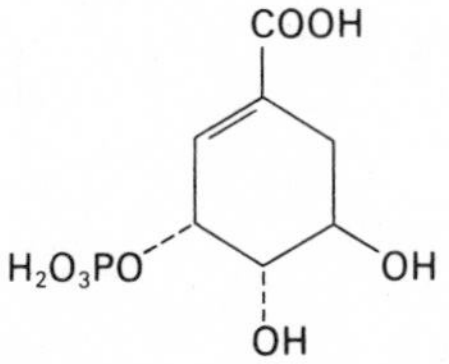

5-phosphoshikimate

5-phosphoshikimate reacts with a molecule of phosphoenolpyruvate to yield 3-enolpyruvyl-5-phosphoshikimate:

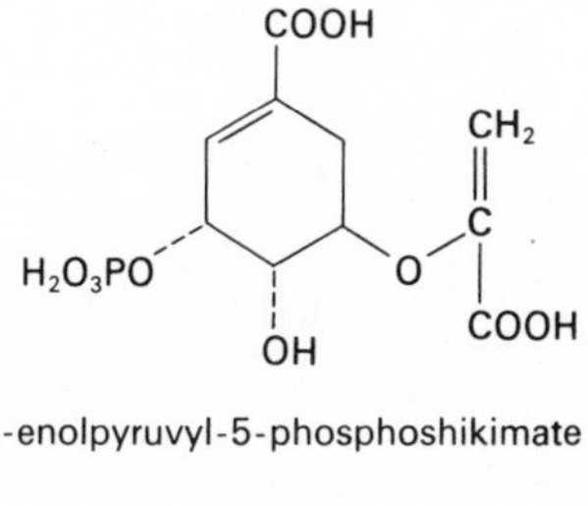

3-enolpyruvyl-5-phosphoshikimate

This loses its phosphate, and the resulting compound is the common precursor from which all the syntheses of aromatic compounds diverge, and is called chorismic acid (from a Greek word meaning separation):

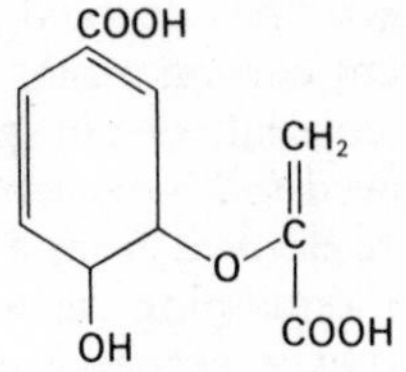

Chorismic acid

BIOSYNTHESIS OF PHENYLALANINE AND TYROSINE FROM CHORISMIC ACID (204, 205)

It is quite plausible that the first precursor identified in the biosynthesis of these two amino acids, prephenic acid, arises by the rearrangement of chorismic acid as shown below (202, 203):

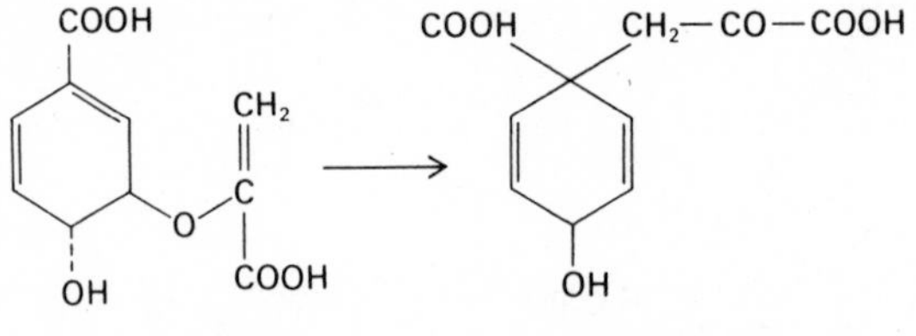

Chorismic acid Prephenic acid

The enzyme catalyzing this rearrangement is called chorismate mutase. The conversion of prephenic acid to the next intermediate, phenylpyruvate, involves a decarboxylation and a dehydration and is accompanied by the aromatization of the ring. The enzyme catalyzing this reaction is called prephenate dehydratase:

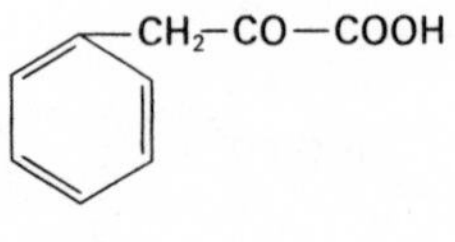

Phenylpyruvic acid

Finally, a transamination converts this α-ketoacid to phenylalanine:

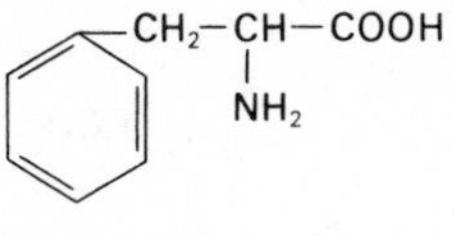

L-phenylalanine

Prephenic acid is a precursor common to both phenylalanine and tyrosine. Prephenate dehydrogenase (which is not to be confused with prephenate dehydratase) catalyzes the oxidative decarboxylation of prephenic acid; this reaction requires the presence of NAD^+ as electron acceptor, and yields the α-ketoacid corresponding to tyrosine:

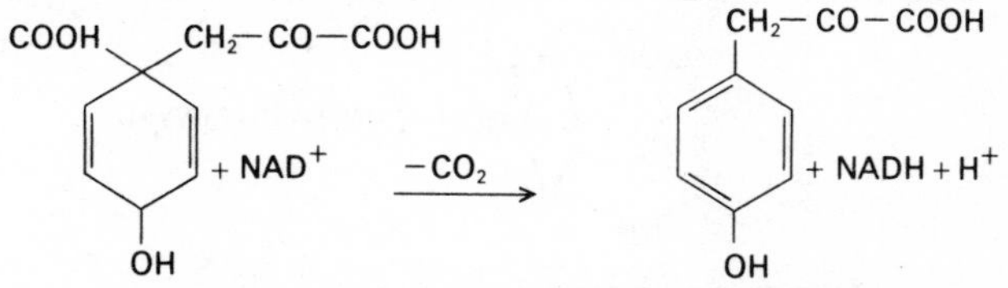

Prephenic acid *p*-hydroxyphenylpyruvic acid

A transamination produces L-tyrosine from the *p*-hydroxyphenylpyruvic acid:

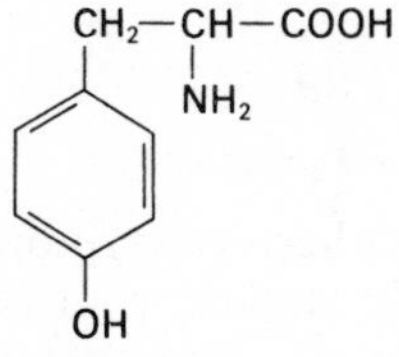

L-tyrosine

Animal tissues possess an enzyme, phenylalanine hydroxylase, able to carry out the direct hydroxylation of phenylalanine to tyrosine. This enzyme is found in a few microorganisms.

BIOSYNTHESIS OF TRYPTOPHAN (206, 207, 208)

Early studies showed that some microorganisms requiring tryptophan for growth could also grow if indole or anthranilic acid were added to the culture medium in place of tryptophan. Some of the reactions involved in the biosynthesis of tryptophan are now known in detail.

Chorismic acid reacts with glutamine in a manner not yet clearly understood; the product of the reaction catalyzed by anthranilate synthetase is anthranilic acid (*o*-aminobenzoic acid):

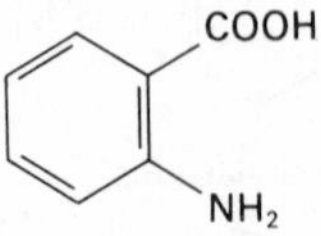

Anthranilic acid

Anthranilate phosphoribosyltransferase catalyzes the reaction between anthranilic acid and 5-phosphoribosyl-1-pyrophosphate to give the ribotide of anthranilic acid. Phosphoribosylanthranilate isomerase converts the ribotide to a deoxyribulotide:

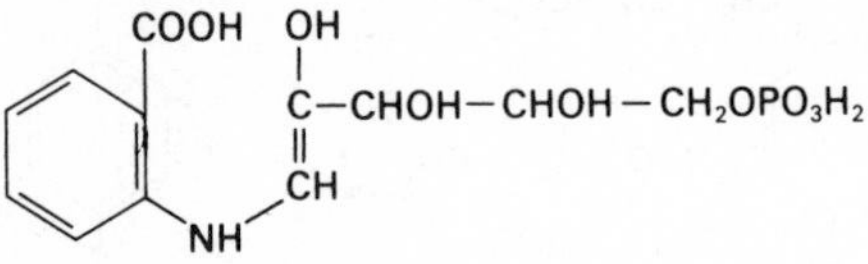

Anthranilate deoxyribulotide

Indoleglycerol phosphate synthetase catalyzes the decarboxylation and ring closure which produces indoleglycerol phosphate:

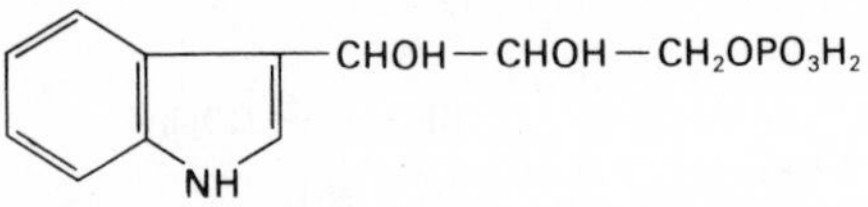

Indoleglycerol phosphate

The final step in the biosynthesis of tryptophan is catalyzed by an enzyme which has been intensively studied with regard to its primary structure, namely tryptophan synthetase. The enzyme extracted from *E. coli* was chosen for studies on the colinearity between nucleotide sequences in DNA and their translation into sequences of amino acids. It has also been an invaluable tool in studies on mutagenesis and the genetic code. As well as these results, it presents other characteristics which deserve our greater attention.

Tryptophan synthetase (209, 210) 4.1.

Both tryptophan synthetase extracted from *E. coli* and the enzyme from *Neurospora crassa* catalyze the three following reactions:

a) The condensation of indoleglycerol phosphate (IGP) and serine, in the presence of pyridoxal phosphate to form tryptophan, with the simultaneous elimination of glyceraldehyde phosphate:

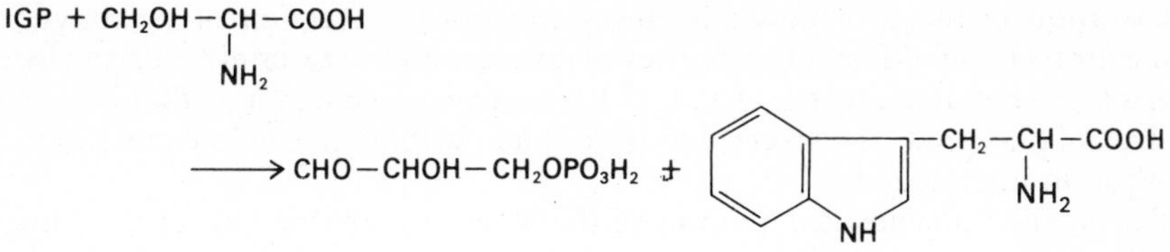

L-tryptophan

b) The condensation of indole and serine in the presence of pyridoxal phosphate to yield tryptophan also:

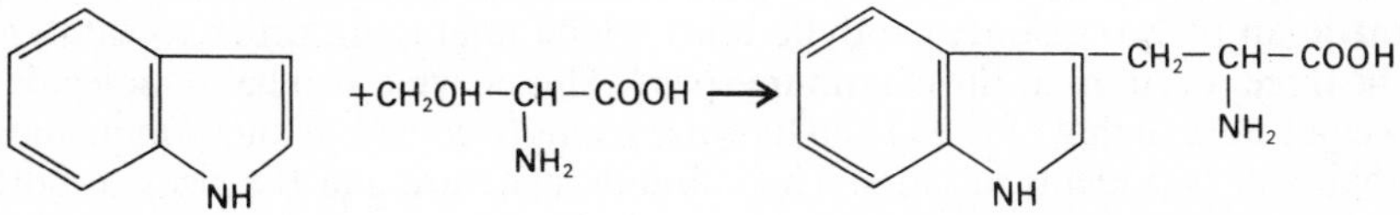

Indole L-serine L-tryptophan

This reaction explains the behaviour of certain microorganisms and mutants which can utilize indole although this compound is not a normal intermediate.
c) The condensation of indole and glyceraldehyde phosphate to give indoleglycerol phosphate:

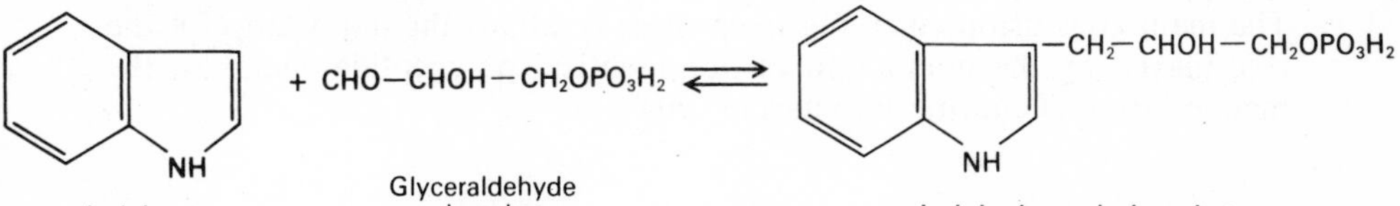

Indole Glyceraldehyde phosphate Indoleglycerol phosphate

The *E. coli* enzyme is made up of two distinct kinds of polypeptide chain, which were early designated as the A and B chains, each one being the translation of a separate cistron. We now know that the A protein is itself composed of two identical chains called α and that the B protein is similarly composed of two β chains. Each α chain has a molecular weight of 29,500 and each β 49,500. Tryptophan synthetase as a whole has therefore a molecular weight of $(29{,}500 + 49{,}500) \times 2 = 158{,}000$. The tryptophan synthetase structure is written as $\alpha_2\beta_2$.
If the A and B chains of the *E. coli* enzyme are separated, neither can catalyze reaction *a*, which is the physiological reaction. However, the A chain can carry out reaction *c* and the B chain reaction *b*. These reactions take place however at very much lower rates than the ones carried out by the intact enzyme. It appears that each of the two chains has a specific combining site for indole, specific for reaction *c* in the case of the A chain and for reaction *b* in the case of the B chain. The reassociation of the two chains results in an

activation of the two individual reactions and the creation of a catalytic site for reaction *a*. The active centres of both chains are certainly reorganized in a very special manner in the (A + B) complex, since we know that indoleglycerol phosphate is converted to tryptophan without free indole participating as an intermediate.

The detailed biochemical analysis of the *N. crassa* enzyme has revealed the following properties: the presence of two separate sites for combination with indole, specific for reactions *b* and *c* respectively; an interdependence of reactions *b* and *c*; no participation of indole as a free intermediate in the synthesis of tryptophan.

As a result, the catalytically active sites of the enzymes extracted from the two organisms must be very similar, since in each case they seem to be made up of two distinct catalytic units which interact in order to catalyze the three reactions at the maximum speed. This enzyme also has a molecular weight close to that of *E. coli* and likewise seems to consist of four polypeptide chains in two identical pairs. The sub-unit structure and the sizes of both enzymes suggest a common origin in evolution.

The tryptophan synthetase enzymes of the blue-green alga *Anabaena variabilis* and the green alga *Chlorella ellipsoidea*, as well as of *B. subtilis*, have also two separate components. Moreover, in these organisms, it would appear that the isolated B chain can catalyze reaction *b* at its maximum rate, while the association of the A and B chains is still essential for reaction *a* and for maximum activity in reaction *c*.

The main conclusion emerging from these results is the importance of the role played by the interaction of non-identical polypeptide chains in the manifestation of enzyme activities in cells.

THE CONTROL OF AROMATIC AMINO ACID BIOSYNTHESIS

Certain aspects of the regulation of aromatic amino acid biosynthesis in *E. coli* are curiously similar to those we have already seen in another branched chain, the biosynthesis of amino acids derived from aspartate.

The first activity of the chain, the condensation between erythrose 4-phosphate and phosphoenolpyruvate is catalyzed by three distinct PADH aldolases (211, 212). The first is subject to feedback inhibition by phenylalanine; its synthesis is repressed by this amino acid in the growth medium. The synthesis of the second is repressed by tyrosine which is an allosteric inhibitor of its activity; finally the third enzyme is not subject to feedback inhibition by any of the essential metabolites of the chain, but its activity is repressed by tryptophan; this aldolase is found only at very low concentrations in *E. coli*. The situation is exactly parallel to that encountered for the three aspartokinases in *E. coli*.

In the same organism, a new example of isofunctional enzymes appears further along the chain: this is the two chorismate mutases, one of which is inhibited by phenylalanine and the other by tyrosine (205); the situation is parallel to the case of the two homoserine dehydrogenases of *E. coli* with the exception that control by repression has not been studied for the chorismate mutases.

The similarity between the two systems is even more obvious when we find that the phenylalanine-sensitive chorismate mutase and prephenate dehydratase are part of the same protein complex. The same is true for the tyrosine-sensitive chorismate mutase and prephenate dehydrogenase.

In *Bacillus subtilis*, only one PDAH aldolase is found; an efficient inhibition by any one of the terminal metabolites would be detrimental to the organism. In an analogous case, we have seen that *Rhodopseudomonas capsulatus* makes use of concerted feedback inhibition and *Rhodospirillum rubrum* the specific reversal of the inhibition caused by one essential metabolite with the help of another essential metabolite. Here, a third solution arises (213): the feedback inhibitor is not an end-product, but a compound whose position in the sequence precedes the branch points leading to the end-products; in fact chorismic acid and prephenic acid are the allosteric feedback inhibitors of PDAH aldolase. This enzyme has been considerably purified. It exhibits no substrate-substrate interactions but molecules of chorismate produce a co-operative inhibition which is strictly non-competitive. This enzyme is therefore a member of the class of allosteric enzymes of the *V* type defined in chapter 2.

The enzyme complexes carrying out the synthesis of tryptophan from chorismate 5.1.

In *Neurospora crassa*, the four enzymatic steps in the synthesis of indoleglycerol phosphate from chorismate are under the control of only three genetic loci. Phosphoribosylanthranilate isomerase and indoleglycerol phosphate synthetase seem to be one and the same enzyme, for point mutations at the same locus, or at another locus, result in the loss of anthranilate synthetase activity. The explanation seems to be that a molecular complex of the products of the two loci catalyzes the three reactions. This complex has been partially purified (214) but it has not proved possible by standard methods to dissociate it into active sub-units. We have already met such complexes in studying the proteins with aspartokinase and homoserine dehydrogenase I and II activities in *E. coli*, and the chorismate mutase activities associated respectively with prephenate dehydrogenase and prephenate dehydratase in the same organism. We recall also the case of the pyruvate and α-ketoglutarate oxidases of *E. coli* and the complex which catalyzes the synthesis of long-chain fatty acids in *Saccharomyces cerevisiae*.

In yeast, a different aggregate is found: the synthesis of anthranilate synthetase and indoleglycerol phosphate synthetase is under the control of a single genetic locus, but phosphoribosylanthranilate isomerase is a quite separate enzyme.

Finally in *E. coli*, a molecular aggregate carries both the anthranilate synthetase and anthranilate phosphoribosyltransferase activities (215). In this particular case, the catalytic activities of the aggregate are physiologically sequential, and we can imagine that anthranilate is never a free intermediate during the synthesis of tryptophan *in vivo*. This argument is valid in every case where the proteins composing the molecular aggregate catalyze consecutive reactions in the same chain, but holds its own with difficulty when the reactions catalyzed are, for example, the first and third of a sequence, as in the case of aspartokinase and homoserine dehydrogenase or in the example of the *Neurospora* aggregate studied in the paragraph above.

The following scheme summarizes the steps identified in the biosynthesis of the aromatic amino acids:

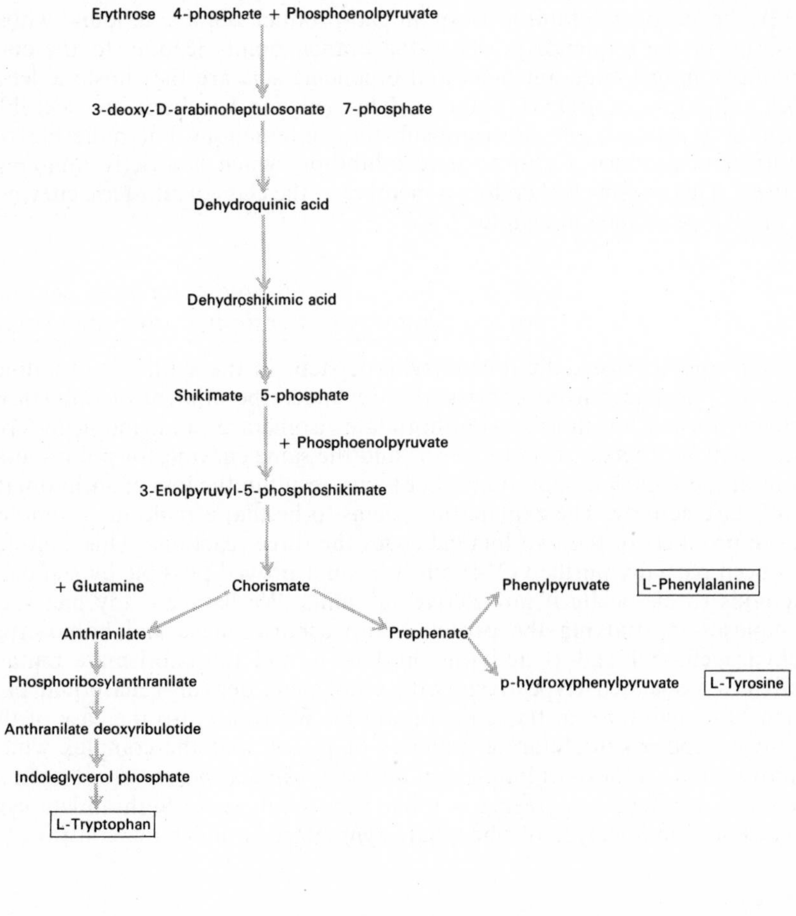

The scheme below summarizes the existing state of our knowledge about feedback inhibition in the biosynthesis of these amino acids in *E. coli*:

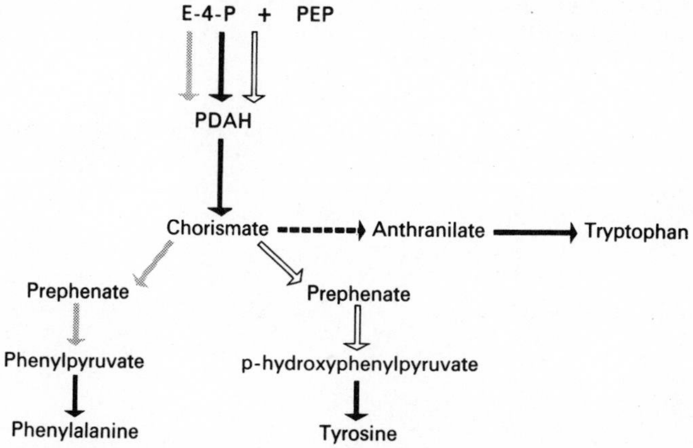

The reactions shown in gray are inhibited by phenylalanine; those in white by tyrosine. The reaction shown by a dotted arrow is inhibited by tryptophan.

In contrast, in *B. subtilis*, there is only one PDAH aldolase which is inhibited by chorismate and prephenate:

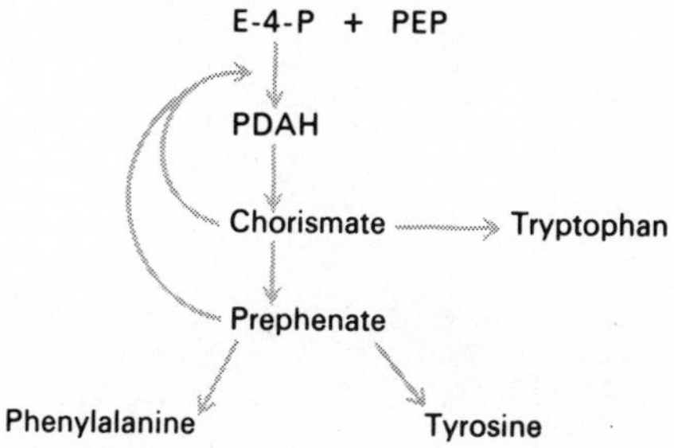

14

Biosynthesis of Histidine
and its Regulation

The enzyme called PR-ATP-pyrophosphorylase for short catalyzes the reaction between ATP and 5-phosphoribosyl-1-pyrophosphate (PRPP) to give N^1-(5′-phosphoribosyl)-ATP (216):

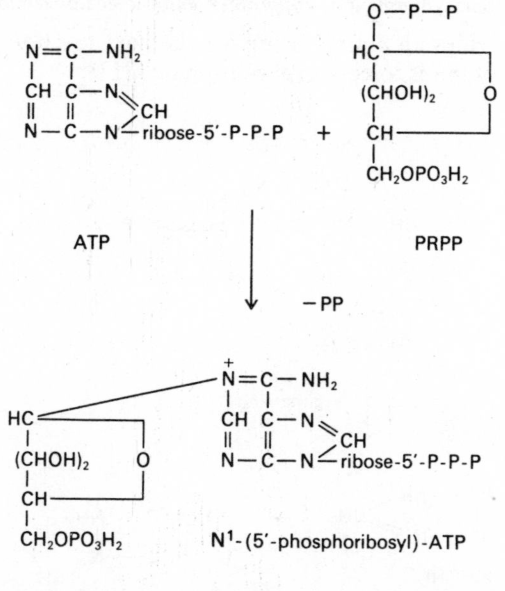

The second intermediate in the biosynthetic chain leading to histidine has recently been identified: this is N^1-(5′-phosphoribosyl)-AMP, formed from the preceding compound by PR-ATP-pyrophosphohydrolase, which removes a pyrophosphate residue. Another enzyme, PR-AMP-1,6-cyclohydrolase, converts this compound to phosphoribosylformimino-aminoimidazole-carboxamide ribotide:

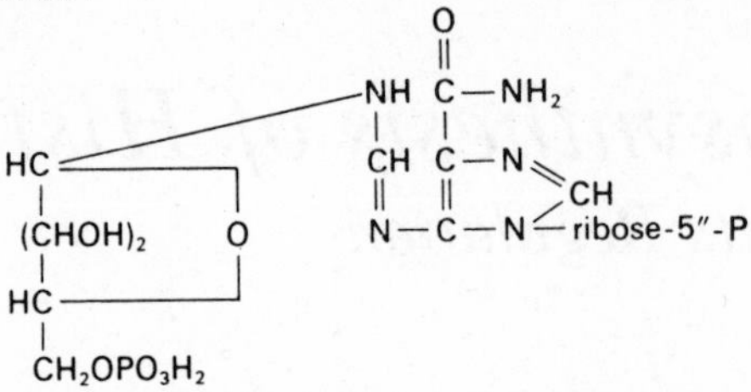

N-(5′-phosphoribosylformimino)-5-amino-4-imidazolecarboxamide-1-(5″-phosphoriboside)

An isomerase converts this compound to the corresponding ribuloside:

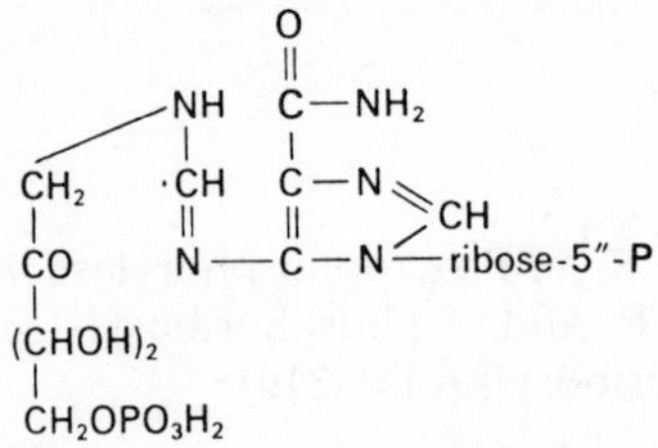

N-(5′-phosphoribulosylformimino)-5-amino-4-imidazolecarboxamide-1-(5″-phosphoriboside)

Glutamine provides an amino group for the next reaction which results in the formation of imidazoleglycerol phosphate (217):

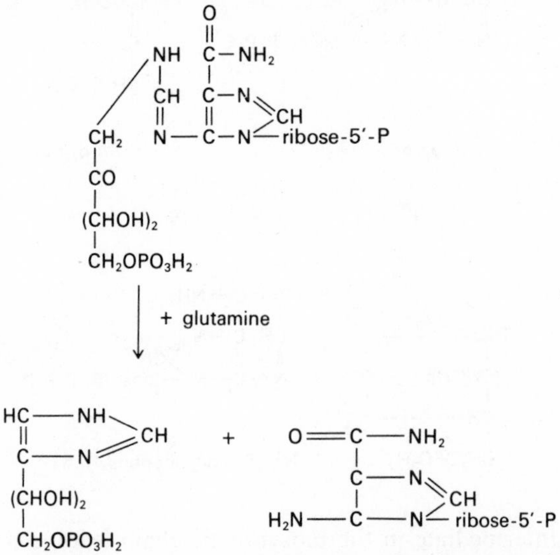

Imidazoleglycerol phosphate

5-amino-4-imidazolecarboxamide-1-(5′-phosphoriboside)

The other product of the reaction, 5-amino-4-imidazolecarboxamide ribotide, is itself a precursor of ATP. In this way the purine nucleus of ATP is recycled during the biosynthesis of histidine.

A specific dehydratase removes a molecule of water from the imidazoleglycerol phosphate molecule and converts it to imidazole acetol phosphate (218):

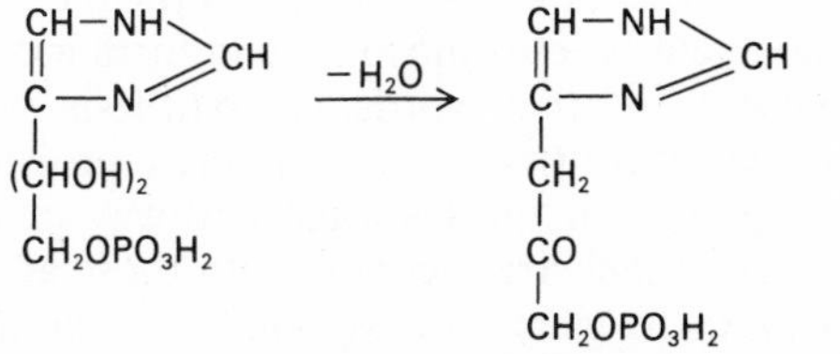

Imidazole acetol phosphate

A transaminase (219) converts this to histidinol phosphate, which is dephosphorylated by a specific phosphatase to histidinol (220). This compound is then oxidized to histidine by histidinol dehydrogenase. The aldehyde derivative, histidinal, is probably an intermediate in this reaction, although it has never been possible to demonstrate its existence (221):

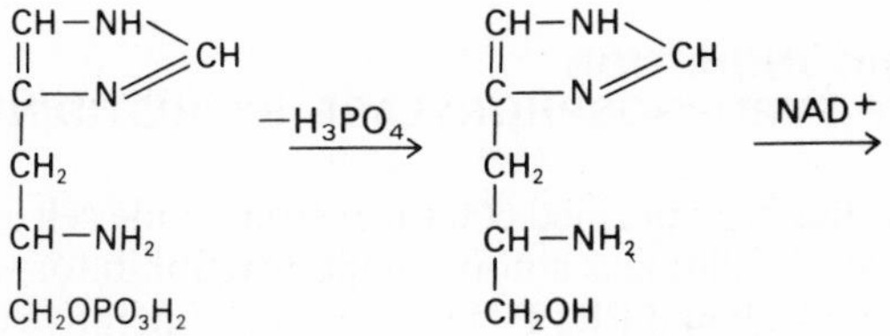

Histidinol phosphate Histidinol

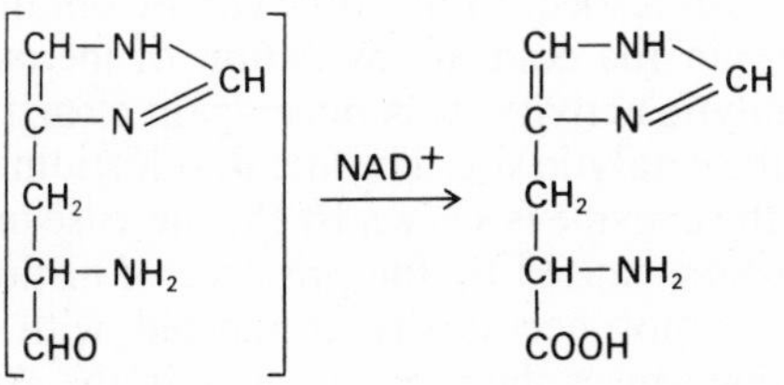

Histidinal L-Histidine

The histidinol dehydrogenase of *Salmonella typhimurium* has been purified: a crystalline homogeneous preparation catalyzes the oxidation of both histidinol and histidinal (221*a*).

Despite the existence of two complementation regions in the gene coding for this protein, it appears to be composed of two very similar or identical sub-units (221*b*). The enzyme probably exists as a functional unit catalyzing both steps of the oxidation without histidinal ever being formed as a free intermediate (222).

In the enterobacteriaceae (*E. coli* and *S. typhimurium*), the genes which control the synthesis of the different enzymes in the biosynthesis of histidine are adjacent on the bacterial chromosome and form a co-ordinated unit of regulation (the operon). In other words, the synthesis of all the enzymes is simultaneously subject to control by co-ordinate repression (223).

The biosynthetic reactions in the histidine pathway in *Neurospora crassa* and *Saccharomyces cerevisiae* are identical with those above for the enterobacteriaceae. However, the genes corresponding to the different enzymatic activities are not grouped together, but separated in different loci on different chromosomes. Whereas in *S. typhimurium*, imidazoleglycerol phosphate dehydratase and histidinol phosphate phosphatase are controlled by the same gene, in *Neurospora crassa* and yeast, the controlling genes are different. It is not beyond possibility that the two activities in *Salmonella* under the control of the same gene, and certain enzymatic activities in *Neurospora*, may belong to multifunctional protein aggregates such as we have already encountered.

ALLOSTERIC INHIBITION OF PR-ATP-PYROPHOSPHORYLASE BY HISTIDINE (224)

This enzyme has been purified 600 times from crude cell extracts of wild-type *S. typhimurium*. Histidine is a non-competitive inhibitor with respect to both the substrates, ATP and PRPP. There is no co-operative interaction between substrate molecules. Unfortunately, such interactions have not been looked for in the case of histidine.

The desensitization with respect to histidine can be obtained spontaneously by aging the enzyme in the cold, or by action of mercurials, without appreciable loss of catalytic activity. It is once again clear that the regulatory site is distinct from the catalytic site. The fact that histidine induces a conformational change in the enzyme is shown by the increase in the rate of tryptic hydrolysis of the enzyme caused by the presence of histidine; but this conformational change is not necessarily connected with the allosteric inhibition, since histidine causes the same increase in the rate of tryptic digestion whether the enzyme is in the native state or desensitized. ATP and PRPP on the other hand protect against digestion. Independent measurements have shown that the native enzyme and the desensitized enzyme are able to combine with histidine equally effectively, suggesting that the observed complexes result from the existence of a site with affinity for histidine which is different from the one involved in the allosteric inhibition. Mercurial concentrations which are quite high compared with those causing desensitization lead to irreversible inactivation of the enzyme, accompanied by a change in the sedimentation coefficient. This implies a dissociation into sub-units. As this change is not observed with lower concentrations of mercurials which produce desensitization, it seems improbable that the monomer-polymer interconversions are associated with the mechanism of control by histidine.

15

Biosynthesis of Pyrimidine Nucleotides and Deoxynucleotides and its Regulation

SYNTHESIS OF CARBAMYL PHOSPHATE (225, 226, 227)

In bacteria, the first step in the synthesis of pyrimidines is the synthesis of carbamyl phosphate from ammonia or an ammonia donor, CO_2 and ATP:

$$NH_3 + CO_2 + ATP \longrightarrow \underset{\text{Carbamyl phosphate}}{H_2N{-}COO{-}PO_3H_2} + ADP$$

In many species, glutamine is the actual donor of ammonia. The enzyme catalyzing this reaction is called carbamate kinase (or carbamoyl phosphomutase) because carbamate is thought to be formed as an intermediate. It differs from another enzyme, carbamyl phosphate synthetase, found in the liver of ureotelic animals, which catalyzes the following reaction:

$$NH_3 + CO_2 + 2\,ATP \longrightarrow H_2N{-}COO{-}PO_3H_2 + 2\,ADP + P_i$$

This second enzyme requires the presence of N-acetylglutamate as cofactor; the N-acetylglutamate does not take part in the reaction but appears to affect the enzyme conformation.

We have seen in chapter XI that carbamyl phosphate is also a precursor of arginine, a fact which creates a problem in the regulation of the two biosyntheses. The first reaction truly specific for the synthesis of pyrimidines is the carbamylation of aspartate.

THE SYNTHESIS OF CYTIDINE AND URIDINE TRIPHOSPHATES (228–232, 30)

Aspartate transcarbamylase (ATCase) is an enzyme which can carry out the condensation of a molecule of aspartate with a molecule of carbamyl phosphate. This reaction is formally similar to the ornithine transcarbamylase reaction (OTCase) which we studied in chapter 11:

$$H_2N-COO-PO_3H_2 \;+\; \underset{\underset{NH_2}{|}}{COOH-CH_2-CH-COOH} \longrightarrow \begin{array}{c} COOH \\ | \\ NH_2 \quad CH_2 \\ | \qquad | \\ CO \qquad CH-COOH \\ \diagdown NH \diagup \end{array} \;+\; H_3PO_4$$

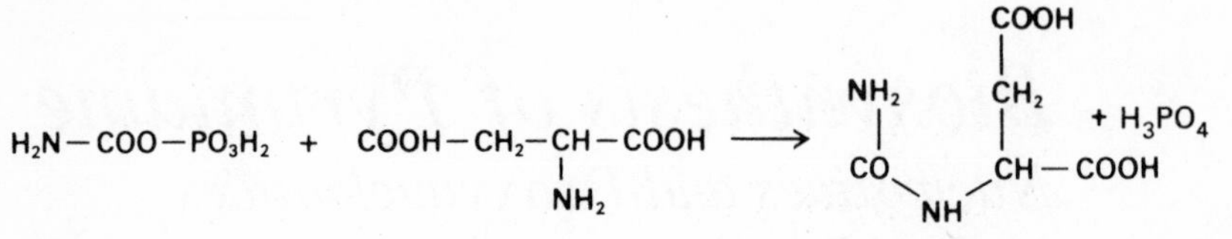

Carbamylaspartate
(or ureidosuccinate)

Dihydroorotase, a dehydratase, catalyzes the cyclization forming the pyrimidine ring:

$$\begin{array}{c} COOH \\ \diagdown \\ NH_2 \quad CH_2 \\ | \qquad | \\ CO \qquad CH-COOH \\ \diagdown NH \diagup \end{array} \xrightarrow{-H_2O} \begin{array}{c} CO \\ \diagup \diagdown \\ HN \qquad CH_2 \\ | \qquad | \\ CO \qquad CH-COOH \\ \diagdown NH \diagup \end{array}$$

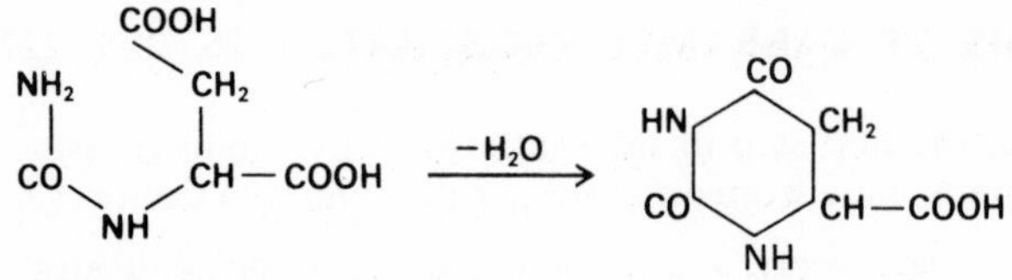

Carbamylaspartate   Dihydroorotate

Dihydroorotate dehydrogenase catalyzes the formation of orotic acid, the hydrogen acceptor being flavin adenine dinucleotide (FAD) in this case, rather than NAD^+ or $NADP^+$:

$$\begin{array}{c} CO \\ \diagup \diagdown \\ HN \qquad CH_2 \\ | \qquad | \\ OC \qquad CH-COOH \\ \diagdown NH \diagup \end{array} \longrightarrow \begin{array}{c} CO \\ \diagup \diagdown \\ HN \qquad CH \\ | \qquad \| \\ OC \qquad C-COOH \\ \diagdown NH \diagup \end{array}$$

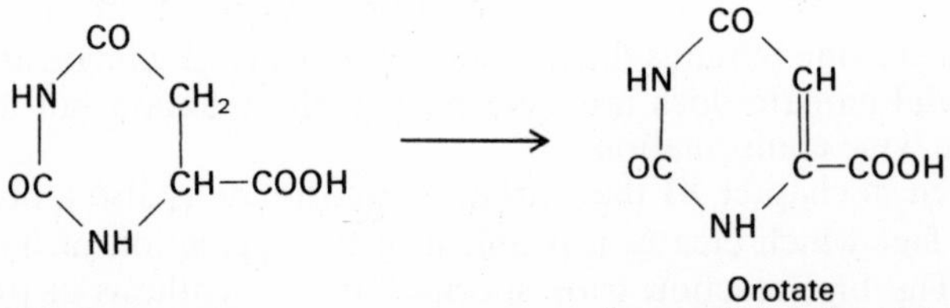

Dihydroorotate   Orotate
(or uracil-4-carboxylate)

The normal pathway of biosynthesis does not involve a direct decarboxylation of orotate to uracil, but a reaction of orotate with 5-phosphoribosyl-1-pyrophosphate (PRPP) to produce orotidine 5'-phosphate, which is converted by a specific decarboxylase to uridine 5'-phosphate (UMP):

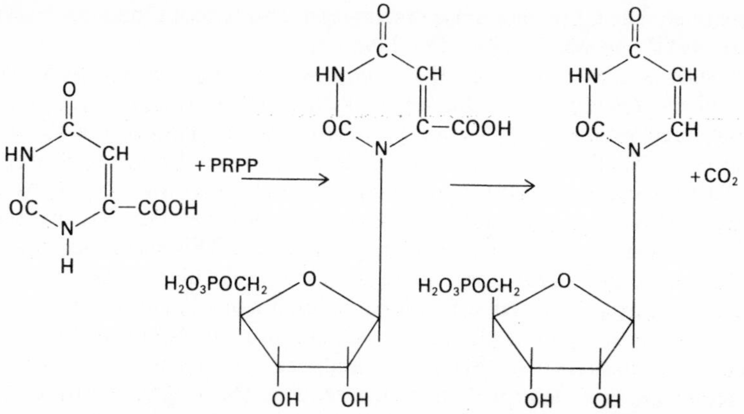

Orotate Orotidine 5′-phosphate Uridine 5′-phosphate (UMP)

Specific kinases convert the nucleoside monophosphate, UMP, to the nucleoside diphosphate, UDP, and triphosphate, UTP. These kinases (233, 234) use ATP as phosphate donor. UDP and UTP are utilized directly in the synthesis of ribonucleic acid (RNA) and certain coenzymes. The second pyrimidine nucleotide, cytidine triphosphate, is formed from UTP by the action of UTP aminase (235):

$$\text{UTP} + \text{NH}_3 + \text{ATP} \longrightarrow \text{CTP} + \text{ADP} + \text{H}_3\text{PO}_4$$

In microorganisms, exogenous uracil can be utilized directly in the synthesis of UTP by means of several enzymes. The first, uridine phosphorylase, catalyzes the following reversible reaction:

$$\text{Uracil} + \text{Ribose 1-phosphate} \rightleftharpoons \text{Uridine} + \text{P}_i$$

This reaction would appear to be of little importance in mammalian cells, though the following reactions can be carried out under conditions of rapid growth at an appreciable rate:

$$\text{Uridine} \xrightarrow{\text{ATP}} \text{UMP} \xrightarrow{\text{ATP}} \text{UDP} \xrightarrow{\text{ATP}} \text{UTP} \longrightarrow \text{CTP}$$

THE SYNTHESIS OF DEOXYCYTIDINE DIPHOSPHATE AND TRIPHOSPHATE

Recent work has established that in *E. coli* the synthesis of deoxycytidine diphosphate (dCDP) is carried out by a direct reduction of cytidine diphosphate (CDP), the ribose moiety of the CDP molecule being reduced to deoxyribose. The CDP-reductase system, comprising more than one enzyme, requires ATP and Mg^{++} (236, 237, 238).

Early observations established that crude extracts required the presence of NADPH for this reduction. During purification of the system, a preparation was obtained which would no longer catalyze the reduction of CDP in the presence of NADPH but instead required reduced lipoic acid. Certain observations suggested that in addition dihydrolipoate was not the natural hydrogen donor, but a "model substance", and that the true hydrogen donor had been eliminated during the purification. This substance has now been shown to be a heat-stable protein of low molecular weight, given the name thioredoxin. Thioredoxin can be isolated from *E. coli* in the oxidized form, referred to as thioredoxin (S_2). Conversion by NADPH to reduced thioredoxin, thioredoxin $(SH)_2$, is catalyzed by thioredoxin reductase. The reductase is a flavoprotein which reduces the single cystine of thioredoxin to two cysteine residues. In the presence of catalytic amounts of thioredoxin and its reductase, other substances with disulfide bridges are reduced (for example oxidized lipoate and glutathione, and insulin). The thioredoxin-thioredoxin reductase system may therefore have a wider role than the reduction of CDP.

The following scheme summarizes the mechanism of reduction of CDP in this complex system:

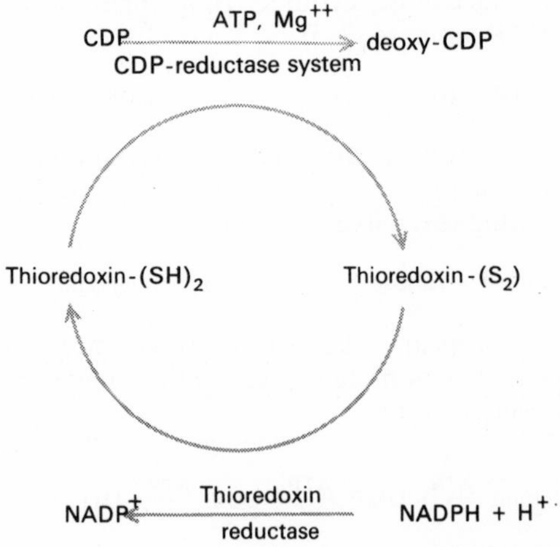

This scheme emphasizes the fact that thioredoxin fulfills a catalytic role in the presence of thioredoxin reductase and excess NADPH.

The molecular weight of thioredoxin is 12,000. This protein is another example of a low molecular weight protein escaping notice because another naturally occurring "model-substance" has been discovered before it (in this case lipoate; in the case of ACP, coenzyme A).

In *Lactobacillus leichmanii*, evidence has been presented for a requirement for the coenzyme of vitamin B 12 in addition to thioredoxin in the reduction of ribonucleotides.
A kinase phosphorylates dCDP to dCTP, one of the precursors of deoxyribonucleic acid.

THE SYNTHESIS OF THE SECOND PYRIMIDINE DEOXYNUCLEOTIDE, DEOXYTHYMIDINE TRIPHOSPHATE

An enzyme, deoxycytidylate aminohydrolase, catalyzes the deamination of deoxycytidylate (dCMP) to deoxyuridylate (dUMP). This enzyme has been found in bacteria, sea-urchin eggs and in the tissues of warm-blooded animals (239):

$$\text{dCMP} + H_2O \longrightarrow \text{dUMP} + NH_3$$

Thymidine synthetase catalyzes the conversion of dUMP to deoxythymidine monophosphate (dTMP). The cofactor in this reaction is 5,10-methylenetetrahydrofolic acid, one of a family of compounds involved in every case of addition of a methyl or hydroxymethyl group:

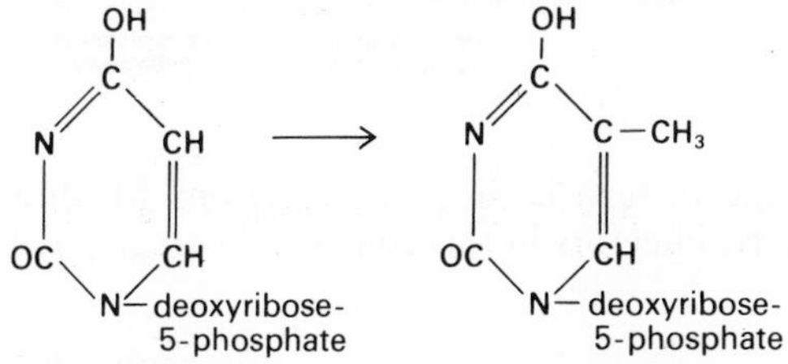

Deoxyuridine monophosphate (dUMP) — Deoxythymidine monophosphate (dTMP)

Specific kinases phosphorylate dTMP to deoxythymidine triphosphate (dTTP).
The only pyrimidines found in DNA are cytosine and thymine. The reason for the absence of uracil is the lack of a specific kinase to convert dUMP to dUTP. If dUTP is artificially synthesized and provided as substrate for DNA polymerase, an artificial DNA containing uracil is obtained.
Deoxythymidine kinase is able to catalyze the direct phosphorylation of the deoxyriboside to dTMP.

THE REGULATION OF THE SYNTHESIS OF PYRIMIDINE RIBO- AND DEOXYRIBO-NUCLEOTIDES

As well as controls of a repressive nature, which we shall not go into in detail here, the control of the activity of the enzymes involved in the synthesis of

the pyrimidine precursors of RNA and DNA occurs at at least six different sites:
1. The carbamylation of aspartate by aspartate transcarbamylase.
2. The conversion of carbamylaspartate to dihydroorotate.
3. The reduction of CDP to dCDP by the deoxycytidine reductase system.
4. The deamination of deoxycytidylate by deoxycytidylate aminohydrolase.
5 and 6. The direct phosphorylation of uridine and deoxythymidine by the corresponding kinases.
The following scheme summarizes the syntheses studied in this chapter and indicates the points of allosteric regulation found in different organisms.

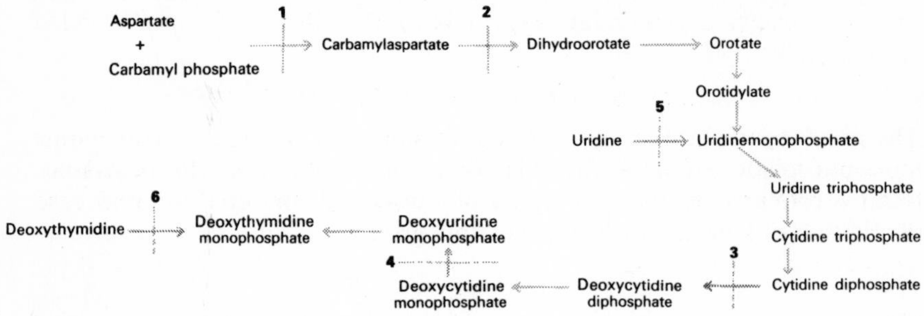

We shall examine in turn each of the reactions which are targets for the action of allosteric effectors in this somewhat complicated scheme.

E. coli aspartate transcarbamylase 5.1.

This enzyme has been crystallized from a pyrimidine-requiring mutant of *E. coli* grown under conditions of physiological derepression which enable crude extracts to be obtained with this protein comprising more than 10% of the total soluble proteins. This is to date the most studied allosteric enzyme and the results have been the foundation for the majority of ideas about metabolic regulation and its mechanism (240, 241, 242). The enzyme saturation curve as a function of aspartate concentration is sigmoid, indicating as we have seen several times, that more than one substrate molecule can complex with each molecule of enzyme, and that the binding of the first molecule facilitates the binding of a second. Cytidine triphosphate, the end product of the biosynthetic pathway starting with the carbamoylation of aspartate, is a specific inhibitor of the enzyme. The inhibition by CTP is competitive with respect to aspartate and appears as a displacement of the aspartate concentration giving 50% of the maximum activity towards higher values of concentration (fig. 38). In other words, the affinity of the enzyme for aspartate decreases in the presence of CTP, but the co-operativity between molecules of substrate is still in evidence. There is no detectable effect on the value of

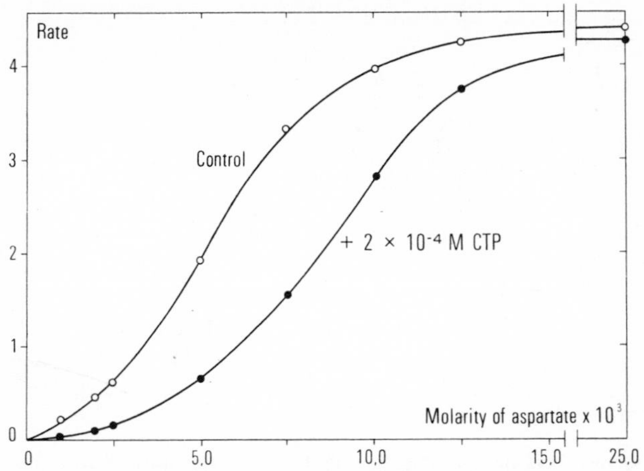

FIGURE 38

Displacement of the sigmoid saturation curve of aspartate transcarbamylase by CTP. The experiment was carried out with a fixed concentration of carbamyl phosphate and variable aspartate concentrations.

V_{max}. The inhibitory effect of CTP is countered by ATP, an antagonist of CTP.

ATP has also an intrinsic activating effect on the uninhibited enzyme. This activation is associated with an increase in the apparent affinity of the enzyme for aspartate and a normalization of the saturation curve with respect to this substrate so as to follow the Michaelis-Henri law. This suggests that ATP induces a conformational change resulting in the loss of the co-operative interactions between substrate molecules.

Although the inhibition by CTP is competitive with respect to aspartate, it has been possible to establish unequivocally that aspartate and CTP combine at different sites on the enzyme surface. This has been shown by desensitization of the enzyme towards its allosteric inhibitor and especially by physical separation into different sub-units, one of which contains the catalytic site and the other the site with affinity for the allosteric inhibitor.

Physical and chemical measurements have shown that the enzyme has a molecular weight of 310,000. The action of low concentrations of urea, or treatment with heat or mercurials, abolishes the sensitivity to CTP, without the catalytic activity being modified. This desensitization is accompanied by major changes in the molecular weight of the enzyme. It can be shown that the action of *p*-mercuribenzoate dissociates the enzyme into two components which can be separated by centrifugation in a sucrose gradient (fig. 39). Whereas the native enzyme has a sedimentation coefficient of 11·8 S, the two components have coefficients respectively 5·8 S and 2·8 S. The 5·8 S fraction has the catalytic activity; it has a greater specific activity than the native enzyme but differs in that it is completely insensitive to CTP or ATP. The 5·8 S component is therefore sufficient for the catalytic activity, but

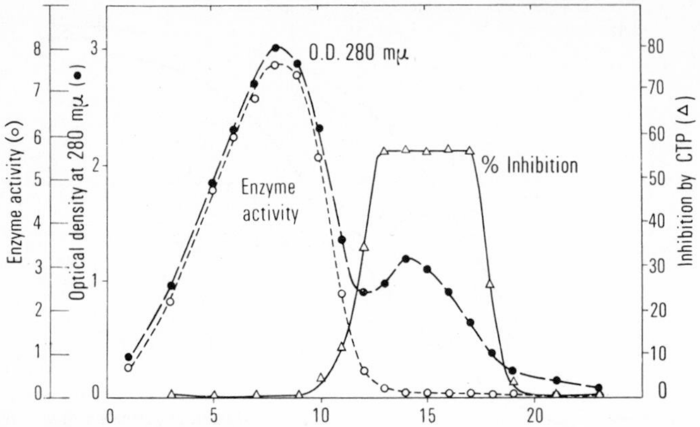

FIGURE 39

Separation by sucrose gradient centrifugation of the two components of *E. coli* aspartate transcarbamylase.
7 milligrams of *p*-MB-treated enzyme were centrifuged at 38,000 rpm for 20 hours at 10°C. The centrifuge tubes were then pierced and fractions of twelve drops collected. The filled circles are the protein elution profile; the white circles indicate catalytic activity, measured after addition of 2-mercaptoethanol. The regulatory protein is identified by adding the test fraction to fraction 6, and measuring the resulting activity in the presence and absence of 4 × 10^{-4} M CTP.

not for its regulation. The kinetics of the activity of this fraction as a function of substrate concentration follow the Michaelis law. The addition of 2-mercaptoethanol to the lighter fraction does not cause any catalytic activity to appear, but allows the fraction to regain the ability to bind CTP which the enzyme had lost when treated with the mercurial. The 2·8 S component is therefore the carrier of the capacity of the enzyme to be inhibited by CTP, and has no catalytic role.

If 2-mercaptoethanol is added to the unseparated mixture of the two fractions produced by treatment with *p*-mercuribenzoate, nearly all the enzyme is recovered with its native properties of sedimentation and inhibition. The 2·8 S component is indispensable for the reaggregation; neither component alone can aggregate upon removal of the mercurial.

Knowing the weight contributions from the 5·8 S and 2·8 S components, it can be calculated that of the 310,000 daltons of the native enzyme, 190,000 belong to the catalytic unit and 120,000 to the regulatory unit. It can be shown by sedimentation equilibrium studies that the approximate molecular weights are 96,000 for the catalytic unit and 30,000 for the regulatory unit, enabling it to be deduced that the native enzyme is made up of two catalytic and four regulatory sub-units. To use the terminology of Monod, Wyman and Changeux, the native enzyme can be considered to be an oligomer consisting of protomers made up from one catalytic unit and two regulatory units[1] (fig. 40).

1. The structure of aspartate transcarbamylase has been re-examined, in terms of actual polypeptide chains rather than of sub-units. The amino acid sequence of the regulatory chain R has

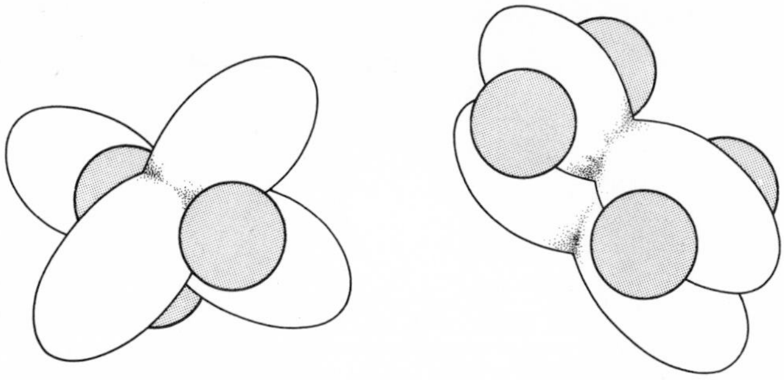

FIGURE 40

Two possible models of the native aspartate transcarbamylase molecule. Both models have two catalytic sub-units (white) and four regulatory sub-units (gray). The elongation and constriction of the catalytic sub-units is merely a product of the imagination, suggested by the existence of smaller sub-units obtained in guanidine hydrochloride. In fact, measurement of viscosity shows that the native molecule is globular and compact (241).

The catalytic sub-unit shows no tendency to dissociate spontaneously in dilute buffer at pH 7. On the other hand, in the presence of 5·8 M guanidine hydrochloride, it dissociates into four chains of molecular weight about 25,000. A preliminary determination of the number of substrate sites suggests that each catalytic unit of molecular weight 96,000 possesses four receptor sites (for maleate, an analog of aspartate). It is interesting to note that the presence of carbamyl phosphate is indispensable for the reversible binding of maleate to the catalytic sub-unit. These experiments are unequivocal proof that this enzyme consists of sub-units and that the competitive inhibition is not due to competition between inhibitor and substrate for a common site, since two distinct sites exist on two chains with are themselves different; another explanation is provided by the results: a conformational change is induced by the allosteric effector and leads to a decrease in the affinity of the enzyme for its substrate at the catalytic site.

According to the proposed model, the protomers are subjected to strong forces of interaction in the native molecule, the enzyme being in a "constrained" form with little affinity for aspartate. Several kinds of change of the environment, including combination with aspartate or nucleotides or variation of pH, affect the interactions between protomers (fig. 41). In particular, CTP increases these interactions, making the enzyme less active at low concentrations of aspartate. The disappearance of the interactions

been determined. Its molecular weight is 17,000 rather than 30,000. The molecular weight of the catalytic chain is 33,000. Since the molecular weight of the native enzyme is 310,000, the calculations indicate clearly a structure of the type R_6C_6 for aspartate transcarbamylase. Reinterpretation of the data shows that *p*-MB cleaves the enzyme into 2 C_3 units and 3 R_2 units (242*a*). A crystallographic study (242*b*) shows that the protein has a 3-fold and a 2-fold symmetry axis, restricting the spatial arrangement of the chains such as each of the six (RC) pairs of the hexamer is in an identical environment. It is obvious that the results of the binding studies (242*c*) will have to be reinterpreted.

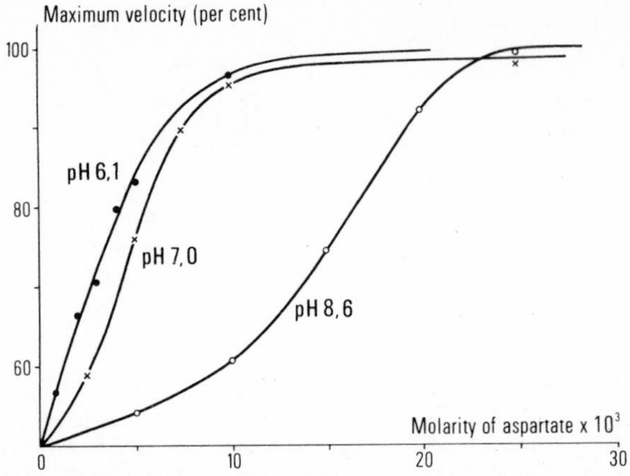

FIGURE 41

Effect of pH on the kinetics of aspartate transcarbamylase. Since the activity at alkaline pH was very much greater, the amount of enzyme used was 10 times less at pH 8·6 than at pH 6·1.

in the case of the isolated catalytic sub-unit is also a fact supporting the model. Another argument, in favor, arises from the observation that there is a slight decrease in the sedimentation coefficient of the enzyme when centrifuged in the presence of its substrate (3–4 %), as if the oligomer were in a "relaxed" form.

This is one of the rare cases of an enzyme for which we can cite arguments other than purely kinetic ones concerning the conformational changes associated with combination with substrates, activators and inhibitors. The regulatory sub-unit is the first example of a class of non-enzymatic proteins produced by the cell to control the activity of the true enzymes. These regulatory proteins can be thought of as arising by mutation of the genes responsible for the structure of primitive enzymes which had an adequate affinity for key-metabolites. It is to be hoped that physical and chemical studies of aspartate transcarbamylase will contribute further to increasing our understanding of the mechanism of allosteric effects.

Control of dihydroorotase activity 5.2.

This enzyme, which catalyzes the second reaction in the synthesis of pyrimidines, is not subject to allosteric regulation in those microorganisms in which it has been studied. The enzyme extracted from ascites cells of a hepatoma is sensitive to inhibition by purine and pyrimidine nucleotides. As aspartate transcarbamylase from the same source is sensitive to the same inhibitors, the possibility of a multifunctional association cannot be ruled out. Derivatives of cytidine and thymidine are the most effective.

Control of nucleoside diphosphate reduction (243, 244) 5.3.

The direct reduction of CDP to dCDP is sensitive to allosteric control. The following facts have recently been discovered: first of all, the purified system from *E. coli* which reduces CDP with thioredoxin is also able to reduce UDP to dUDP. In the presence of suitable allosteric effectors, the reduction of ADP and GDP to the corresponding deoxyribonucleoside phosphates is also catalyzed by this system which in future should be called "ribonucleoside diphosphate reductase" rather than "CDP reductase".

ATP, which stimulates the reduction of pyrimidine ribonucleotides, has practically no effect on purine ribonucleotides; the reduction of the latter is stimulated on the other hand by dTTP and dGTP, the first activating the reduction of GDP especially, and the second ADP. dATP strongly inhibits both reactions, the effect being reversed by ATP but not by dTTP.

The current explanation of these interactions, which seem so complicated at first, is as follows: different nucleotides behave as allosteric effectors stabilizing certain states of one or several of the enzymes involved, and so determining the substrate specificity. Thus ATP stabilizes a state favorable to the reduction of pyrimidine ribonucleotides: dGTP stabilizes a state favorable to the reduction of purine ribonucleotides: dTTP stabilizes a state favorable to both kinds of reduction, and dATP stabilizes an inactive state. These effects may be the foundation of a physiological mechanism for obtaining a balanced supply of the different substrates required for the enzymatic synthesis of DNA (fig. 42).

Figure 43 summarizes the different interrelations listed above.

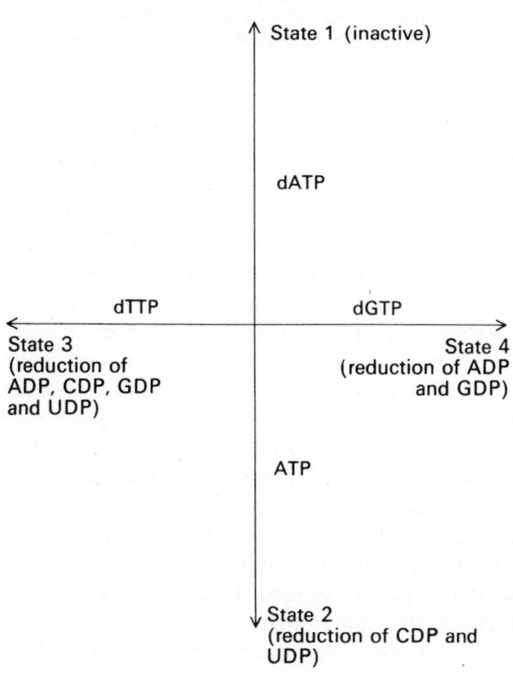

FIGURE 42

Schematic interpretation of the allosteric effects in the reduction of ribonucleotides.

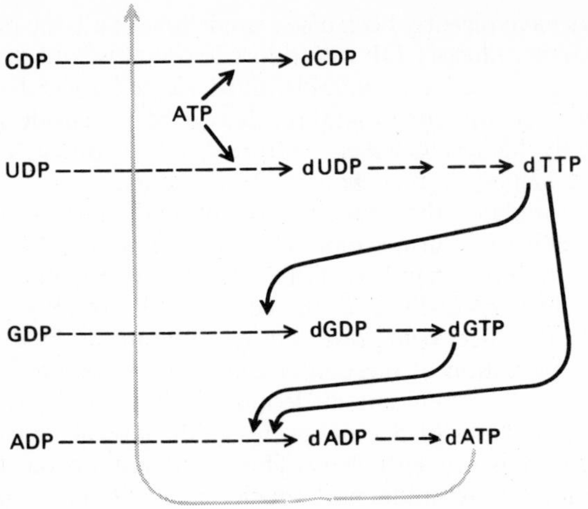

FIGURE 43

Hypothetical scheme for the physiological regulation of the synthesis of deoxyribonucleotides. The black arrows indicate stimulations; the gray arrow shows the inhibition by dATP.
Synthesis of dCDP and dUDP requires ATP as allosteric effector. Other enzymes transform dUDP to dTTP. dTTP occupies a central position in this scheme: in the presence of ATP, low concentrations of dTTP can cause an additional stimulation of the reduction of pyrimidine ribonucleotides, but higher concentrations are inhibitory; this is not shown in the scheme, as the principal effect of dTTP is the stimulation of the synthesis of dGDP. The dGTP formed from this in turn stimulates the formation of dADP. This nucleotide becomes dATP, which is an allosteric inhibitor of the four reduction reactions. The extent of inhibition depends on the concentration of ATP, which reverses the effect of dATP.

Control of deoxycytidylate deaminase activity (245) 5.4.

The sigmoid form of the substrate saturation curves for deaminases obtained from a great variety of sources, ranging from chicken to bacteria infected with bacteriophage T 4, as well as their sensitivity to allosteric inhibition, reminds us that this enzyme is an important target in the control of deoxynucleotide syntheses. The enzymes of every source studied are inhibited with complex kinetics by dTTP, purine mononucleotides, and competitively by dUMP and dTMP. Furthermore, dCTP activates the enzyme at low concentrations of dCMP, the substrate. This activation is accompanied by a decrease in the apparent order of the reaction and an increase in the affinity for substrate. In the case of the chicken enzyme, there is also a change in the state of aggregation of the enzyme: whereas at saturating concentrations of substrate and in the absence of inhibitor, the sedimentation coefficient is 2·0 S, at low substrate concentrations and in the presence of dCTP, it becomes 7·5 S. Inhibition by dTTP of the dCTP-activated form restores the enzyme to a state with sedimentation coefficient 3·0 S. Although these results suggest that the activation of the enzyme by dCTP is associated with conversion to an aggregated form, aggregation alone is not sufficient to explain the activation, for it is also obtained in the presence of dGMP, which is an inhibitor of the enzyme. The experimental data can be interpreted as follows: the enzyme possesses at least two sites for the substrate dCMP, one of which is a catalytic site (whether the other site is a purely regulatory one cannot be decided with the available data). In addition, the enzyme possesses at least two kinds of allosteric site, one to combine with dCTP, the other with dTTP: the interactions at these two sites with the corresponding effectors produce opposite effects. The possibility of an additional allosteric site for dGTP cannot be ruled out. Finally, although dUMP and dTMP are competitive inhibitors, it is not proved that the competition is at the catalytic site.

Although this enzyme deserves a more detailed study, the opposing effects of dCTP and dTTP are understandable in terms of cell physiology, since these two products are essential ultimate metabolites resulting from the metabolism of dCMP. These opposing controls may perhaps secure the desired balance between the relative concentrations of these two DNA precursors.

Control at the levels of uridine and deoxythymidine kinase 5.5

It can be shown that uridine kinase is the limiting step in the synthesis of uridine nucleotides from exogenous uridine, in several cell-free preparations of mouse or human tissues. This enzymatic activity is subject to feedback inhibition by the pyrimidine nucleoside triphosphates, UTP and especially CTP. The inhibition can be partially removed by increasing the concentration of the substrates, uridine or ATP. The phosphorylation of cytidine to CMP is also subject to feedback inhibition by the same allosteric effectors. These facts show that feedback inhibition plays a regulatory role not only at the level of endogenous synthesis of pyrimidine nucleotides, but also at the stage of direct utilization of preformed nucleosides.

The same kind of control has been found in the utilization of preformed deoxynucleosides. Highly purified preparations of *E. coli* deoxythymidine kinase (246) show characteristics similar to those of many of the allosteric enzymes which we have already discussed: the phosphorylation of deoxythymidine is a sigmoid function of the ATP concentration. At low ATP concentrations, the enzyme is strongly stimulated by a large number of deoxynucleoside diphosphates, dCDP, dADP, dGDP, hydroxymethyl-dCDP, and also by GDP. This activation is accompanied, as in many other cases, by normalization of the kinetics and by an increased affinity for the two substrates, deoxythymidine and ATP. This enzyme is very strongly inhibited by low concentrations of dTTP. The authors of these experiments rightly note that deoxythymidine kinase is inhibited, as is the case for other biosynthetic enzymes, by the end product of its action, dTTP, and is activated by a compound, dCDP, which in the synthesis of DNA would accumulate for lack of the necessary concentration of dTTP.

16

Biosynthesis of Purine
Nucleotides and Deoxynucleotides and its Regulation

THE SYNTHESIS OF 5-AMINO-4-IMIDAZOLE CARBOXAMIDE RIBONUCLEOTIDE (247–252)

Ribose 5-phosphate, a normal intermediate of glucose degradation by the pentose oxidative pathway, is phosphorylated by ATP to yield 5-phosphoribosyl-1-pyrophosphate (PRPP), a compound which as we have already seen occurs in the biosynthesis of tryptophan, histidine and UTP:

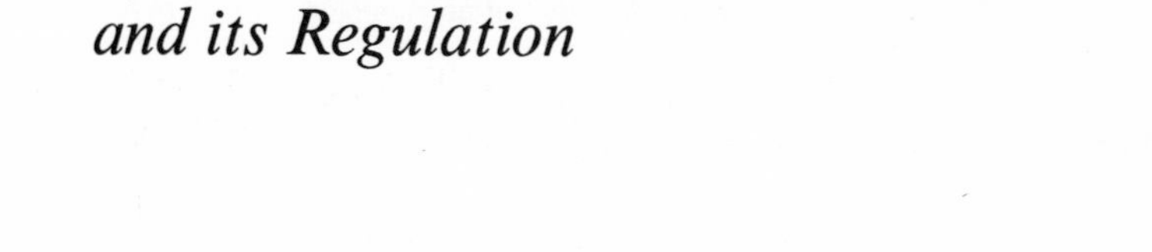

PRPP

Glutamine serves as donor of the amino group to PRPP. The reaction produces 5-phosphoribosylamine with the loss of the pyrophosphoryl residue:

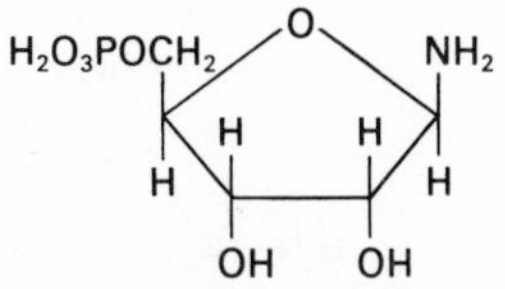

5-phosphoribosylamine

The amino acid glycine is added to the phosphoribosylamine molecule in a reaction which uses ATP as an energy source, and the product is glycinamide ribonucleotide:

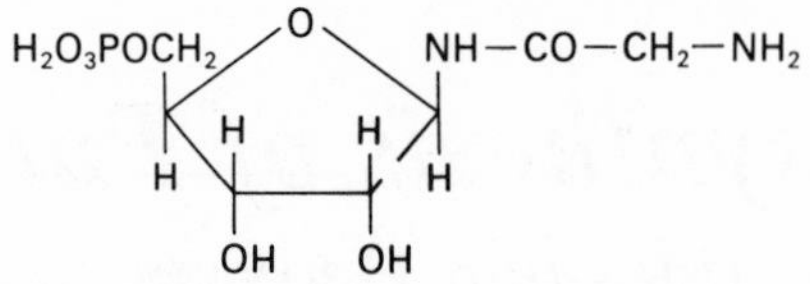

"Ribonucleotide" of glycinamide

An enzyme with a formyl derivative of tetrahydrofolic acid as cofactor adds on a formyl residue, to yield formylglycinamide ribonucleotide:

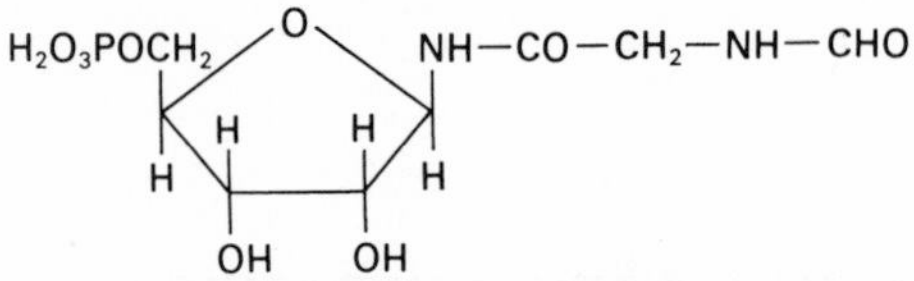

"Ribonucleotide" of formylglycinamide

This compound is converted to formylglycinamidine ribonucleotide in the presence of glutamine and ATP:

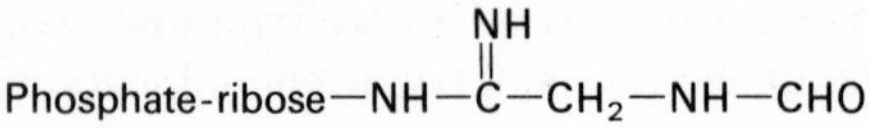

This cyclizes to aminoimidazole ribonucleotide in a reaction involving more ATP:

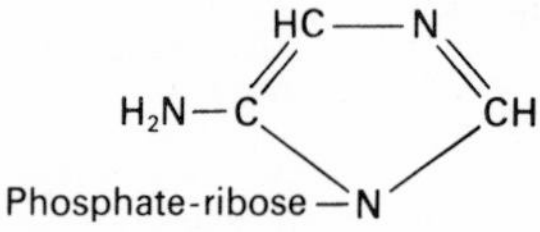

"Ribonucleotide" of aminoimidazole

A fixation of CO_2 results in the formation of 5-amino-4-imidazole carboxylic acid ribonucleotide:

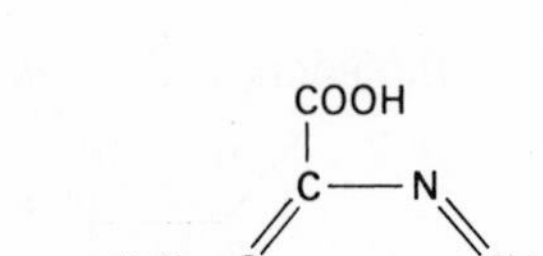

"Ribonucleotide" of 5-amino-4-imidazole carboxylic acid

This is followed by the addition of a molecule of aspartic acid in the presence of ATP to yield 5-amino-4-imidazole-N-succinylcarboxamide ribonucleotide:

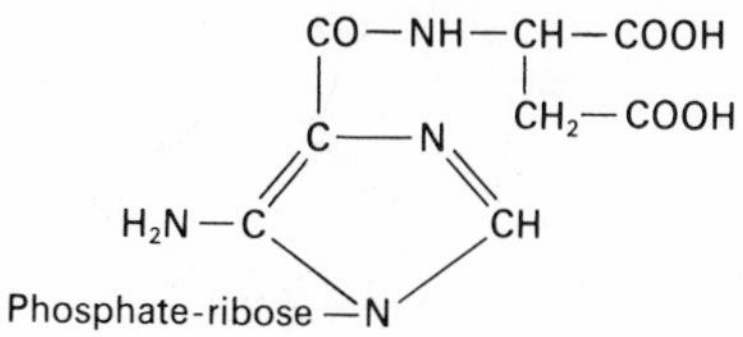

The ribonucleotide of 5-amino-4-imidazole carboxamide is reached after elimination of fumaric acid:

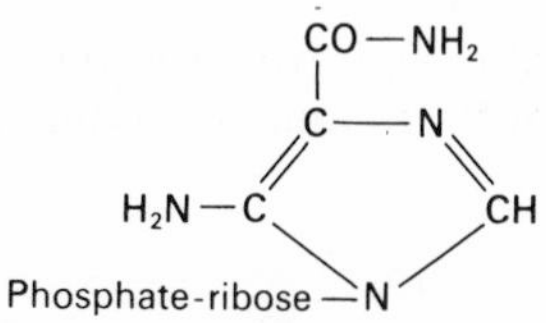

"Ribonucleotide" of 5-amino-4-imidazole carboxamide (AICAR)

This is the second time we have met this curious amination procedure which consists of adding an aspartic acid molecule and then eliminating a fumaric acid molecule (cf. the synthesis of argininosuccinate, the intermediate between citrulline and arginine). We shall soon see a third example. Note that AICAR is also a product formed in the synthesis of imidazoleglycerol phosphate (see the synthesis of histidine).

SYNTHESIS OF PURINE RIBONUCLEOTIDES (253–256)

AICAR is formylated to 5-formamido-4-imidazole carboxamide ribonucleotide:

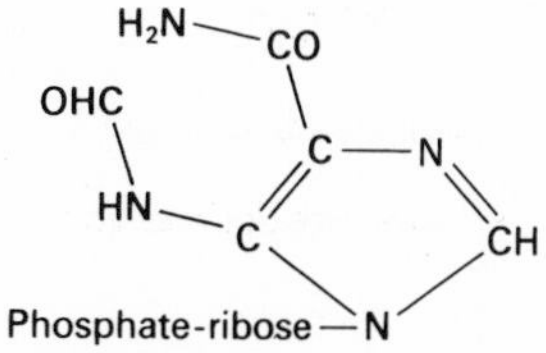

"Ribonucleotide" of 5-formamido-4-imidazole carboxamide

The loss of a molecule of water leads to cyclization and the production of inosinic acid, where the purine ring appears for the first time:

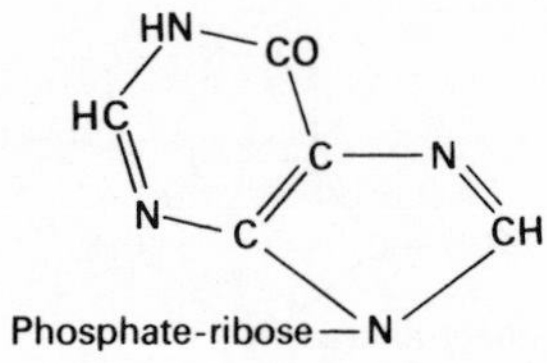

Inosinic acid (IMP)

Inosinic acid is the precursor of two of the nucleotides found in ribonucleic acid, guanylic and adenylic acids.

1) It is oxidized to xanthylic acid, which is then aminated either directly by ammonia (in bacteria) or by glutamine (in animal tissues):

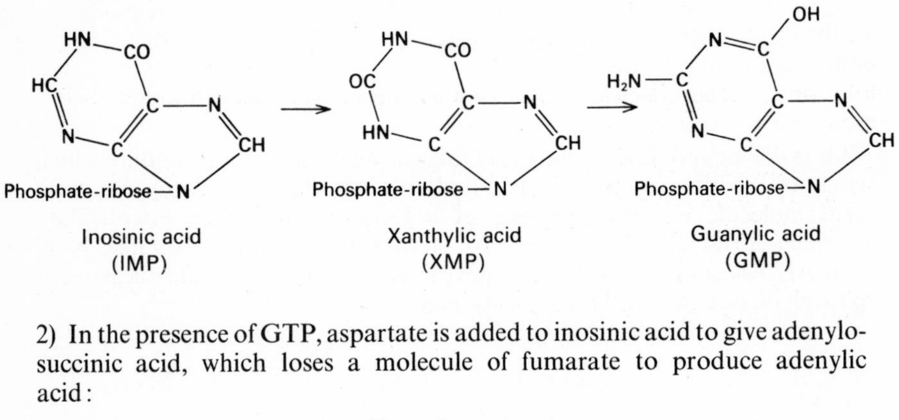

Inosinic acid (IMP) | Xanthylic acid (XMP) | Guanylic acid (GMP)

2) In the presence of GTP, aspartate is added to inosinic acid to give adenylosuccinic acid, which loses a molecule of fumarate to produce adenylic acid:

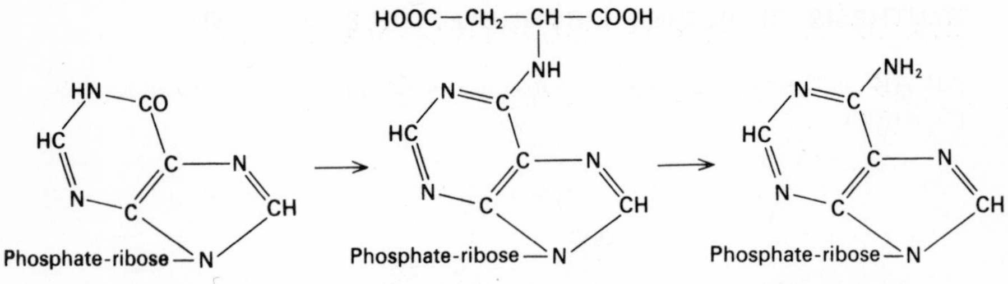

Inosinic acid (IMP) | Adenylosuccinic acid | Adenylic acid (AMP)

As in the case of the pyrimidine nucleotides, specific kinases phosphorylate the purine nucleoside monophosphates to di- and triphosphates.

A specific enzyme, myokinase, carries out the following reaction:

$$AMP + ATP \rightleftarrows 2\,ADP$$

The ATP required here is generated during glycolysis and the oxidative phosphorylation of reduced nicotinamide nucleotides.
The formation of purine deoxynucleotides has been studied very little to date. It is likely that they arise directly from nucleotides by the reduction of ribose to deoxyribose, as is found for the pyrimidines.

CONTROL OF THE ACTIVITY OF THE ENZYMES OCCURRING IN PURINE NUCLEOTIDE BIOSYNTHESIS

Study of the control mechanisms is complicated by the fact that during the biosynthesis of the purine nucleus, a by-product is a precursor of histidine. Also, hypoxanthine and xanthine, purine bases not found in RNA, can be respectively converted to inosinic and xanthylic acids, precursors of the two "natural" nucleotides. In addition, there exist enzymes responsible for the direct formation of nucleotides from preformed bases or nucleosides. Some idea of the complexity of this network of reactions is given by the following scheme onto which the direct interconversions of nucleotides by reduction or amination reactions have been grafted.

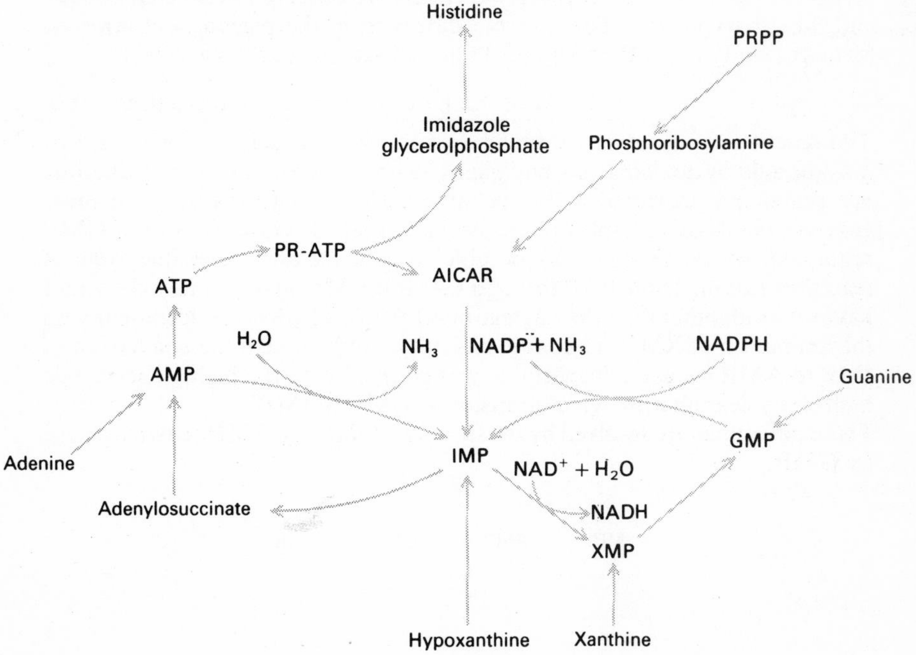

In this scheme, a certain number of the reactions are subject to allosteric activation or inhibition effects. We shall examine only some of them here.

Control of glutamine: 5-phosphoribosylpyrophosphate amidotransferase 3.1.

Under this uncouth name is concealed the enzyme responsible for the synthesis of 5-phosphoribosylamine from PRPP and glutamine. It is inhibited by many purine nucleotides (ATP, ADP, GDP, GMP, IMP). The inhibitions are competitive with respect to PRPP. However, there are a great many arguments to support the view that the inhibition site and the catalytic site are distinct: the enzyme from pigeon liver (257) can be more or less desensitized by freezing, aging at 4°C, dialysis, or heat treatment; this desensitization is not associated with a change in the apparent affinity of the enzyme for its two substrates. Mixtures of a 6-hydroxypurine (GMP, GDP or IMP) and a 6-aminopurine (AMP, ADP or ATP) give total inhibitions higher than the sum of the individual inhibitions. On the other hand, mixtures of homologous purines do not produce this synergistic effect. This shows that at least two sites exist for combination with the inhibitors, one specific for 6-hydroxypurines and the other for 6-aminopurines. The desensitization is not associated with any appreciable change in the sedimentation coefficient of the enzyme.
An enzyme catalyzing the same reaction has been studied in *Aerobacter aerogenes* (258): the same synergistic effects are observed between 6-amino- and 6-hydroxypurines. This enzyme differs from the pigeon one however, by insensitivity to ATP and by the failure of attempts to desensitize it.

Control of nucleotide interconversions (259, 260) 3.2.

The reactions converting xanthylic acid to guanylic acid, adenylic acid to inosinic acid by deamination, and guanylic acid to inosinic acid by reduction, are practically irreversible. In the absence of a rigid control, the three enzymes (xanthosine 5′-phosphate aminase, IMP dehydrogenase and GMP reductase) would theoretically be able to catalyze an irreversible cycle of reactions leading from IMP through GMP to IMP again. This cycle would have no result other than the wastage of ATP by the hydrolysis accompanying the amination of XMP. The same difficulty would arise if the conversion of IMP to AMP *via* adenylosuccinate was coupled with the highly endergonic hydrolytic deamination which transforms AMP to IMP.
These difficulties are resolved by the specific inhibition of IMP dehydrogenase by GMP:

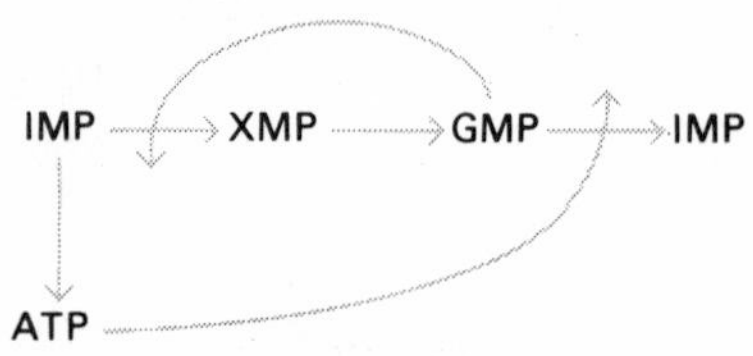

In the same way, adenylosuccinate synthetase in *E. coli* is inhibited by ADP:

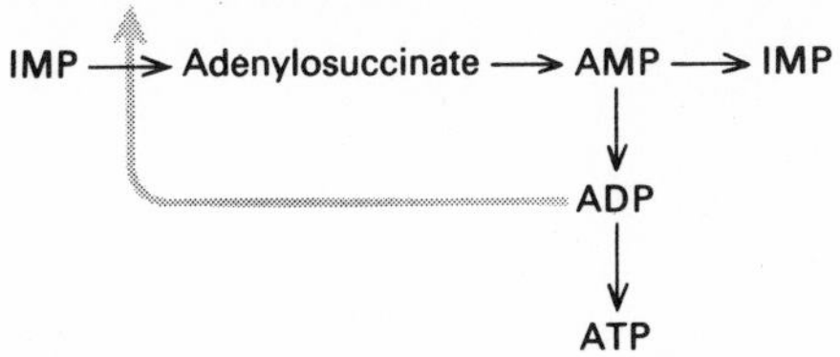

Control of the purine mononucleotide pyrophosphorylases 3.3.

These enzymes catalyze the entry into the cycle of exogenous purine bases, which as we have seen are not normal intermediates in the synthesis of nucleotides. They catalyze the following type of reaction:

Base + PRPP ⟶ Nucleoside monophosphate + Pyrophosphate

In *Bacillus subtilis*, all these reactions are inhibited by a large number of purine nucleotides (261). From the standpoint of cellular control, it is significant that the nature of the inhibitors and the comparative sensitivity of the different reactions can be understood in terms of intracellular equilibrium. For example, XMP pyrophosphorylase is especially sensitive to the guanine nucleotides dGTP and GTP: so an excess of either of these prevents the accumulation of XMP, the direct precursor of the guanine nucleotides; incidentally, the alternative pathway for the synthesis of XMP from IMP is also inhibited by GMP, making GMP the regulator of every step in its synthesis.
It is interesting to note that the observed inhibitions can have repercussions on the activity of the specific permeation systems for purines, since the uptake of purines by *B. subtilis* seems to be obligatorily connected with the synthesis of purine nucleotides.

17

Biosynthesis of Some
Water-Soluble Vitamins and their Coenzyme Forms

For a great many of the substances dealt with in this chapter, our knowledge is fairly rudimentary, and in some cases even non-existent. We shall limit ourselves to setting forth the firmly established facts and to showing the directions in which the work relating to this difficult subject is progressing.

BIOSYNTHESIS OF THIAMINE AND COCARBOXYLASE

Thiamine, also called vitamin B_1, can be considered made up of two parts, one being 2-methyl-6-amino-5-hydroxymethyl pyrimidine ("pyrimidine" for simplicity in presentation) and the other 4-methyl-5-hydroxyethylthiazole ("thiazole"):

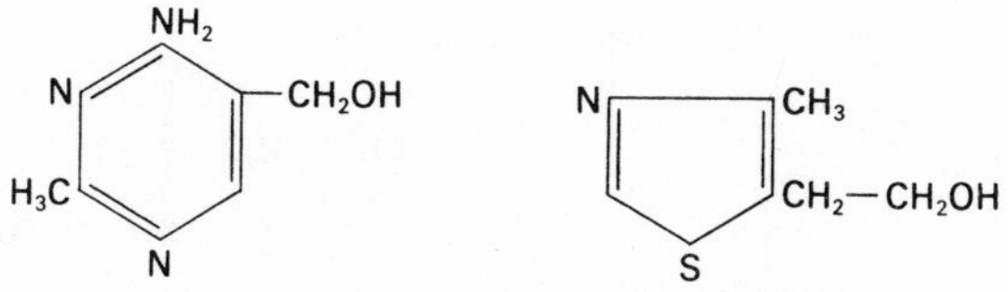

" Pyrimidine "   " Thiazole "

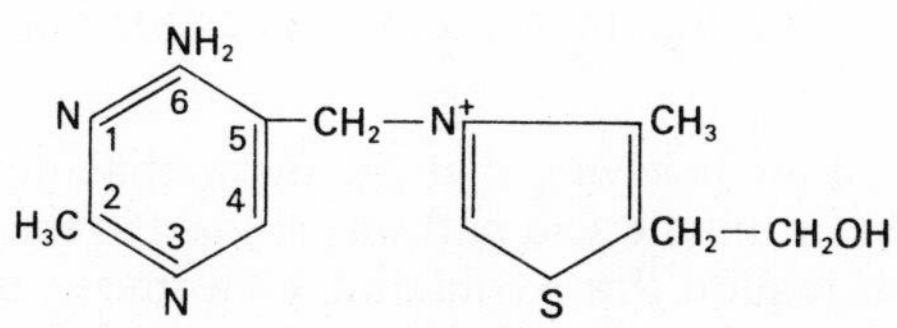

Thiamine

Very little is known about the biosynthesis of the individual compounds, except that in growth experiments with radioactive isotopes, the carbon of formate is incorporated into the pyrimidine and the $-S-CH_3$ residue of methionine is incorporated as a whole into the thiazole.
In contrast, the condensation of the two parts of the thiamine molecule has been well characterized in yeast and bacteria.
In thiamine requiring microorganisms, three groups of mutants can be distinguished:
1) mutants requiring added pyrimidine only, and which are therefore able to synthesize the thiazole moiety;
2) mutants requiring thiazole and which can therefore synthesize the pyrimidine moiety;
3) finally, those requiring preformed thiamine for growth and unable to condense the two parts when they are provided.
The study of these mutants justifies our conclusion that both parts are synthesized separately and then connected. Experiments carried out with cell-free extracts support the following scheme to account for the synthesis of thiamine from its component parts (262):

Pyrimidine + ATP ⟶ Pyrimidine pyrophosphate

Thiazole + ATP ⟶ Thiazole monophosphate

Pyrimidine pyrophosphate + Thiazole monophosphate
⟶ Thiamine phosphate + pyrophosphate

Thiamine phosphate + H_2O ⟶ Thiamine + P_i

It is interesting to find out that thiamine monophosphate, which is a normal intermediate in the synthesis of thiamine, is not the substrate from which thiamine diphosphate or cocarboxylase is synthesized; the synthesis of the cofactor occurs in yeast by the action of thiaminokinase, which acts on thiamine and ATP (263):

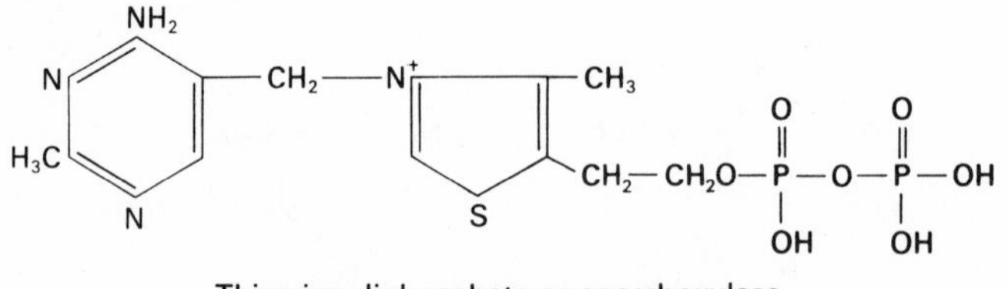

Thiamine diphosphate or cocarboxylase

Speculation on the possible origin of "pyrimidine" and "thiazole" 1.1.

There is no reason for believing that the pyrimidine moiety of thiamine is synthesized by the orotidylic acid pathway studied in chapter 15. As mutants are known which require this pyrimidine preformed yet are certainly able to synthesize the pyrimidines of their nucleic acids, it is clear that: 1) either the biosynthetic pathways of the two kinds of pyrimidine are completely different; 2) or the mutants are unable to attach the substituents at the C-2 and (or) C-5 positions; 3) or they cannot remove the ribose 5-phosphate moiety of UMP (we recall that the synthesis of nucleic acids from pyrimidines occurs at the nucleoside phosphate level, while the synthesis of thiamine must take place with free "pyrimidine" as substrate). A recent theory (264) about the synthesis of "thiazole" has a condensation reaction between cysteine and glutamate occurring to form a derivative of thiazolidine as precursor of the thiazole moiety of thiamine. This hypothetical condensation is formally analogous to the one known in the case of penicillin synthesis from cysteine and valine:

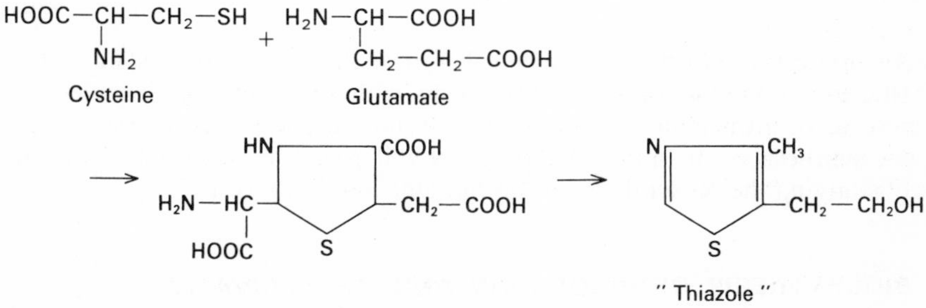

To date there is no experiment with enzyme preparations to allow justification of this scheme. We have merely presented it as a model of a possible hypothesis.

Control of thiamine biosynthesis (265) 1.2.

The pathway of thiamine synthesis differs from all those we have studied so far in that whereas the latter can be represented in the form of linear or diverging sequences of reactions, the thiamine pathway consists of two converging biosynthetic pathways each of which synthesizes products which do not normally accumulate. In addition, the amounts of the compounds synthesized are several orders of magnitude below the amino acids and nucleotides.

The control mechanism found in *Salmonella typhimurium* is summarized in the following figure.

The gray arrows interrupting the biosynthetic reactions represent repressive controls, while the white arrow represents control by feedback inhibition. The final product, cocarboxylase, can be seen to repress the synthesis of the enzymes involved in both the initial biosynthesis as well as the enzyme which condenses the pyrimidine and thiazole. In addition, thiazole exerts an inhibitory effect on an enzyme (not identified) involved in its biosynthesis.

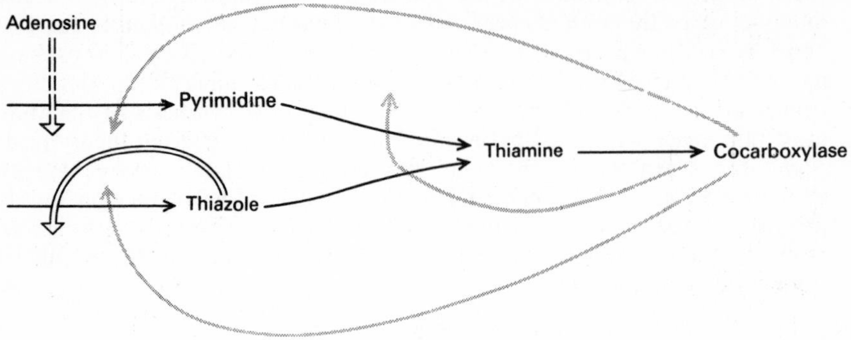

An interesting effect of adenosine has been found in this system: where studied, preincubation of the organism with this compound depletes its reserve of intracellular thiamine, so causing an enormous derepression of the synthesis of thiamine; this property will assuredly be useful as a means of studying the biosynthesis of "pyrimidine" and "thiazole".

BIOSYNTHESIS OF RIBOFLAVIN AND ITS DERIVATIVES

Some lower fungi, like *Eremothecium ashbyii* or *Ashbya gossypii*, synthesize so much riboflavin that the compound crystallizes in the growth medium (266). It is obvious that such organisms are the tools of choice for studying the biosynthesis of riboflavin (which is also known as vitamin B_2).

Many experiments have shown that addition of purines to the growth medium stimulates the synthesis of riboflavin. Experiments carried out with compounds labelled in different carbon atoms suggest that the purine carbon skeleton, with the exception of carbon 8, is incorporated as such into the isoalloxazine ring of riboflavin (267). This points to 4,5-diaminouracil or a ribityl derivative of the same, as a possible intermediate; furthermore, this compound has been found to accumulate in a mutant of *Aspergillus nidulans* which requires riboflavin (268):

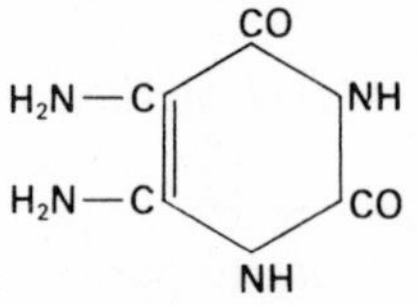

4,5-diaminouracil

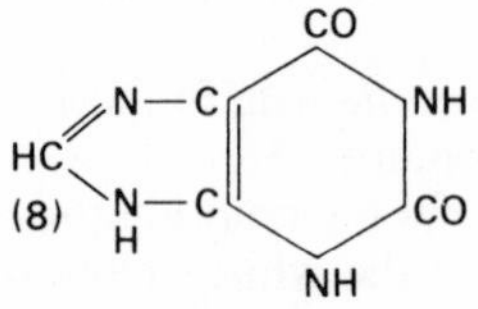

Xanthine

The next precursor of riboflavin to have been identified with certainty is 6,7-dimethyl-8-ribityllumazine. It is assumed that this compound arises from the ribityl derivative of diaminouracil by a nonenzymatic condensation with butanedione; 5-amino-4-ribitylamincuracil has since been isolated from filtrates of cultures of another riboflavin requiring mutant of *Aspergillus nidulans* (269):

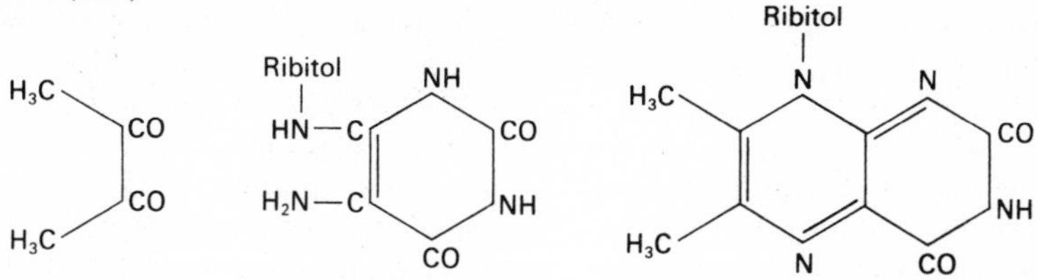

Butanedione 4,5-diaminouracil (ribityl derivative) 6,7-dimethyl-8-ribityllumazine

We have no information as to whether the ribose residue is attached to the purine before the loss of carbon 8, and whether the phosphorylated form is an intermediate. Cell-free systems have been obtained which can synthesize ribityllumazine from the ribityl derivative of diaminouracil (270).

The condensation of butanedione with 4-ribitylamino-5-amino-2,6-dihydroxypyrimidine can be achieved by the methods of organic chemistry, and it has been suggested that the biological pathway is the same. Unfortunately, although acetoin, $CH_3-CHOH-CO-CH_3$, is a normal metabolite in *E. ashbyii*, it has never been shown that this compound (or its oxidized derivative, butanedione) is actually involved in the biological synthesis of lumazine.

The proof that lumazine is an intermediate rests on its isolation from all those organisms which produce riboflavin. The incorporation of radioactive formate occurs in analogous positions in lumazine and riboflavin. The relative rates of incorporation are such that it is more probable that lumazine is an intermediate in the biosynthesis of riboflavin rather than a product of its degradation. The most convincing argument is the conversion of lumazine to riboflavin by cell-free extracts of a great number of microorganisms. Examination of the formulas of lumazine and riboflavin emphasizes that four more carbon atoms have to be added to lumazine to complete the *o*-xylene residue of riboflavin.

The ease with which lumazine condenses chemically (i.e. nonenzymatically) with butanedione suggests the following reaction as the final step in the synthesis of riboflavin:

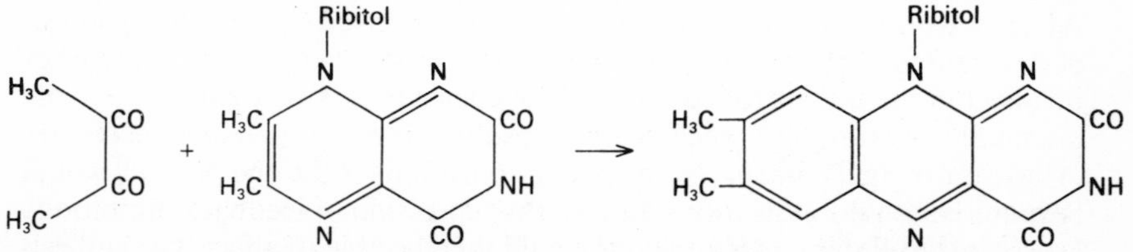

Butanedione 6,7-dimethyl-8-ribityllumazine Riboflavin

In reality, it is not so simple. It appears that the four-carbon unit, or two two-carbon units, come from lumazine itself: cell-free extracts of *E. ashbyii* can synthesize riboflavin from lumazine without the addition of other exogenous precursors. More than two molecules of lumazine are used up per molecule of riboflavin produced (271).

If we add to this the admission that we know nothing about how or at what stage in the biosynthesis of riboflavin the ribityl residue is incorporated, we can see how much work is still to be done to elucidate the details of this biosynthesis. Although enzymatic systems converting riboflavin to flavin mononucleotide and flavin adenine dinucleotide have been identified, it is not impossible that the real intermediate in the synthesis of lumazine may be the adenine dinucleotide derivative of 4,5-diaminouracil and that the synthesis of riboflavin occurs at the flavin adenine dinucleotide level.

In different animals and plant tissues and in bacteria, the existence has been shown of a flavokinase which catalyzes the phosphorylation of riboflavin at the terminal position of the ribitol chain (272):

$$\text{Riboflavin} + \text{ATP} \longrightarrow \text{Riboflavin 5'-phosphate} + \text{ADP}$$

Riboflavin 5′-phosphate is also called flavin adenine mononucleotide, abbreviated to FMN.

An enzyme has been purified from yeast which catalyzes the formation of flavin adenine dinucleotide (FAD) from FMN and ATP (273):

$$\text{FMN} + \text{ATP} \longrightarrow \text{FAD} + \text{Pyrophosphate}$$

The synthesis of flavins is not adjusted as precisely to the physiological needs of bacteria as the synthesis of major metabolites, the amino acids and nucleotides, as is shown by the following results, obtained in *E. coli* (274):

1) Flavins are produced in large excess during exponential growth; the amount excreted can reach as much as eight times the intracellular concentration.

2) The synthesis is not linked closely to growth: it can continue for a long time after growth has ceased in *E. coli*; conversely, the growth of lactic acid bacteria which require riboflavin, can continue for quite a long time after they have been deprived of this growth factor. It can be shown that flavins have no feedback inhibitory effect on their synthesis; through control by repression, the amounts of the enzymes necessary for the synthesis of flavins do not vary by more than a factor of two.

Bacteria would probably not benefit by very strict control of the synthesis of flavins and certain other coenzymes. The wastage of matter and energy involved in the uncontrolled synthesis of coenzymes is very slight. To avoid the small excretion observed (small in absolute terms), it would be necessary to have more rigid control: i.e. lower concentrations of the end product would be required to inhibit its own synthesis (by repression or feedback inhibition). Lower intracellular concentrations would then be able to affect the synthesis of macromolecules in which enzymes with flavin coenzymes are involved

at different points. To give a figure, the internal concentration of free flavins in *E. coli* is already lower than 4×10^{-6} M.
This absence of a fine control can result in monstrosities such as *E. ashbyii* where filtrates of the culture medium can reach a concentration of 1 g/litre or more in riboflavin.

BIOSYNTHESIS OF NICOTINAMIDE, NAD$^+$ AND NADP$^+$

The details of the biosynthesis of nicotinic acid have been worked out only in animals and fungi. It appears that bacteria and plants synthesize their nicotinamide by quite a different route, one about which we know very little.
In animals and fungi, the precursor of nicotinic acid is tryptophan. Tryptophan pyrrolase, a heme enzyme, catalyzes the opening of the pyrrole ring by an oxygenation reaction which adds molecular oxygen (275):

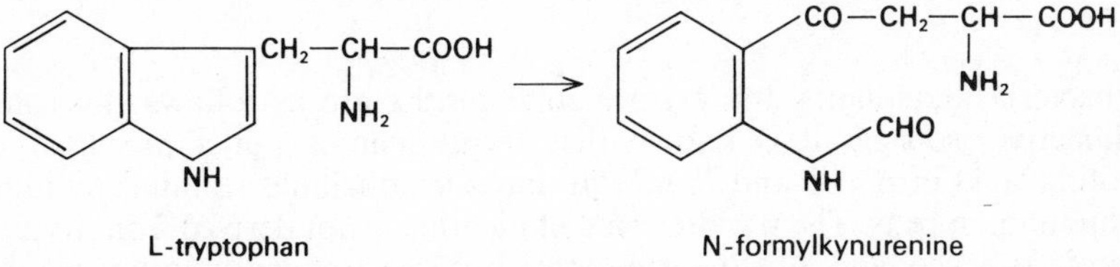

The compound produced loses its formyl group by the action of a specific formamidase (276) and the kynurenine obtained is hydroxylated by kynurenine 3-hydroxylase; the oxygen atom of the hydroxyl group comes from molecular oxygen and not from water. The reason why the hydroxylase requires NADPH to function is not known (277).

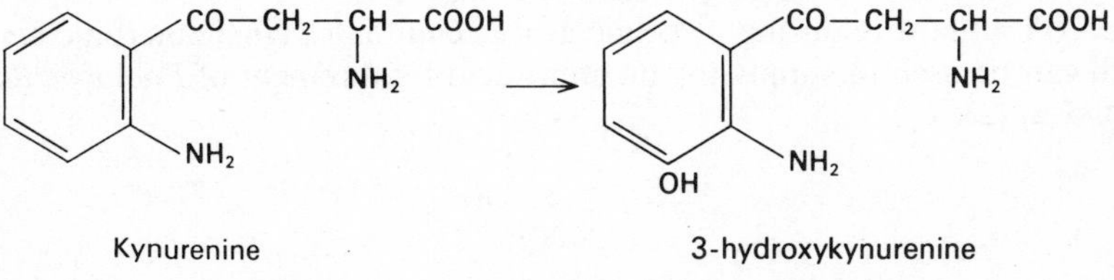

Kynureninase is an enzyme with pyridoxal phosphate as cofactor; it hydrolyzes 3-hydroxykynurenine to 3-hydroxyanthranilic acid and alanine (278). The benzene ring of 3-hydroxyanthranilic acid is then opened by the action of an oxygenase which has been highly purified from ox liver and is activated by ferrous ions and sulfhydryl compounds (279). The oxidation product is 1-amino-4-formyl-1,3-butadiene-1,2-dicarboxylic acid:

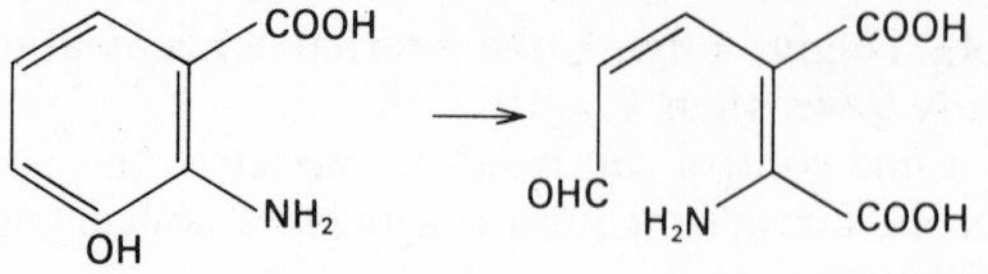

3-hydroxyanthranilic acid   1-amino-4-formyl-1,3-butadiene-1,2-dicarboxylic acid

Specific enzymes carry out the cyclization of this compound to form quinolinic acid and the decarboxylation to form pyridine 3-carboxylic or nicotinic acid (280):

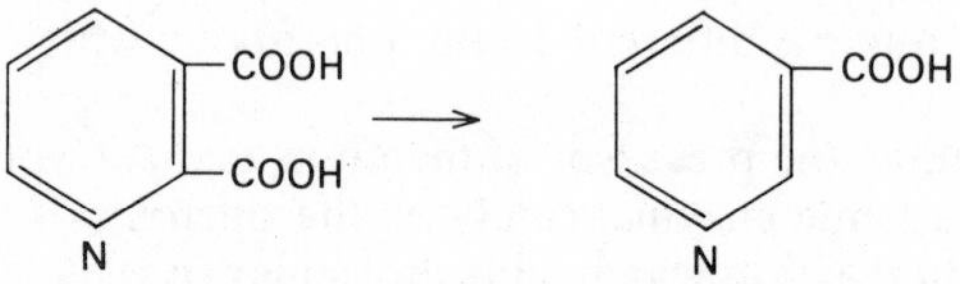

Quinolinic acid   Nicotinic acid

In bacteria and plants, the experimental results are as follows: by using radioactive isotopes it is known that tryptophan is not a precursor of nicotinic acid in *E. coli* and *B. subtilis* nor is trigonelline, a similar pyridine compound, in peas. The pyridine ring of nicotine is not derived from tryptophan in tobacco, and labelled tryptophan or 3-hydroxyanthranilic acid are not the precursors of nicotinic acid extracted from maize germ.
Recent experiments with *E. coli* and *Mycobacterium tuberculosis* (281, 282) would appear to show that a three-carbon compound such as glycerol, and a four-carbon compound such as succinate or aspartate, might be possible precursors, and condensation of these compounds followed by decarboxylation would provide the carbon skeleton of nicotinic acid, with the carboxyl group coming from the C-4 compound.
An *E. coli* mutant requiring nicotinic acid accumulates cinchomeronic acid which can be used to supply the nicotinic acid requirement of *Lactobacillus arabinosus* (283).

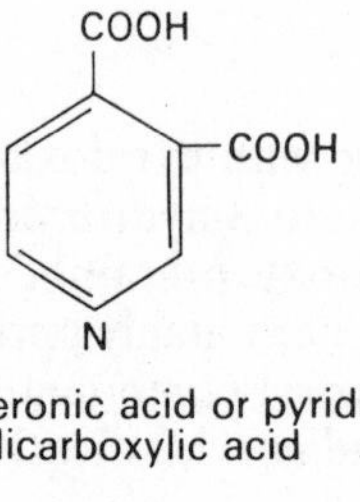

Cinchomeronic acid or pyridine 3,4-dicarboxylic acid

There is no doubt that much more information is necessary to obtain a complete picture of the synthesis of nicotinic acid in plants and bacteria. The only bacterial species studied which synthesizes nicotinic acid by the pathway from tryptophan is *Xanthomonas pruni.*

The cofactors for dehydrogenation reactions, NAD^+ and $NADP^+$, are derivatives not of nicotinic acid but of nicotinamide. Nicotinamide found in biological fluids comes from the degradative action of NADase or the degradation of nicotinamide mononucleotide. The amidation of nicotinic acid occurs at the level of the dinucleotide, as we shall see below. The first precursor of NAD^+ (284) is the mononucleotide of nicotinic acid, synthesized by the action of phosphoribosyl nicotinate transferase:

$$\begin{array}{c}\text{Nicotinic acid + Phosphoribosylpyrophosphate} \\ \downarrow\uparrow \text{ (NMN-pyrophosphorylase)} \\ \text{Nicotinic acid mononucleotide (NMN) + Pyrophosphate.}\end{array}$$

The mononucleotide reacts with ATP to yield the dinucleotide of nicotinic acid and adenine:

$$\text{NMN + ATP} \rightleftarrows \text{Deamido-NAD}^+ \text{ + Pyrophosphate}$$
$$\text{(nicotinate-adenine-dinucleotide pyrophosphorylase)}$$

Finally, NAD^+-synthetase adds an amide group to the nicotinic acid moiety of deamido-NAD^+. Glutamine is the source of this NH_2:

$$\text{Deamido-NAD}^+ \text{ + ATP + Glutamine} \xrightarrow[\text{Synthetase}]{\text{NAD}^+} \text{NAD}^+ \text{ + AMP + Pyrophosphate + Glutamate}$$

The synthesis of $NADP^+$ is catalyzed by NAD^+ kinase which transfers a phosphate from ATP to carbon 2 of the ribose moiety adjacent to adenine in NAD^+ (285):

$$\text{NAD}^+ \text{ + ATP} \longrightarrow \text{NADP}^+ \text{ + ADP}$$

To help us to understand the details of this biosynthesis, the structural formulas of NAD^+ and $NADP^+$ are set out on page 196.

The control of the synthesis of pyridine nucleotides seems to be quite efficient. In *Aerobacter aerogenes*, the addition of exogenous nicotinic acid causes the endogenous synthesis to fall to 3% of its rate: the total intracellular concentration of pyridine nucleotides remains constant.

The mechanism of this control has been analyzed in the case of *E. coli* (286): a mutant requiring nicotinic acid was grown with varying concentrations of

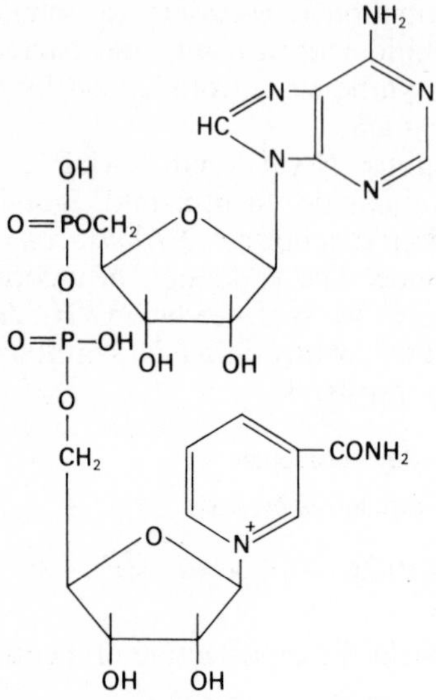

Nicotinamide adenine dinucleotide (NAD^+)

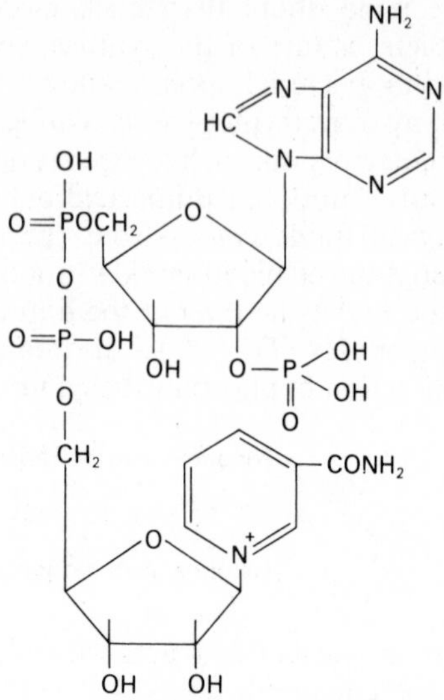

Nicotinamide adenine dinucleotide phosphate ($NADP^+$)

NAD^+ or nicotinic acid and the four enzymatic activities following were measured *in vitro*: NMN-pyrophosphorylase, nicotinate adenine dinucleotide pyrophosphorylase, NAD^+ synthetase and NAD^+ kinase. Whereas the activity of the last three enzymes seemed to be independent of the growth conditions, the specific activity of NMN-pyrophosphorylase was increased 200 times in cultures with limiting nicotinate. It is deduced that the synthesis of this enzyme is subject to control by repression which regulates the intracellular concentrations of NAD^+ and $NADP^+$. In other organisms, such as *B. subtilis*, *Serratia marcescens*, *Torula cremoris* and *Tetrahymena pyriformis*, this control is absent. On the other hand, a different kind of regulation has been demonstrated in *B. subtilis*, the activation of NMN-pyrophosphorylase by ATP (287). This enzyme possesses a site for combination with ATP which activates the enzyme and stimulates the formation of NAD^+ in non-proliferating cells. The fact that ATP stimulates the formation of NAD^+ has interesting implications for control (288), since ATP is an indirect product of the reoxidation of NADH in oxidative phosphorylation. The availability of energy in the form of ATP would thus influence the rate of intracellular oxidation-reduction reactions by controlling the rate of NAD^+. In turn, NAD^+ would influence the production of the energy required for the different cell functions. The cell would be greatly benefited by the working of such a co-ordinated system of interconnecting controls, which appears very likely.

BIOSYNTHESIS OF *p*-AMINOBENZOIC ACID, AND FOLIC ACID AND ITS DERIVATIVES

On examining the structural formula of folic acid:

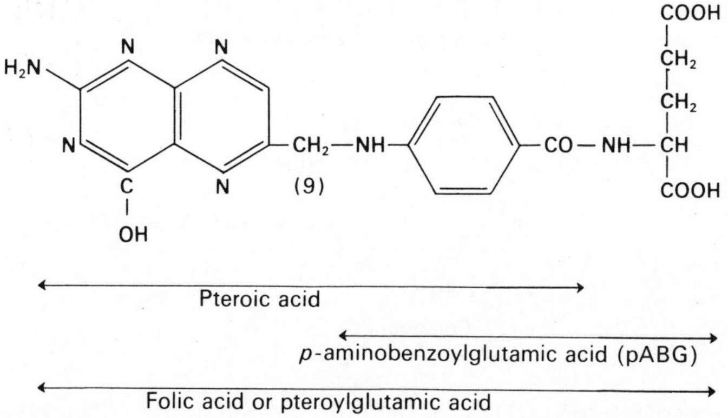

we see that it can be considered as composed of three parts, glutamic acid, *p*-aminobenzoic acid (pAB) and 2-amino-4-hydroxypteridine. The combination of pteridine and pAB through the methylene bridge (numbered 9 in the formula) is called pteroic acid. We can therefore imagine the synthesis of folic acid to take place either by the condensation of pteroate with glutamate, or by the condensation of pteridine with pABG. Chorismic acid, the common precursor of the three aromatic amino acids, is also the precursor of pAB (289). Prephenic acid and *p*-hydroxybenzoic acid are inactive as substrates for the cell-free system which synthesizes pAB from chorismate. The nitrogen atom of pAB is derived from the amide nitrogen of glutamine. We have no actual details of the mechanism of this reaction. As in the riboflavin case, a purine residue which has lost carbon 8 is incorporated as such into the pteridine molecule (290). Guanine is active only in the presence of PRPP, but guanosine and guanine nucleotides are better substrates (291). A hypothetical scheme for the biosynthesis is given below:

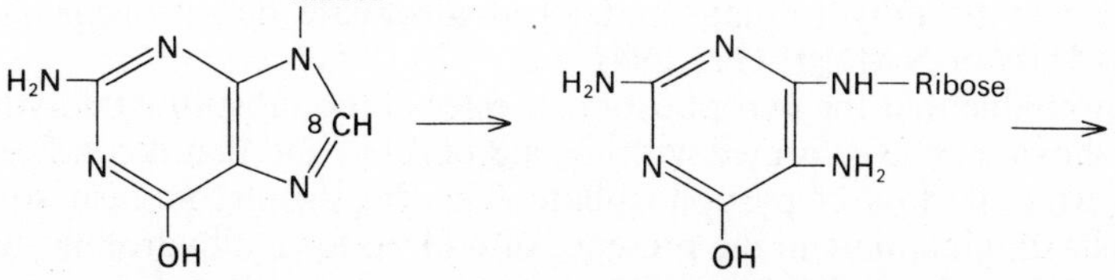

Guanosine　　　Triaminouracil riboside

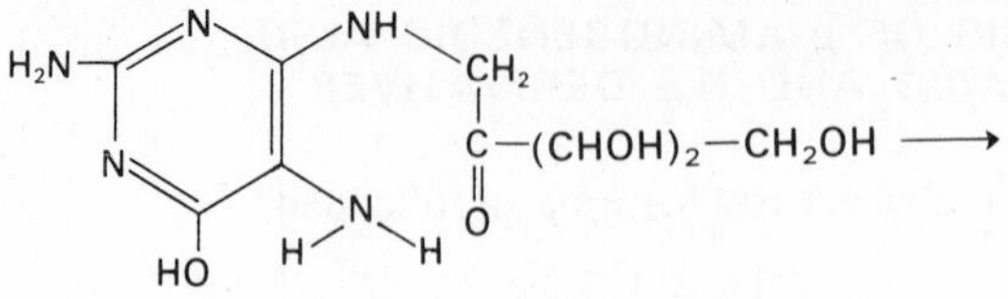

Triaminouracil deoxypentuloside

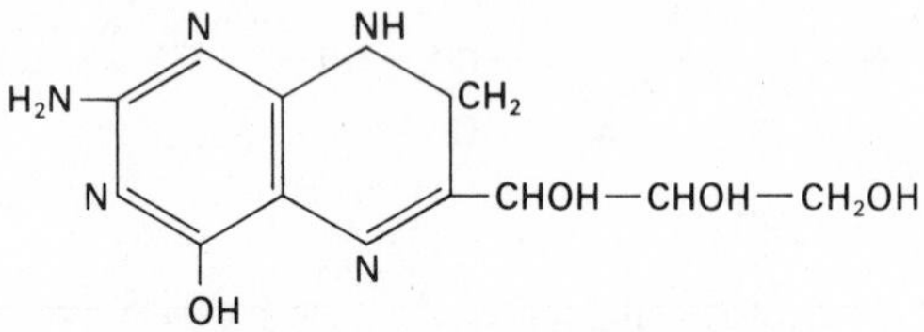

Compound A

If this scheme is correct, two of the three carbon atoms of the side chain of biopterin must be removed to obtain 2-amino-4-hydroxy-6-hydroxymethyl-dihydropteridine, characteristic of the folic acid structure. This scheme seems likely since it can be shown that an enzymatic system extracted from yeast can synthesize folate from tetrahydrobiopterin, a compound analogous to compound A (292):

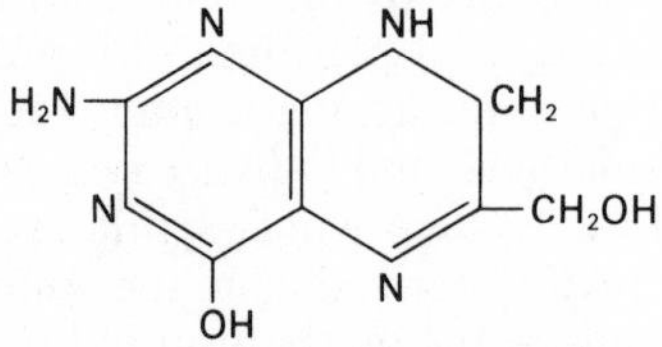

2-amino-4-hydroxy-
6-hydroxymethyldihydropteridine

We should note that folic acid is probably not an intermediate in the *de novo* biosynthesis of tetrahydrofolic acid. It is isolated in the oxidized form from natural sources, because of the ease of oxidation of the reduced species. Fortunately for the economy of the cell, there are enzymes which reduce folic acid, the dihydrofolate and tetrahydrofolate dehydrogenases, which use NADH or NADPH (293, 294).

It is probable that the pyrophosphoric ester of the substituted dihydropteridine shown above is formed with the aid of ATP, and that it condenses with pAB with the loss of pyrophosphate. The dihydropteroic acid so formed reacts with glutamate in the presence of ATP to form dihydrofolic acid.

Other derivatives of folic acid are known: we have already seen briefly tetrahydrofolic acid and N^5,N^{10}-methylenetetrahydrofolic acid, in connection with the biosynthesis of serine and methionine where these compounds act as carriers of one-carbon units. Also known is another kind of tetrahydrofolate derivative, which is used in the transfer of formimino groups (—CH=NH). Other naturally occurring forms are the triglutamic and heptaglutamic derivatives of folic acid. In these, the glutamyl residues are linked by their γ carboxyl groups.

BIOSYNTHESIS OF DERIVATIVES OF VITAMIN B_6 OR PYRIDOXINE

Only a few lines will be taken for this subject, for we know almost nothing about the reactions with which the cell synthesizes these pyridine derivatives whose formulas are given below:

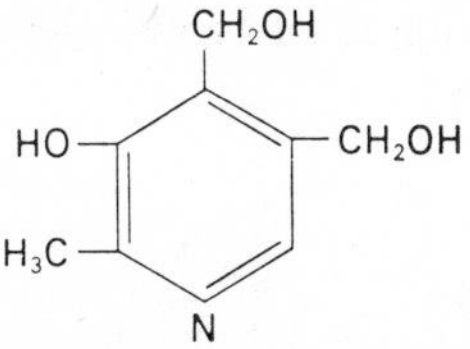

Pyridoxine

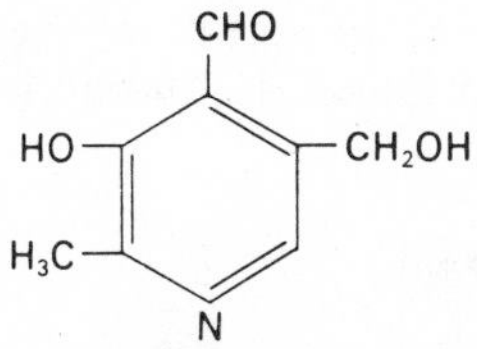

Pyridoxal

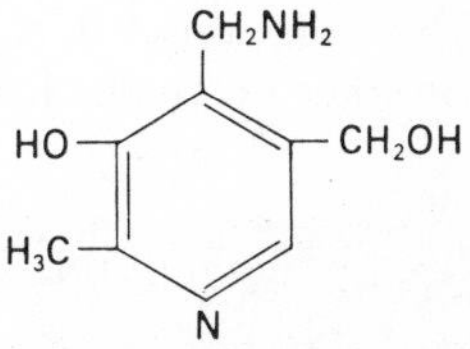

Pyridoxamine

As all three forms of vitamin B_6 are equally active for the growth of B_6-requiring organisms, it is to be expected that they are readily interconvertible. Pyridoxal phosphokinase, which catalyzes the reaction:

$$\text{Pyridoxal} + \text{ATP} \longrightarrow \text{Pyridoxal phosphate} + \text{ADP}$$

also catalyzes the phosphorylation of pyridoxine and pyridoxamine. Pyridoxine phosphate and pyridoxamine phosphate are oxidized to pyridoxal phosphate by a specific oxidase.

Quite recently, experiments in syntrophy with a series of independent *E. coli* mutants enabled these mutants to be classified into seven different phenotypes. One group of mutants lacks the specific oxidase which acts on pyridoxine phosphate, and accumulates pyridoxine and pyridoxine phosphate. The latter compound seems therefore to be a normal intermediate in the synthesis of pyridoxal phosphate (295).

The synthesis of compounds of this family seems to be under control by feedback inhibition: addition of pyridoxine at a concentration of 4×10^{-7} M to exponentially growing cultures of *E. coli* immediately stops all synthesis of pyridoxine derivatives. This conclusion must nevertheless be verified as soon as the specific enzymes of the synthetic pathway are identified (296).

BIOSYNTHESIS OF BIOTIN, "BIOTIN-CO_2" AND BIOCYTIN

Biotin can be thought of formally as a thiophen ring with an *n*-pentanoyl side-chain and a urea moiety:

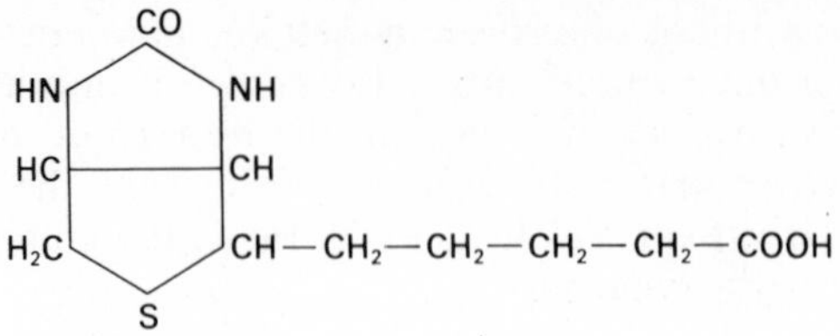

Biotin

Studies carried out quite a long time ago showed that certain mycobacteria requiring biotin could utilize pimelic acid in its place (297):

$$HOOC-CH_2-CH_2-CH_2-CH_2-CH_2-COOH$$

Pimelic acid

This compound is considered to be one of the precursors of biotin (298). Another precursor has been found, desthiobiotin (299):

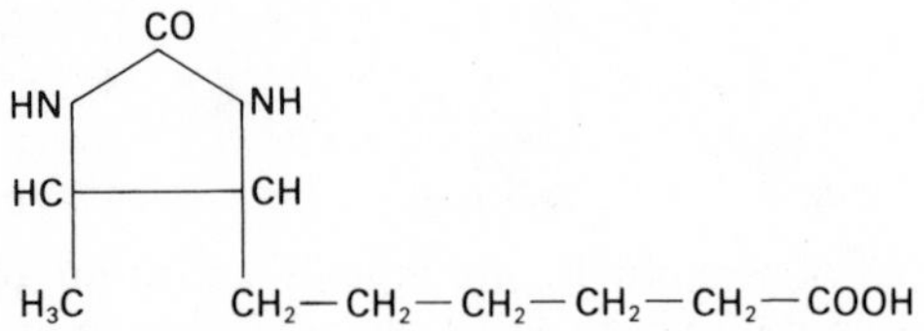

Desthiobiotin

The pimelic acid moiety can be recognized in this compound.
The immediate source of the sulphur atom required to complete the thiophen ring is not known.
We have seen that acetyl CoA carboxylase and many other carboxylases contain biotin. In several instances it has been shown that CO_2-activation which occurs in those reactions results from the carboxylation of biotin to form an energy-rich compound, biotin $\sim CO_2$ (300):

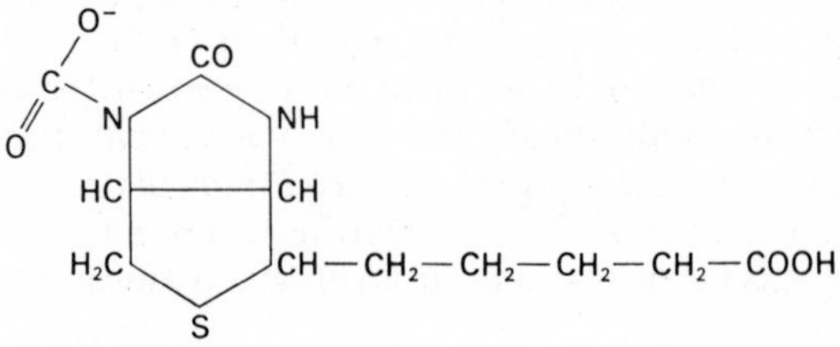

Biotin $\sim CO_2$

With acetyl CoA carboxylase, some authors postulate a mechanism different from the one worked out for other known carboxylases: the carbon atom of the urea moiety would be the active carbon. This implies the existence of a compound which for simplicity can be called "diamino-biotin":

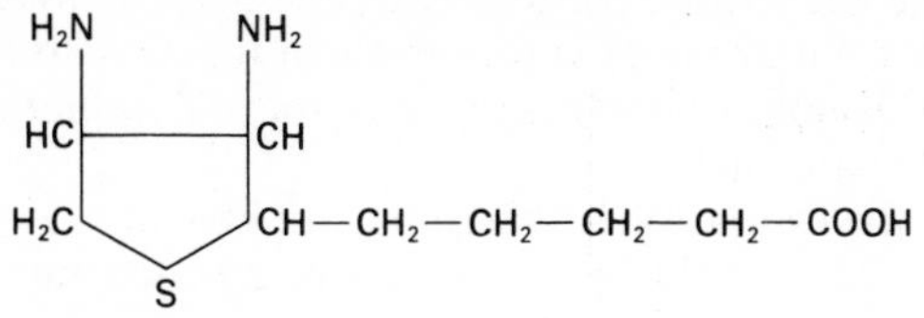

"Diamino-biotin"

The ureido-carbon would be transferred to acetyl CoA during the carboxylation reaction and regenerated from bicarbonate in the presence of ATP. This is questioned by the majority of workers specializing in this field; and the participation of "diamino-biotin" in the biosynthesis of biotin is definitely ruled out. A "combined" form of biotin, called biocytin (ε-N-biotinyllysine) was known for a long time. This suggested that biotin was bound to the carboxylase apoenzyme through the ε-amino groups of lysine. This is now unequivocally established for propionyl carboxylase (301, 302, 303). A specific enzyme, acting on radioactive biotin, propionylapocarboxylase and ATP, enables the radioactive holoenzyme to be obtained, from which radioactive biocytin can be isolated after proteolytic digestion. The following generalized formula can then be written:

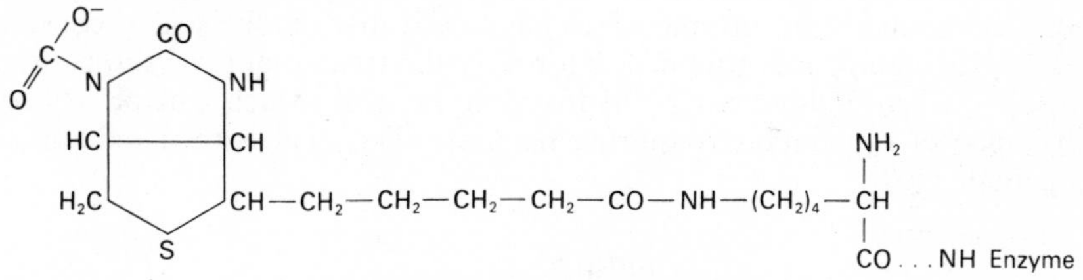

A carboxylated holocarboxylase

in which the carboxyl group of lysine is used to bind the active form of the vitamin to apocarboxylase by a peptide bond.
The reaction synthesizing holocarboxylases probably involves the intermediate formation of biotinyladenylate.

THE BIOSYNTHESIS OF PANTOTHENIC ACID AND COENZYME A

The details here are well known. Pantothenic acid is composed of two parts, β-alanine and β,β-dimethyl-γ-hydroxybutyric acid (pantoic acid). Mutants of *E. coli* unable to synthesize pantothenate fall into three classes, formally

analogous to those we studied in the synthesis of thiamine: 1) those which can synthesize pantoic acid but require β-alanine; 2) those which can synthesize β-alanine but require pantoic acid; and 3) those which can synthesize both compounds but are unable to join them together to form pantothenic acid because of lacking the necessary enzyme. These mutants require preformed pantothenate (304).
Two routes for the formation of β-alanine are known.
It can be obtained directly by the action of an aspartate-4-decarboxylase (305):

$$\underset{\text{Aspartate}}{HOOC{-}CH_2{-}\underset{NH_2}{\underset{|}{C}H}{-}COOH} \longrightarrow \underset{\beta\text{-alanine}}{HOOC{-}CH_2{-}CH_2{-}NH_2} + CO_2$$

and also from propionic acid with the intermediate formation of acrylyl CoA (306):

$$CH_3{-}CH_2{-}COOH \longrightarrow \underset{\text{Acrylyl CoA}}{CH_2{:}CH{-}CO{-}S{-}CoA} \xrightarrow{+NH_3} \underset{\beta\text{-alanyl CoA}}{H_2N{-}CH_2{-}CH_2{-}CO{-}S{-}CoA}$$

With regard to pantoic acid, we have already met its precursor, α-keto-isovaleric acid, the precursor of valine. A hydroxymethyl group is added to this compound by an enzyme which has a derivative of folic acid as cofactor (307). The compound obtained, known by the trivial name of ketopantoic acid, is α-keto-β,β-dimethyl-γ-hydroxybutyric acid, which can be utilized by some of the mutants requiring pantoate. This acid is then reduced to pantoate (308):

$$\underset{\alpha\text{-ketoisovalerate}}{(CH_3)_2CH{-}CO{-}COOH} \xrightarrow{+\,HCHO} \underset{\text{Ketopantoate}}{HO{-}CH_2{-}C(CH_3)_2{-}CO{-}COOH} \longrightarrow \underset{\text{Pantoate}}{HO{-}CH_2{-}C(CH_3)_2{-}CHOH{-}COOH}$$

Pantothenate synthetase joins β-alanine and pantoate to give pantothenate (309). This enzyme requires ATP: besides pantothenate, the other products of the reaction are AMP and pyrophosphate (310).
This reaction is of some historic importance: it is the first known reaction in which the net synthesis of a peptide bond is found, and in which an enzyme-substrate complex has been clearly demonstrated. The reaction can be split up as follows (311):

Enzyme + ATP + Pantoate $\longrightarrow$ Enzyme-pantoyl adenylate + Pyrophosphate
Enzyme-pantoyl adenylate + β-alanine $\longrightarrow$ Pantothenate + AMP + Enzyme

Pantoate + ATP + β-alanine $\longrightarrow$ Pantothenate + AMP + Pyrophosphate

$$
\begin{array}{c}
CH_3 \\
| \\
HO-CH_2-C-CHOH-CONH-CH_2-CH_2-COOH \\
| \\
CH_3
\end{array}
$$

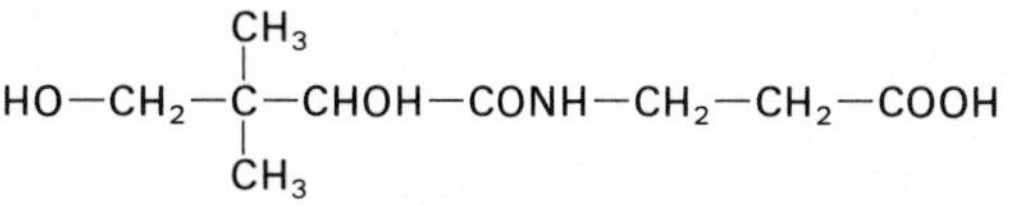

Pantothenic acid

The first reaction leading from pantothenate to coenzyme A is a phosphorylation of the hydroxymethyl group of pantothenate by pantothenate kinase
to produce 4'-phosphopantothenic acid (312):

$$
\begin{array}{c}
CH_3 \\
| \\
H_2O_3PO-CH_2-C-CHOH-CONH-CH_2-CH_2-COOH \\
| \\
CH_3
\end{array}
$$

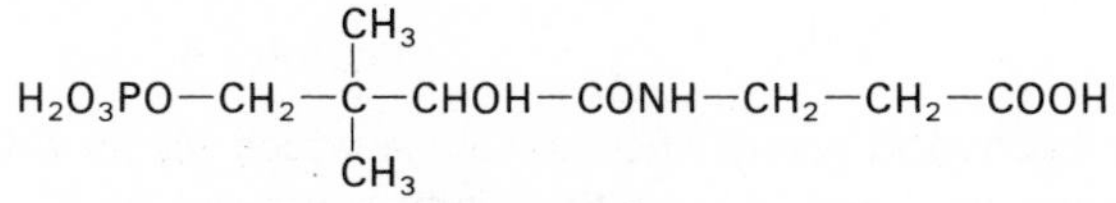

4'-phosphopantothenic acid

The phosphopantothenate is coupled with cysteine by phosphopantothenyl-
cysteine synthetase, which requires ATP or CTP:

$$
\begin{array}{cc}
CH_3 & COOH \\
| & | \\
H_2O_3PO-CH_2-C-CHOH-CONH-CH_2-CH_2-CONH-CH-CH_2SH \\
| & \\
CH_3 &
\end{array}
$$

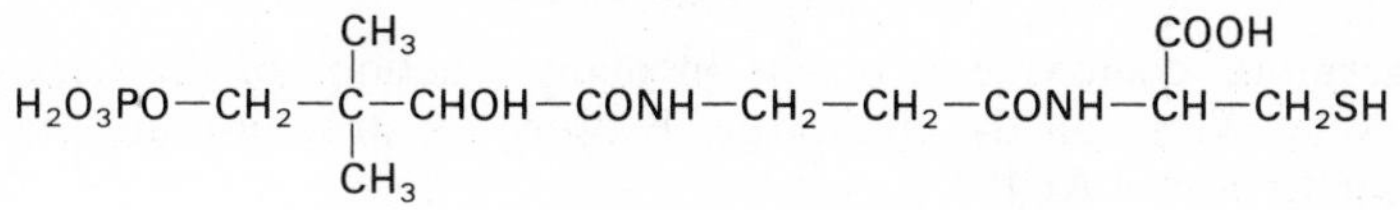

4'-phosphopantothenylcysteine

A specific decarboxylase gives 4'-phosphopantetheine, in which the reader
will note that the cysteine residue of the preceding compound has been
replaced by a 2-mercaptoethylamine residue:

$$
\begin{array}{c}
CH_3 \\
| \\
H_2O_3PO-CH_2-C-CHOH-CONH-CH_2-CH_2-CONH-CH_2-CH_2SH \\
| \\
CH_3
\end{array}
$$

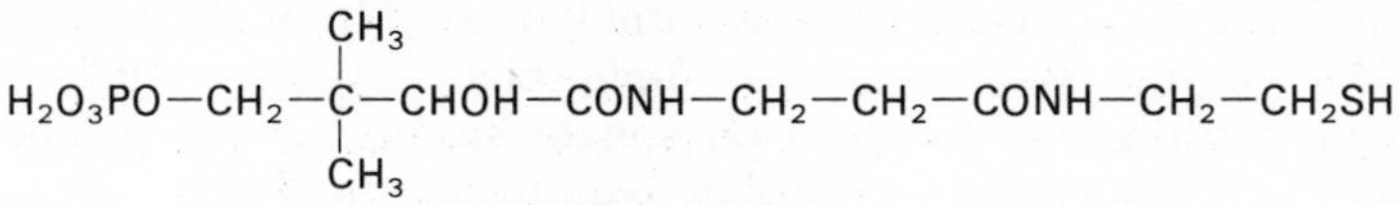

4'-phosphopantetheine

An adenylyl transferase causes a reaction with ATP to form dephosphocoenzyme A and pyrophosphate:

$$
\begin{array}{c}
CH_3 \\
| \\
H_2O_3PO-CH_2-C-CHOH-CONH-CH_2-CH_2-CONH-CH_2-CH_2SH \quad + ATP \\
| \\
CH_3
\end{array}
$$

$$
\begin{array}{c}
\qquad\qquad O \qquad\qquad CH_3 \\
\qquad\qquad \| \qquad\qquad | \\
\Longleftrightarrow \quad HO-P-O-CH_2-C-CHOH-CONH-CH_2-CH_2-CONH-CH_2-CH_2SH \\
\qquad\qquad | \qquad\qquad | \\
\qquad\qquad O \qquad\qquad CH_3 \qquad\qquad\qquad\qquad + \text{ Pyrophosphate} \\
\qquad\qquad | \\
\qquad\qquad O=P-O\text{-adenosine} \\
\qquad\qquad | \\
\qquad\qquad OH
\end{array}
$$

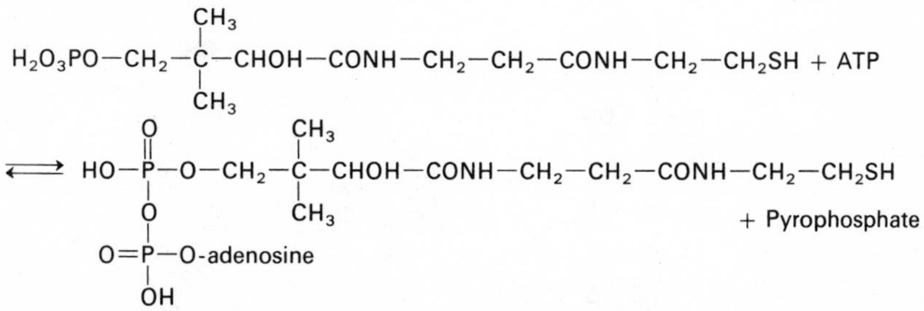

Dephosphocoenzyme A

Finally, dephosphocoenzyme A kinase adds a phosphate residue to one of the ribose hydroxyls and thus coenzyme A is synthesized (313):

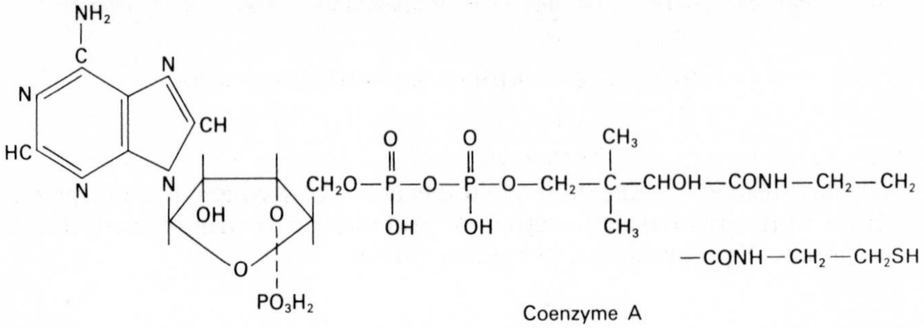

Coenzyme A

It is the free sulfhydryl group of coenzyme A which reacts with acyl groups (acetyl, succinyl, malonyl etc.) in the many syntheses which we have previously studied:

$$R{-}S{-}CO{-}CH_3$$

Acetylcoenzyme A

Furthermore, coenzyme A occurs in many reactions of the tricarboxylic acid cycle. We recall the similarities between its structure and that of the acyl-carrier site of ACP.

SYNTHESIS OF INOSITOL

If one compares the structural formulas of glucopyranose and inositol, one can immediately assume that inositol is derived from glucose by cyclization. An enzyme system, glucose 6-phosphate cyclase, which converts glucose 6-phosphate to inositol 1-phosphate, has been clearly demonstrated in yeast. This system has an absolute requirement for NAD^+. In a second step, a phosphatase which requires Mg^{++} ions hydrolyzes inositol phosphate (314). The same results have been obtained in testicular extracts from mammals.

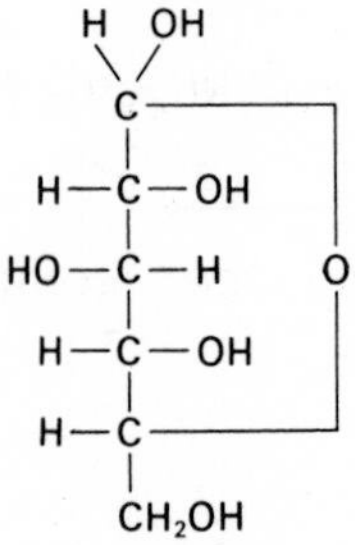

Glucose

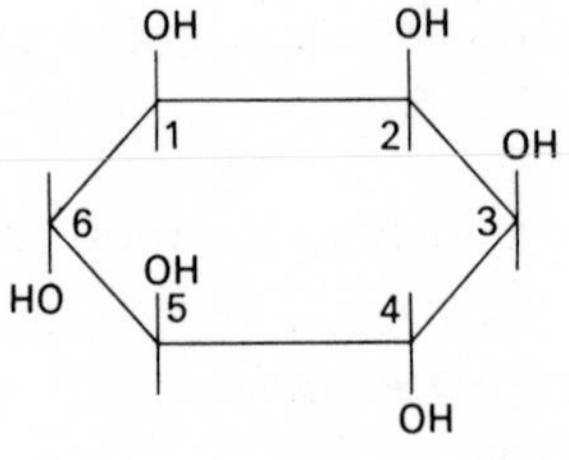

Inositol

BIOSYNTHESIS OF VITAMIN B_{12}

An outline of the synthesis of this complex molecule will be found when we study the tetrapyrrole ring system.

18

Biosynthesis of Carotene,
Vitamin A and Sterols

SYNTHESIS OF ISOPENTENYLPYROPHOSPHATE

The enzyme β-ketothiolase condenses two molecules of acetyl CoA to form acetoacetyl CoA (see p. 83).
In a reaction analogous to the condensation of acetyl CoA with oxaloacetate to give citrate, β-hydroxy-β-methylglutaryl CoA synthetase catalyzes the condensation of acetoacetyl CoA with a new molecule of acetyl CoA (315):

$$CH_3{-}CO{-}CH_2{-}COSCoA + CH_3COSCoA \longrightarrow CH_3{-}\overset{\overset{\displaystyle OH}{|}}{\underset{\underset{\displaystyle CH_2{-}COOH}{|}}{C}}{-}CH_2{-}COSCoA + CoASH$$

β-hydroxy-β-methylglutaryl CoA

Arguments have recently been advanced which tend to prove finally that acetoacetyl-ACP is the true intermediate in this condensation (316, 317).
A specific reductase reduces β-hydroxy-β-methylglutaryl CoA to mevalonic acid (318):

$$CH_3{-}\overset{\overset{\displaystyle OH}{|}}{\underset{\underset{\displaystyle CH_2{-}COOH}{|}}{C}}{-}CH_2{-}CH_2OH$$

Mevalonic acid

Mevalonate kinase catalyzes the phosphorylation of mevalonic acid at position 5 (319):

grow normally in the conditions of anaerobic photosynthesis, it is rapidly killed by simultaneous exposure to light and oxygen. Death is accompanied by destruction of the bacteriochlorophyll. Further experiments have shown that this destruction is a secondary phenomenon and that the mortality curves are the same if the experiment is carried out at a low temperature without destruction of chlorophyll. The mechanism of the protection conferred by carotenoids against photo-oxidation remains obscure (327).

It is very likely that vitamin A is synthesized in the following way (328): β-carotene, which is a "provitamin A", splits in the middle (at the point indicated by the arrow in the formula on page 209). The product is the aldehyde corresponding to vitamin A (retinene) which is then reduced to vitamin A (329):

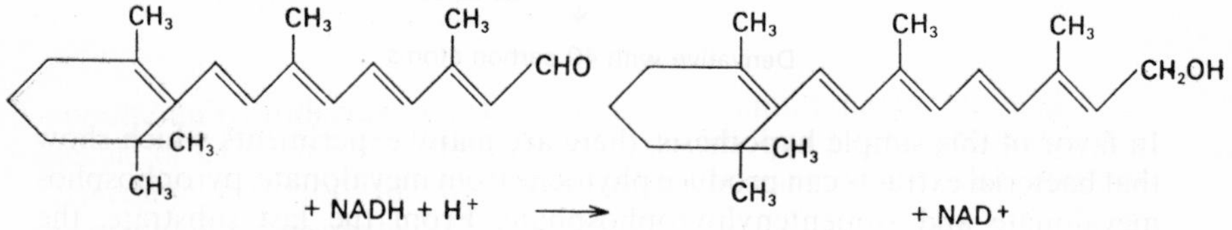

Retinene Vitamin A

SYNTHESIS OF STEROLS

The synthesis of sterols can be considered to be identical with the synthesis of carotenoids as far as the stage of formation of farnesyl pyrophosphate, the 15-carbon atom derivative:

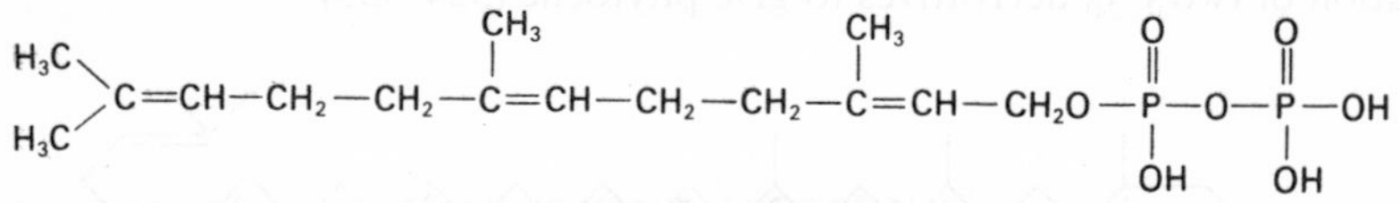

Farnesyl pyrophosphate

A particulate system isolated from yeast can condense two molecules of farnesyl pyrophosphate to form squalene in the presence of NADPH (330). An analogous system has been obtained in liver microsomes (331).

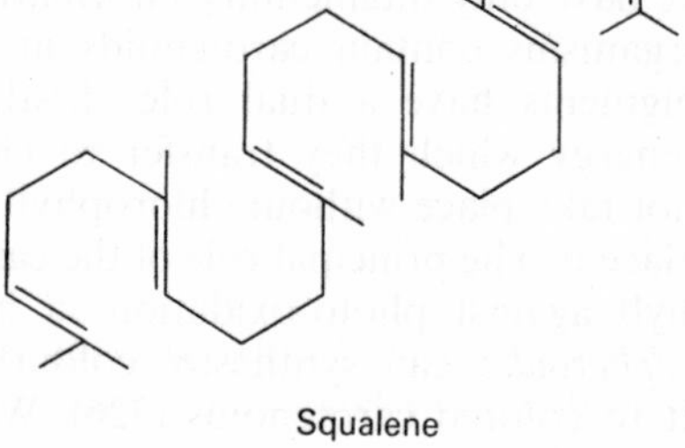

Squalene

The conversion of squalene to cholesterol involves cyclization, reduction and molecular rearrangement steps, all of which are so complex as to be outside the scope of this book[1]. It is enough to say here that at least fifteen successive reactions are involved in the conversion.

It has been known since 1951 (332) that the addition of cholesterol to the diet of laboratory animals reduces the rate of synthesis of cholesterol by the liver. It can be shown that this reduction is caused by the feedback inhibition of β-hydroxy-β-methylglutarate reductase (333); this is a striking example of the absence of structural similarity between an allosteric inhibitor and the substrates of the reaction which it inhibits:

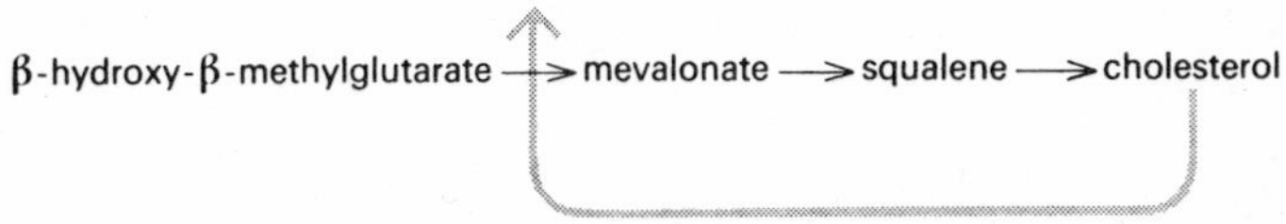

It should be emphasized that the inhibited reaction is the first practically irreversible reaction in the synthesis of sterols.

1. The reader wishing to learn the details of these reactions must consult the specialized literature of the organic chemistry of natural substances.

19

Biosynthesis

of Tetrapyrrole ring system. Its Regulation and an outline of the functions of Vitamin B_{12}

The pathways for the biosynthesis of chlorophyll and respiratory pigments of the heme type make use of the same series of reactions up to the protoporphyrin stage. Judicious use of isotopes, of cell preparations catalyzing some of the reactions involved and degradation techniques specially devised for the task, have allowed the brilliant elucidation of this pathway by some groups of workers.

SYNTHESIS OF PROTOPORPHYRIN

Particulate preparations from lyzed chicken erythrocytes, and cell-free extracts of the photosynthetic bacterium *Rhodopseudomonas spheroides*, are able to carry out the net synthesis of δ-aminolevulinic acid from succinyl CoA and glycine (334):

$$HOOC-CH_2-CH_2-COSCoA + H_2C\begin{matrix}\diagup NH_2\\ \diagdown COOH\end{matrix}$$

$$\downarrow$$

$$HOOC-CH_2-CH_2-CO-CH_2-NH_2 + CO_2$$

δ-aminolevulinic acid (ALA)

ALA synthetase has pyridoxal phosphate as a cofactor.
ALA dehydratase catalyzes a reaction between two molecules of δ-aminolevulinic acid to form the pyrrole derivative, porphobilinogen (335, 336):

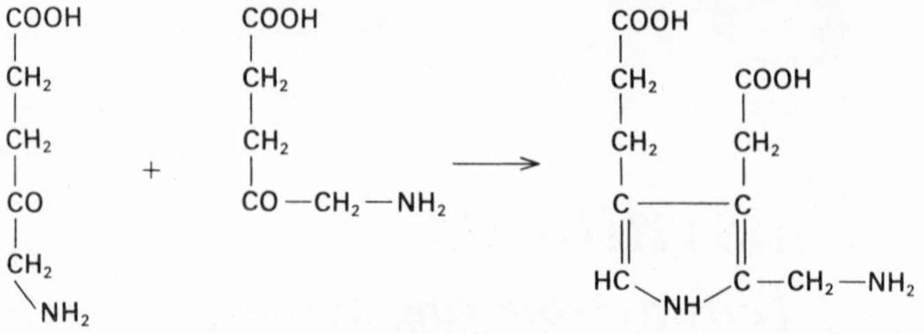

Porphobilinogen

The mechanism and the intermediates of the next reaction have not been elucidated, but it involves two distinct enzymes, porphobilinogen deaminase (337, 338) (prepared from spinach chloroplasts and *R. spheroides*) and uroporphyrinogen III cosynthetase (339) (from wheat germ). The overall stoichiometry of the reaction is as follows:

$$4 \text{ Porphobilinogen} \longrightarrow \text{Uroporphyrinogen III} + 4\,NH_3$$

Uroporphyrinogen III is a tetrapyrrole in which the acetyl residues of the porphobilinogen molecule remain intact. Decarboxylation producing coproporphyrinogen III, in which these acetyls have become methyls, occurs in steps, since porphyrin intermediates with seven, six or five carboxyl groups have been detected. We do not know whether one or more enzymes are involved in the transformation (338, 340):

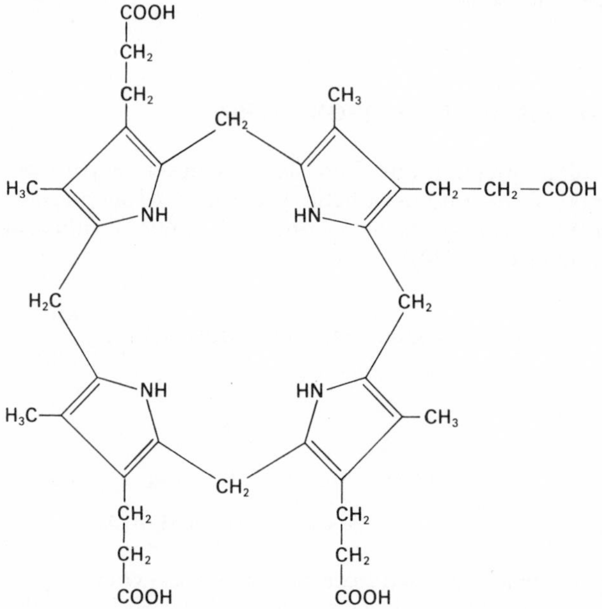

Coproporphyrinogen III

An enzyme system, apparently firmly bound to mitochondria in ox liver, carries out two oxidative decarboxylation reactions, the effect of which is to convert two of the propionyl residues of coproporphyrinogen III to vinyl groups, forming protoporphyrinogen which then becomes oxidized to protoporphyrin:

$$\text{Coproporphyrinogen III} \xrightarrow[-4H]{-2CO_2} \text{Protoporphyrinogen} \xrightarrow{-6H} \text{Protoporphyrin IX}$$

The number of enzymes involved here is not known, and there is no information on the oxidative decarboxylation mechanism (341, 342).

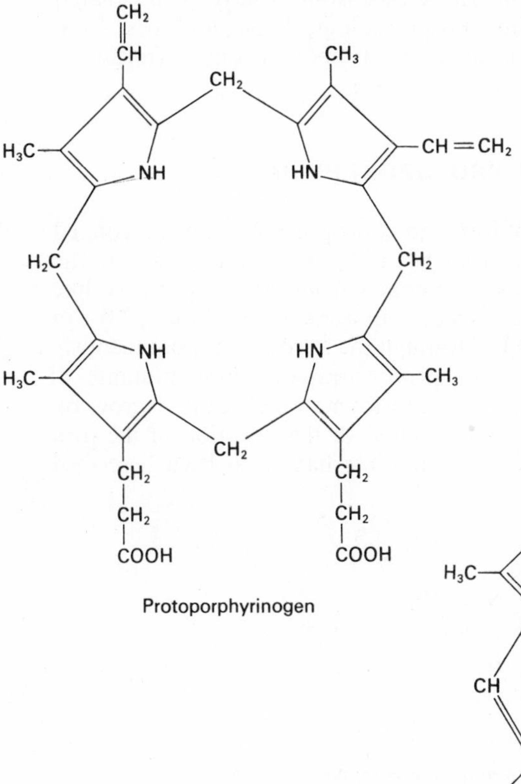

Protoporphyrinogen

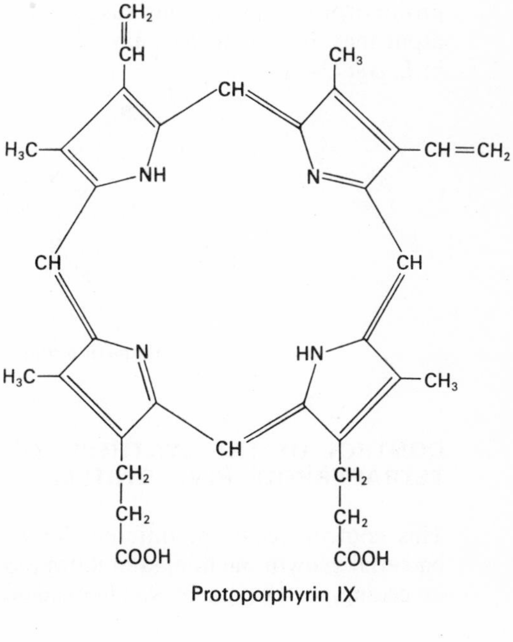

Protoporphyrin IX

The porphyrinogens are colorless substances. The color of the porphyrins is due to dehydrogenation which sets up a system of conjugated double bonds, a chromophore with strong characteristic absorption bands in the near ultraviolet and visible regions of the spectrum.
The Roman numerals following the names of different porphyrinogens and porphyrins are to distinguish the different possible isomers. For example, the methyl, vinyl and propionyl chains in protoporphyrin can be arranged to form fifteen different isomers. In fact, a single series of isomers exists in nature, the protoporphyrin IX series, which for the rest of this chapter we shall refer to simply as protoporphyrin. Other isomers have been isolated from natural sources, but they have no physiological role, and arise from disorders in tetrapyrrole metabolism, or from spontaneous chemical reactions among the precursors of the tetrapyrroles.

SYNTHESIS OF HEME FROM PROTOPORPHYRIN

The fact that natural complexes of iron and coproporphyrin can be isolated strongly suggests that the metal atom is incorporated into heme at the protoporphyrin stage. Further evidence comes from microorganisms, like *Hemophilus influenzae*, where the growth requirement for heme (343) can be satisfied by protoporphyrin (344). Although the ferrous ion spontaneously forms co-ordination complexes with protoporphyrin (345), mutants of *Staphylococcus aureus*, requiring hemin, are found which cannot grow on protoporphyrin (346). This suggests that after all the insertion of the iron atom may be due to an enzyme. Such mutants have also been described in *E. coli* (347).

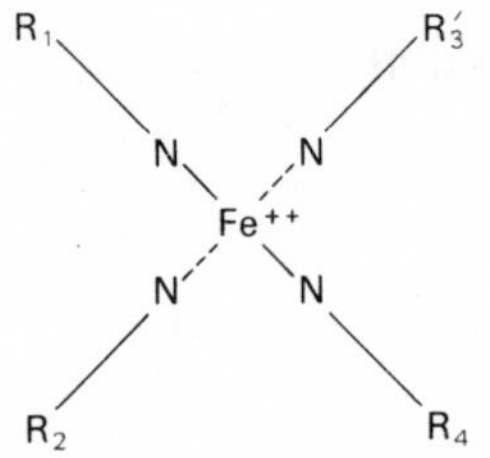

Heme or ferrous protoporphyrin

CONTROL OF THE SYNTHESIS OF THE TETRAPYRROLE RING SYSTEM

This control occurs at different levels. Firstly, an iron deficiency in the bacterial growth medium stimulates a considerable build-up of porphyrins, exceeding, in the case of *Rhodopseudomonas spheroides*, one hundred times the amount of all tetrapyrrole derivatives (bacteriochlorophyll + heme derivatives) normally synthesized in media not lacking iron (348).

This phenomenon has been analyzed in detail with cell-free extracts, and it can be shown that ALA synthetase is very sensitive to inhibition by hemin (336), the effect being appreciable even at a concentration of 10^{-7} M. This inhibition is non-competitive with respect to both the substrates, succinyl CoA and glycine, and can be reversed by dilution. Interpretation of the results obtained *in vivo* is as follows: the control of tetrapyrrole biosynthesis in *R. spheroides* occurs by feedback inhibition of ALA synthetase by hemin, the formation of hemin itself depending on the concentration of iron in the medium:

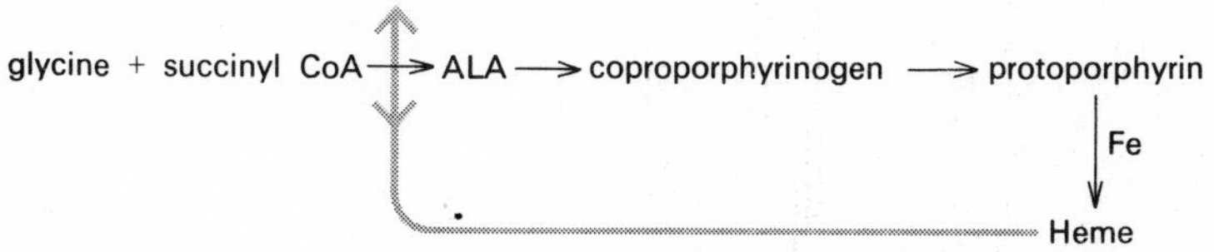

The addition of ALA to cultures of *R. spheroides* also causes severe repression of the synthesis of ALA synthetase and ALA dehydratase (349). It so happens that the only organism in which the control of heme synthesis has been carefully studied is a photosynthetic organism possessing bacteriochlorophyll, another tetrapyrrole compound. This introduces a new parameter in the control of tetrapyrrole synthesis to which we shall return after examining the biosynthesis of chlorophyll.

SYNTHESIS OF CHLOROPHYLL FROM PROTOPORPHYRIN

We know very few of the enzymatic steps involved in this transformation and the intermediates assumed are compounds accumulated by mutant strains of algae or photosynthetic bacteria incapable of carrying out the total synthesis of chlorophyll.

All such compounds contain magnesium. A mutant of *Chlorella* accumulates the most simple of these compounds, magnesium protoporphyrin, whose structure, except for the metal, is identical with that of heme. We know nothing about the mechanism of insertion of the magnesium, except that certain mutants accumulate free protoporphyrin and apparently lack an enzyme required for the addition of the metal (350). Another compound which accumulates in another mutant is the monomethyl ester of the preceding one. The chromatophores of *R. spheroides* catalyze the reaction (351):

Mg-protoporphyrin + S-adenosylmethionine

⟶ Mg-protoporphyrin monomethyl ester + S-adenosylhomocysteine

Examination of the structure of chlorophyll indicates which of the two residues of propionic acid is esterified. This step is the only one which has been studied at the enzymatic level between protoporphyrin and chlorophyll. Another mutant accumulates a third compound which can only be derived from the preceding one by a series of reactions. This is Mg vinylpheoporphyrin a_5 (352):

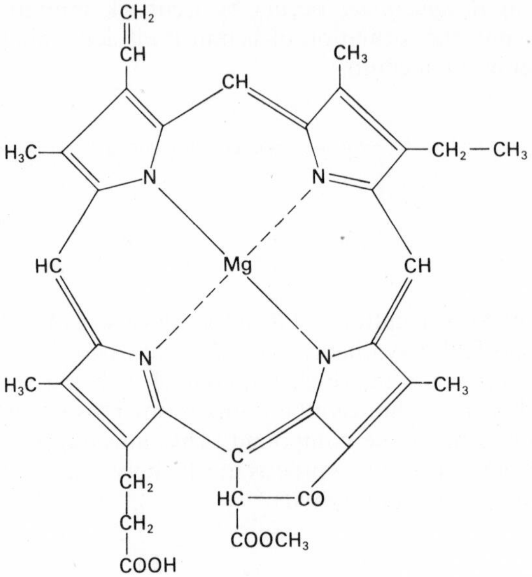

Mg vinylpheoporphyrin a_5
(protochlorophyll)

It can be seen that one of the vinyl groups has been reduced to an ethyl group, that the monomethyl ester of the propionic residue has been oxidized and that the modified chain has cyclized to form a substituted cyclopentanone.

The reduction of this compound to chlorophyll involves reduction of the tetrapyrrole ring carrying the unchanged propionyl residue and an esterification of this residue by phytol, a long-chain alcohol. The intermediates in these reactions probably never occur in the free state (353). It should be mentioned that the reactions take place in higher plants and in some algae only in the presence of light. The structural formulas of chlorophyll *a*, bacteriochlorophyll and phytol are to be found below.

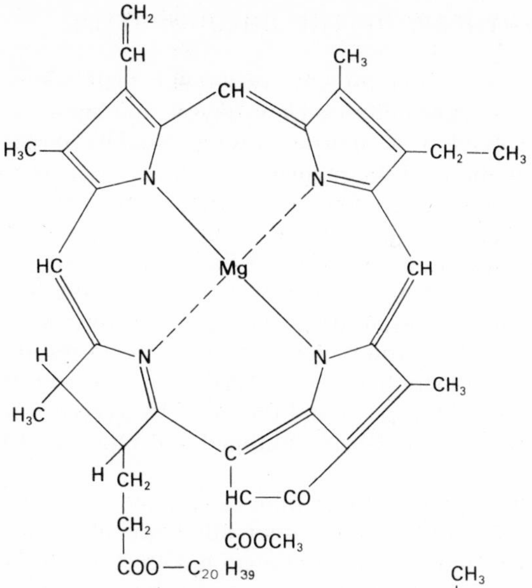

Chlorophyll *a*

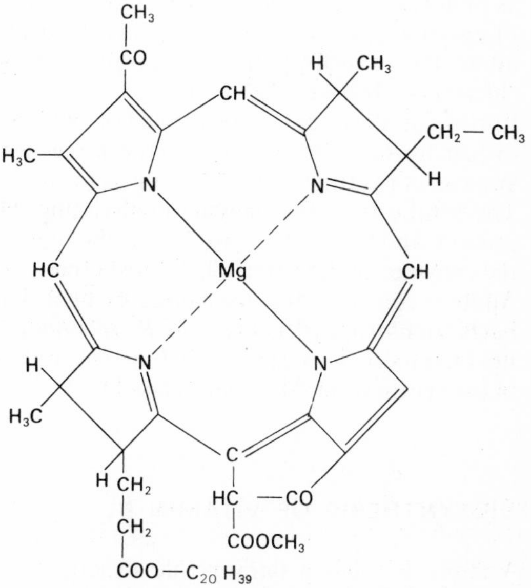

Bacteriochlorophyll

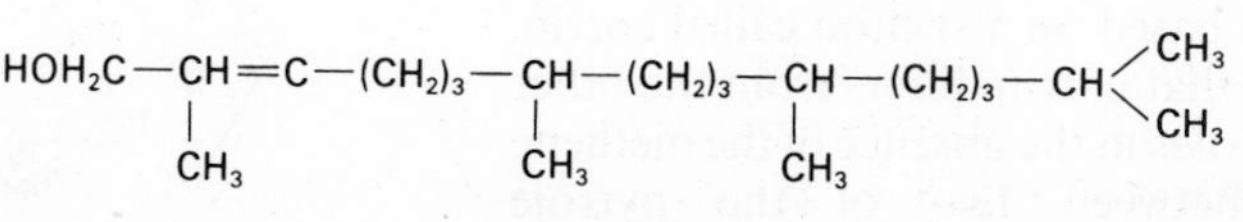

Phytol $C_{20}H_{40}$

CONTROL OF THE BIOSYNTHESIS OF THE CHLOROPHYLLS

Certain photosynthetic bacteria show an impressive variation in their chlorophyll content as a function of external factors such as oxygen and light.
The synthesis of bacteriochlorophyll by *R. spheroides* is repressed by oxygen even in the light (354). The synthesis of the pigment, which occurs anaerobically in light, ceases when air is admitted. On the other hand, the synthesis of bacteriochlorophyll takes place normally in the dark, but at very low partial pressures of oxygen. This phenomenon has been attributed with certainty to repression of the synthesis of ALA synthetase by oxygen (349). The synthetase is never totally repressed, even at high oxygen tensions, while the synthesis of bacteriochlorophyll completely ceases. This raises the question of the existence of two functionally specialized ALA synthetases, the first acting in the synthesis of chlorophyll and repressed by oxygen, and the second in the synthesis of hemin, feedback inhibited and repressed by hemin (355).
Oxygen acts at still other levels, for repression cannot explain the immediate stoppage of the synthesis of bacteriochlorophyll upon admission of oxygen, as preformed ALA synthetase would continue to function. Direct inhibition of enzyme activity has not been observed in *R. spheroides*, but oxygen inhibits the transformation of porphobilinogen to uroporphyrinogen in chicken erythrocytes (356).
Further studies have shown that not only ALA synthetase is repressed by oxygen in *R. spheroides* but also this is true for ALA dehydratase and for the systems converting porphobilinogen to uro- and copro-porphyrinogen III. The synthesis of the enzyme methylating Mg protoporphyrin is also repressed, and it is quite possible that the repression extends to synthesis of all the enzymes of the chlorophyll biosynthetic pathway (351).
Another control is the one caused by light. Under anaerobic conditions, the bacteriochlorophyll content of *R. spheroides* is an inverse function of the light intensity. This can be attributed as in the case of oxygen to a repression of the synthesis of ALA synthetase (354).

BIOSYNTHESIS OF VITAMIN B_{12}

Vitamin B_{12} has a tetrapyrrole structure which can be formally classed with the tetrapyrrole derivatives we have already met. It is based on a skelton called corrin. We note that corrin differs from the other tetrapyrroles in the absence of the methene bridge between two of the pyrrole rings.

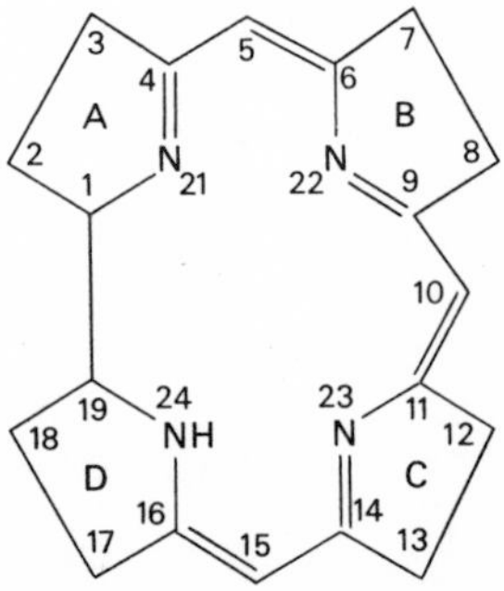

Corrin

In numbering the atoms in this formula, we deliberately omit number 20 in order that all the corrin atoms should correspond to those of the other tetrapyrrole compounds. The structural formula of vitamin B_{12} (or rather of the coenzyme form) is to be found below (fig. 44).

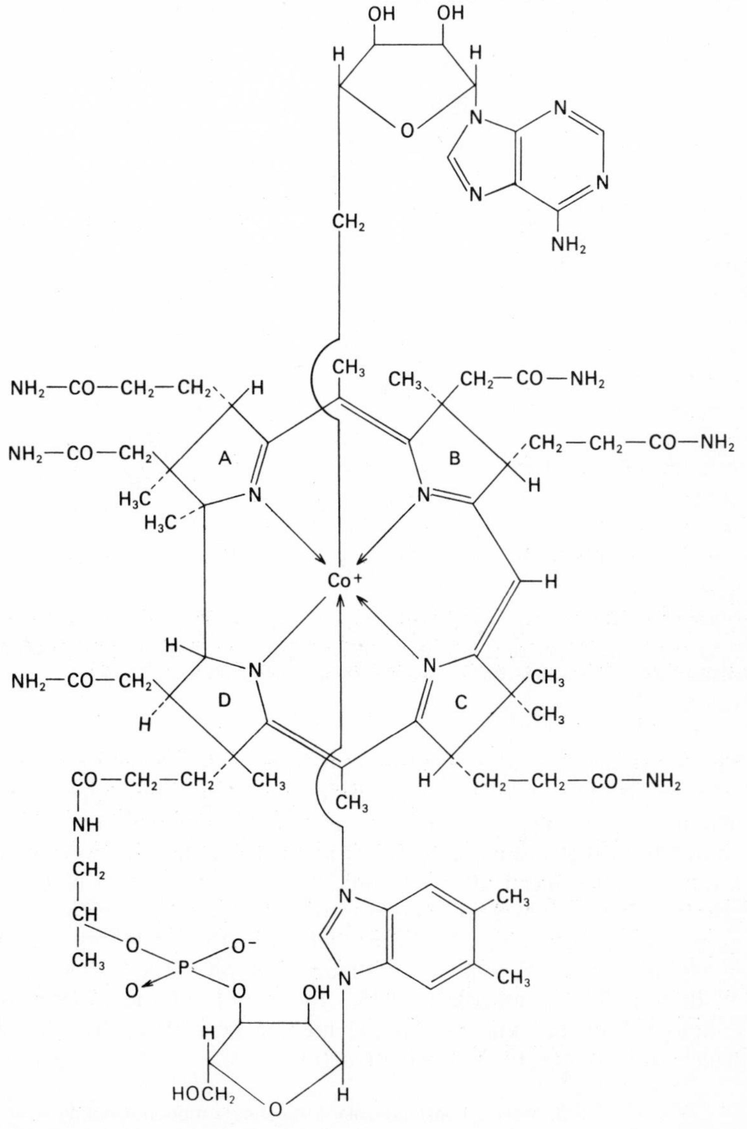

FIGURE 44

Coenzyme form of vitamin B_{12}, (5′-deoxyadenosyl)-B_{12}.

Detailed research work has shown that the first steps in the biosynthesis of the vitamin are the same as for hemin and chlorophyll. Glycine, δ-amino-levulinic acid and porphobilinogen are readily identified intermediates (357). The first part of the synthesis of corrinoids can be considered complete when cobyrinic acid is obtained (fig. 45).

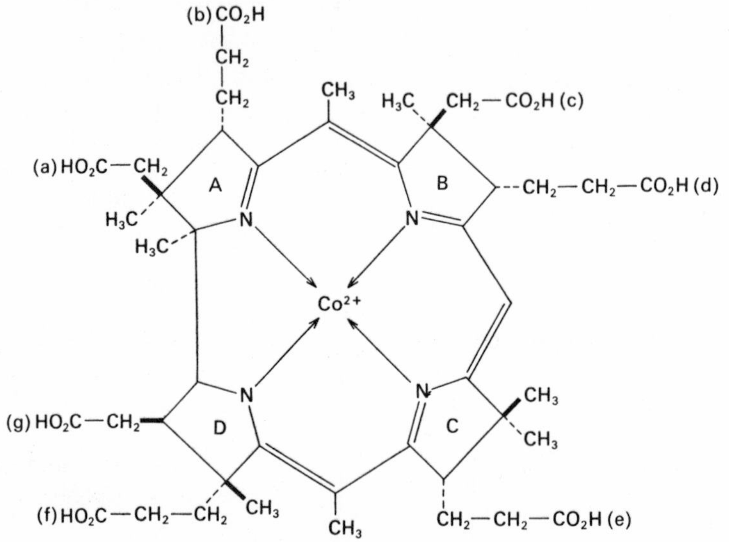

FIGURE 45

Cobyrinic acid. This acid has been isolated from cultures of *Propionibacterium shermanii* (358). If the corrin ring is considered to be in the plane of the paper, the full lines denote substituents above this plane, and the dotted lines bonds from the ring to substituents below the plane.

The incorporation of the isopropanolamine group probably occurs at this stage at position (*f*) of ring D, to produce a compound called cobinic acid. The six carboxyl groups at *a*, *b*, *c*, *d*, *e* and *g* are then amidated to produce a compound called cobinamide. It is quite possible that the isopropanolamine residue is introduced after the amidation of one or two of the carboxyl groups of cobyrinic acid. The isopropanolamine group comes from de-carboxylated threonine. The introduction of the nucleotide characteristic of vitamin B_{12} occurs at the cobinamide level. This nucleotide contains 5,6-dimethylbenzimidazole as base; the details of the biogenesis of this compound are not known. An enzyme can be isolated from *P. shermanii* which will catalyze the following reaction (359):

$$\text{5,6-dimethylbenzimidazole} + \text{nicotinate mononucleotide}$$
$$\downarrow$$
$$\text{1-}\alpha\text{-D-5'-phosphoribofuranosyl-5,6-dimethylbenzimidazole} + \text{nicotinate}$$

A phosphatase next liberates the free nucleoside, which is simply referred to as α-ribazole.

It may be assumed that in certain organisms, the final steps in the synthesis of vitamin B_{12} occur according to the following scheme (360):

Cobinamide + ATP ⟶ Cobinamide-P + ADP

Cobinamide-P + GTP ⟶ Cobinamide-P-P-G + Pyrophosphate

Cobinamide-P-P-G + α-ribazole ⟶ Vitamin B_{12} + GMP

In the corrinoids, the cobalt atom is particularly stable. It is co-ordinated on the one hand by four nitrogen atoms from the tetrapyrrole ring and on the other by one of the nitrogens of the benzimidazole ring. The sixth co-ordination position is the only known case in biology of an organometallic metal-carbon bond. When the substituent in this position is a 5′-deoxy-adenosyl residue, the resulting compound is one of the coenzyme forms of vitamin B_{12}.

The conversion of vitamin B_{12} to coenzyme by extracts of *P. shermanii* (361) or *Clostridium tetanomorphum* (362) requires the presence of ATP, NADH, FAD and a reducing agent which can be reduced glutathione or 2-mercapto-ethanol. ATP is the source of the deoxyadenosyl residue but the mechanism of the reaction is obscure; it is known however that ATP is cleaved in a reaction which produces triphosphoric acid.

The mechanism of the reactions involving this coenzyme are unknown or only partially elucidated. It is nevertheless interesting to describe three of them here.

Glutamate mutase 6.1.

The first reaction in the utilization of glutamate by *Clostridium tetanomorphum* is its conversion to L-*threo*-β-methylaspartate by an enzyme system called glutamate mutase, which depends on the presence of coenzyme B_{12}. The enzyme reaction can be written:

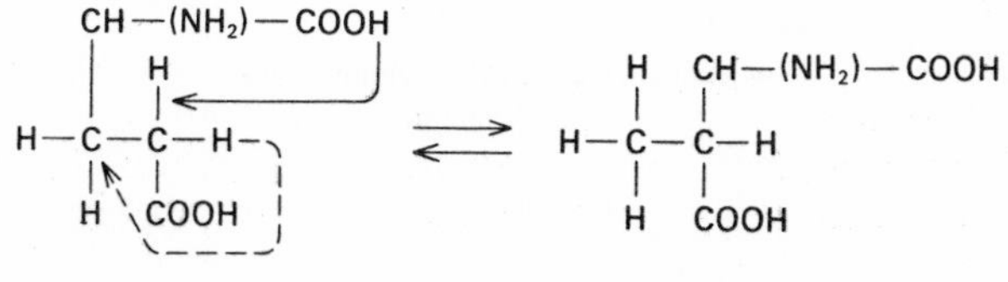

L-glutamate L-β-methylaspartate

It can be seen that this reaction behaves as a double rearrangement by transfer of a hydrogen atom and a glycyl residue (363).

The intramolecular transfer of hydrogen is stereospecific and results in inversion at carbon 4 of glutamic acid.

L-methylmalonyl CoA mutase 6.2.

This reaction is found in microorganisms and animal tissues and is important in the metabolism of propionate, which involves the carboxylation of propionyl CoA to form D-methylmalonyl CoA, isomerization to the L-isomer, and conversion of the L-derivative to succinyl CoA. The isomerization of methylmalonyl CoA, as in the preceding reaction, involves a double re-arrangement (364):

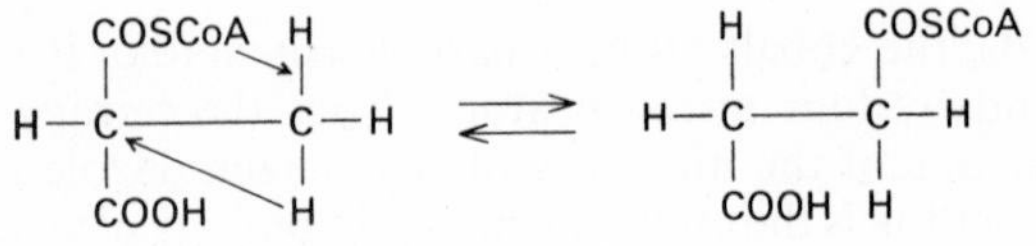

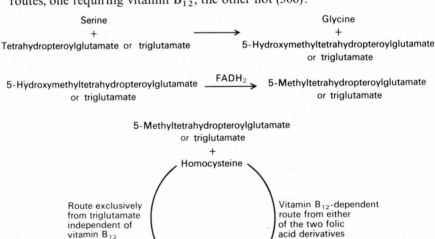

Methylmalonyl CoA Succinyl CoA

Biosynthesis of methionine 6.3.

In addition to nutritional mutants requiring cystathionine, homocysteine or even preformed methionine, there are mutants of *E. coli* which require *either* methionine (to the exclusion of its precursors) *or* vitamin B_{12} for growth (365). From other work, it is known that the methyl donor for the methylation of homocysteine is the carbon of serine and the methyl carrier is tetrahydropteroylglutamic acid. The work of several groups of specialists has gradually produced the view that the synthesis of methionine from methyltetrahydropteroylglutamate and homocysteine can occur by two different routes, one requiring vitamin B_{12}, the other not (366):

Serine + Tetrahydropteroylglutamate or triglutamate ⟶ Glycine + 5-Hydroxymethyltetrahydropteroylglutamate or triglutamate

5-Hydroxymethyltetrahydropteroylglutamate or triglutamate $\xrightarrow{FADH_2}$ 5-Methyltetrahydropteroylglutamate or triglutamate

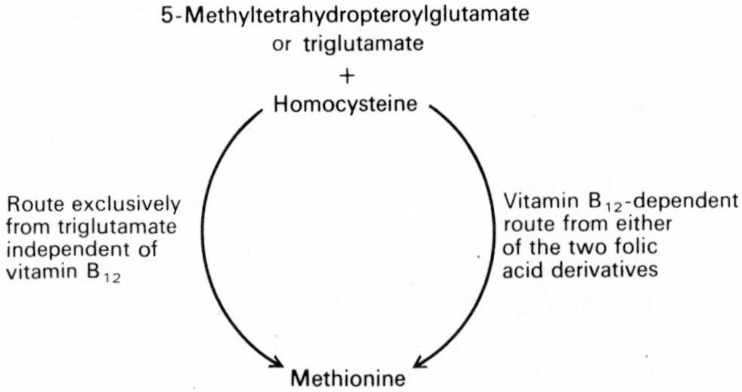

The enzyme of the independent pathway is absent in mutants requiring either methionine or vitamin B_{12}.

The mechanism of the dependent pathway is as follows: a 5-methyltetrahydrofolatehomocysteine transmethylase contains a vitamin B_{12} derivative as prosthetic group. This derivative can have either a hydroxyl group (B_{12}—OH), or a methyl group (B_{12}—CH_3) co-ordinated in the sixth position of the cobalt atom. The additional information that catalytic amounts of S-adenosylmethionine are required for the functioning of this system enables us to write the following cycle of reactions as a working hypothesis:

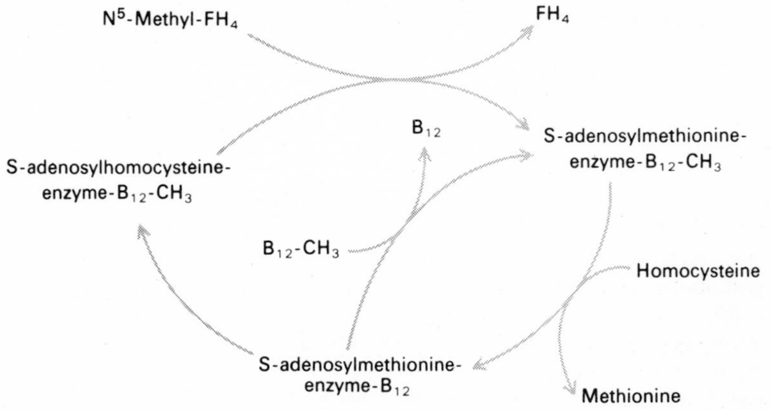

The S-adenosylmethionine required in catalytic amounts comes from a reaction discovered independently in 1957:

$$\text{Methionine} + \text{Adenosine}-\underset{\alpha}{P}-\underset{\beta}{P}-\underset{\gamma}{P} \longrightarrow \text{S-adenosylmethionine} + \text{Pyrophosphate} + P_i$$

This reaction is interesting because it is the phosphorus moieties in positions α and β which are the source of the pyrophosphate produced. Until this discovery, it was believed that ATP reacted in three ways: 1) as phosphate donor to form ADP; 2) as pyrophosphate donor to form AMP; 3) as adenylate donor to form pyrophosphate. This reaction shows for the first time that ATP can also react as an adenosine donor and that the ribose-phosphate bond is not as inert as had been thought.

It is still not known what significance should be attributed to the existence in the same cell of two independent systems for the methylation of homocysteine. We can imagine an ancestor of *E. coli* possessing only the independent pathway; a mutation leading to the ability to form the apoenzyme of the B_{12} enzyme would acquire a selective advantage in the presence of vitamin B_{12}; this organism would no longer be limited to using the triglutamate forms of folic acid, but would be able to utilize the monoglutamate form when present. Furthermore, it would be able to survive in the absence of vitamin B_{12} by synthesizing its methionine by the other pathway. This hypothetical ancestor would also be a forerunner of plants: the latter contain no vitamin B_{12} and synthesize their methionine solely from N-methyltetrahydropteroyltriglutamate. If, conversely, we postulate that the ancestral organism possessed only the B_{12}-dependent pathway, a mutation leading to the acquisition of the independent pathway would give the organism the ability to survive in the absence of vitamin B_{12}. This primitive organism could not be an ancestor of present-day plants. A third possibility assumes an ancestral organism with a genetic constitution allowing it to synthesize the enzyme of the independent route and the apoenzyme of the B_{12} enzyme, the independent enzyme not being able to function for lack of the ability of this organism to synthesize the triglutamic form of folic acid.

References

1. G. N. Cohen and J. Monod, *Bacterial Permeases, Bact. Revs.*, *21* (1957), 169.
2. H. V. Rickenberg, G. N. Cohen, G. Buttin and J. Monod, *Ann. Inst. Pasteur*, *91* (1956), 829.
3. B. Helferich and D. Türk, *Chem. Ber.*, *89* (1956), 2215.
4. W. A. Newton, J. R. Beckwith, D. Zipser and S. Brenner, *J. Mol. Biol.*, *14* (1965), 290.
5. C. F. Fox and E. P. Kennedy, *Proc. Nat. Acad. Sci. U.S.*, *54* (1965), 891.
6. A. Kepes and G. N. Cohen, *Permeation, The Bacteria*, vol. 4, p. 179; New York, Acad. Press, (1962).
7. R. J. Britten, R. B. Roberts and E. F. French, *Proc. Natl. Acad. Sci. U.S.*, *41* (1955), 863.
8. G. N. Cohen and H. V. Rickenberg, *Ann. Inst. Pasteur*, *91* (1956), 693.

8*a*. Y. Anraku, *J. Biol. Chem.*, *243* (1968), 3116.

8*b*. J. R. Piperno and D. L. Oxender, *J. Biol. Chem.*, *241* (1966), 5732.

9. J. H. Schwartz, W. K. Maas and E. J. Simon, *Biochim. Biophys. Acta*, *32* (1959), 582.
10. M. Lubin, D. H. Kessel, A. Budreau and J. D. Gross, *Biochim. Biophys. Acta*, *42* (1960), 535.
11. H. R. Kaback and E. R. Stadtman, *Proc. Natl. Acad. Sci. U.S.*, *55* (1966), 920.
12. B. L. Horecker, J. Thomas and J. Monod, *J. Biol. Chem.*, 235 (1960), 1580 and 1586.
13. H. Wiesmeyer and M. Cohn, *Biochim. Biophys. Acta*, *39* (1960), 440.
14. F. Stoeber, *Compt. rend.*, *244* (1957), 1091.
15. J. Monod, H. O. Halvorson and F. Jacob, unpublished results described in ref. 1.
16. P. Hoffee, E. Englesberg and F. Lamy, *Biochim. Biophys. Acta*, *79* (1964), 337.
17. C. Novotny and E. Englesberg, *Proc. 6th Intern. Congr. Biochem.*, New York, *3* (1964), 46.
18. M. Shilo and R. Y. Stanier, *J. Gen. Microbiol.*, *16* (1957), 472 and 482.
19. H. C. Lichstein and R. B. Ferguson, *J. Biol. Chem.*, *233* (1958), 243.
20. A. B. Pardee and L. S. Prestidge, *Proc. Natl. Acad. Sci. U.S.*, *55* (1966), 189.
21. A. B. Pardee, L. S. Prestidge, M. B. Whipple and J. Dreyfuss, *J. Biol. Chem.*, *241* (1966), 3962.

21*a*. A. B. Pardee, *Science*, *156* (1967), 1627.

22. W. KUNDIG, S. GHOSH and S. ROSEMAN, *Proc. Natl. Acad. Sci. U.S.*, *52* (1964), 1067.
23. W. KUNDIG, F. D. KUNDIG, B. ANDERSON and S. ROSEMAN, *J. Biol. Chem.*, *241* (1966), 3243.
23*a*. R. D. SIMONI, M. LEVINTHAL, F. D. KUNDIG, W. KUNDIG, B. ANDERSON, P. E. HARTMAN and S. ROSEMAN, *Proc. Natl. Acad. Sci. U.S.*, *58* (1967), 1963.
24. R. B. ROBERTS, P. H. ABELSON, D. B. COWIE, E. T. BOLTON and R. J. BRITTEN, *Studies in biosynthesis in Escherichia coli.*, Carnegie Inst. of Washington, publ. n° 607, 1955.
25. J. MONOD and G. COHEN-BAZIRE, *Compt. rend.*, *236* (1953), 530.
26. M. COHN, G. N. COHEN and J. MONOD, *Compt. rend.*, *236* (1953), 746.
27. L. GORINI and W. K. MAAS, *Biochim. Biophys. Acta*, *25* (1957), 208.
28. H. J. VOGEL, in *The Chemical Basis of Heredity*, W. D. MCELROY and B. GLASS, ed., p. 276, Baltimore, *The Johns Hopkins Press*, (1957).
29. H. E. UMBARGER, *Science*, *123* (1956), 848.
30. R. A. YATES and A. B. PARDEE, *J. Biol. Chem.*, *221* (1956), 757.
31. W. K. MAAS and E. MCFALL, *Ann. Rev. Microbiol.*, *18* (1964), 95.
32. J. MONOD and F. JACOB, *Cold Spring Harbor Symp. Quant. Biol.*, *26* (1961), 389.
33. J. MONOD, J.-P. CHANGEUX and F. JACOB, *J. Mol. Biol.*, *6* (1963), 306.
34. J. MONOD, J. WYMAN and J.-P. CHANGEUX, *J. Mol. Biol.*, *12* (1965), 88.
35. D. E. KOSHLAND, G. NÉMETHY and D. FILMER, *Biochemistry*, *5* (1966), 365.
36. D. E. ATKINSON, *Ann. Rev. Biochemistry*, *35* (1966), 85.
37. L. E. DEN DOOREN DE JONG, *Bijdrage tot de kennis van het mineralisatieproces*, Delft, (1926).
38. D. H. BROWN and C. F. CORI, in *The Enzymes*, vol. V.; P. D. BOYER, H. LARDY and K. MYRBÄCK, ed., New York, Academic Press, (1961).
39. A. A. GREEN and G. T. CORI, *J. Biol. Chem.*, *151* (1943), 21.
40. G. T. CORI and A. A. GREEN, *J. Biol. Chem.*, *151* (1943), 31.
41. A. A. YUNIS, E. H. FISCHER and E. G. KREBS, *J. Biol. Chem.*, *235* (1960), 3163.
42. A. B. KENT, E. G. KREBS and E. H. FISCHER, *J. Biol. Chem.*, *232* (1958), 549.
43. E. H. FISCHER, D. J. GRAVES, E. R. S. CRITTENDEN and E. G. KREBS, *J. Biol. Chem.*, *234* (1959), 1698.
43*a*. V. L. SEERY, E. H. FISCHER and D. C. TELLER, *Biochemistry*, 6 (1967), 3315.
44. N. B. MADSEN and C. F. CORI, *J. Biol. Chem.*, *233* (1956), 1055.
45. E. H. FISCHER, A. B. KENT, E. R. SNYDER and E. G. KREBS, *J. Am. Chem. Soc.*, *30* (1958), 2906.
46. D. J. GRAVES, E. H. FISCHER and E. G. KREBS, *J. Biol. Chem.*, *235* (1960), 805.
47. E. HELMREICH and C. F. CORI, *Proc. Natl. Acad. Sci. U.S.*, *51* (1964), 131.
48. A. ULMANN, P. R. VAGELOS and J. MONOD, *Biochem. Biophys. Res. Comm.*, *17* (1964), 86.
49. N. B. MADSEN, *Biochem. Biophys. Res. Comm.*, *15* (1964), 390.
50. E. G. KREBS, A. B. KENT, D. J. GRAVES and E. H. FISCHER, in *Proc. Intern. Symp. on Enzyme Chemistry*, Tokyo and Kyoto, p. 41. London, Pergamon Press (1958).
51. R. A. DARROW and S. P. COLOWICK, in *Methods in Enzymology*, vol. V., p. 226, New York, Academic Press, (1962).
52. H. W. KOSTERLITZ, *Biochem. J.*, *37* (1943), 322.
53. R. K. CRANE and A. SOLS, *J. Biol. Chem.*, *203* (1953), 273. See also R. K. CRANE, in *The Enzymes*, vol. VI, P. D. BOYER, H. LARDY and K. MYRBÄCK, ed., New York, Academic Press, (1963).
54. G. DE LA FUENTE and A. SOLS, *Abstr. Intern. Congr. Biochem.*, New York, *6* (1964), 506.
55. I. A. ROSE, J. V. B. WARMS and E. L. O'CONNELL, *Biochem. Biophys. Res. Comm.*, *15* (1964), 33.
56. I. A. ROSE and E. L. O'CONNELL, *J. Biol. Chem.*, *239* (1964), 12.

57. V. A. NAJJAR, in *The Enzymes*, vol. VI, P. D. BOYER, H. LARDY and K. MYRBÄCK, ed., New York, Academic Press, (1963).
58. A. PARMEGGIANI and E. G. KREBS, *Biochem. Biophys. Res. Comm.*, *19* (1965), 89.
59. T. E. MANSOUR, N. W. WAKID and H. M. SPROUSE, *Biochem. Biophys. Res. Com.*, *19* (1965), 721.
60. E. VIÑUELA, M. L. SALAS and A. SOLS, *Biochem. Biophys. Res. Comm.*, *12* (1963), 140.
61. J. V. PASSONNEAU and O. H. LOWRY, *Biochem. Biophys. Res. Comm.*, *13* (1963), 372.
62. E. VIÑUELA, M. L. SALAS, M. SALAS and A. SOLS, *Biochem. Biophys. Res. Comm.*, *15* (1964), 243.
63. O. H. LOWRY, J. V. PASSONNEAU, F. X. HASSELBERGER and D. W. SCHULTZ, *J. Biol. Chem.*, *239* (1964), 18.
63*a*. K. KAWAHARA and C. TANFORD, *Biochemistry*, *5* (1966), 1578.
63*b*. W. CHAN, D. E. MORSE and B. L. HORECKER, *Proc. Natl. Acad. Sci. U.S.*, *57* (1967), 1013.
64. S. F. VELICK and C. FURFINE, in *The Enzymes*, vol. VII, p. 343, P. D. BOYER, H. LARDY and K. MYRBÄCK, ed., New York, Academic Press, (1963).
64*a*. M. COHN, *J. Biol. Chem.*, *201* (1953), 735.
65. M. COHN, *Biochim. Biophys. Acta*, *20* (1956), 92.
66. D. G. FRAENKEL and B. L. HORECKER, *J. Biol. Chem.*, *239* (1964), 2765.
67. N. ENTNER and M. DOUDOROFF, *J. Biol. Chem.*, *196* (1952), 853.
68. V. JAGANNATHAN and R. S. SCHWEET, *J. Biol. Chem.*, *196* (1952), 551 and 563.
69. M. KOIKE, L. J. REED and W. R. CARROLL, *J. Biol. Chem.*, *235* (1960), 1924.
69*a*. M. KOIKE, L. J. REED and W. R. CARROLL, *J. Biol. Chem.*, *238* (1963), 30.
70. D. B. KEECH and M. F. UTTER, *J. Biol. Chem.*, *238* (1963), 2603 and 2609.
71. R. S. BANDURSKI and F. LIPMANN, *J. Biol. Chem.*, *219* (1956), 741.
72. S. OCHOA, J. R. STERN and M. C. SCHNEIDER, *J. Biol. Chem.*, *193* (1951), 691.
73. A. KORNBERG and W. E. PRICER, *J. Biol. Chem.*, *189* (1951), 123.
74. J. A. HATHAWAY and D. E. ATKINSON, *J. Biol. Chem.*, *238* (1963), 2875.
74*a*. D. E. ATKINSON, J. A. HATHAWAY and E. C. SMITH, *J. Biol. Chem.*, *240* (1965), 2682.
75. P. R. VAGELOS, A. W. ALBERTS and D. B. MARTIN, *J. Biol. Chem.*, *238* (1963), 533.
76. V. MASSEY, *Biochem. J.*, *51* (1952), 490.
77. V. MASSEY, *Biochem. J.*, *53* (1953), 67 and 72; *ibid.*, *55* (1953), 172.
78. C. J. R. THORNE, *Biochim. Biophys. Acta*, *42* (1960), 175.
79. H. L. KORNBERG, in *Essays in Biochemistry*, vol. 2, p. 1; P. N. CAMPBELL and G. D. GREVILLE, ed., London, Academic Press, (1966).
80. M. F. UTTER, D. B. KEECH and M. C. SCRUTTON, in *Advances in Enzyme Regulation*, Vol. 2, p. 49; G. WEBER, ed., Pergamon Press, (1964).
81. M. C. SCRUTTON and M. F. UTTER, *J. Biol. Chem.*, *240* (1965), 1.
82. M. C. SCRUTTON, D. B. KEECH and M. F. UTTER, *J. Biol. Chem.*, *240* (1965), 574.
83. R. C. VALENTINE, N. G. WRIGLEY, M. C. SCRUTTON, J. J. IRIAS and M. F. UTTER, *Biochemistry*, *5* (1966), 3111.
84. F. LYNEN, J. KNAPPE, E. LORCH, G. JUTTING, R. RINGLEMANN and J. P. LACHANCE, *Biochem. Z.*, *335* (1961), 123.
85. H. A. KREBS, in *Advances in Enzyme Regulation*, vol. 1, p. 385; G. WEBER, ed., Pergamon Press, (1963).
86. K. TAKETA and B. M. POGELL, *J. Biol. Chem.*, *240* (1965), 651.
87. K. TAKETA and B. M. POGELL, *Biochem. Biophys. Res. Comm.*, *12* (1963), 229.
88. S. PONTREMOLI, S. TRANIELLO, B. LUPPIS and W. A. WOOD, *J. Biol. Chem.*, *240* (1965), 3459.
89. S. PONTREMOLI, B. LUPPIS, W. A. WOOD, S. TRANIELLO and B. L. HORECKER, *J. Biol. Chem.*, *240* (1965), 3464 and 3469.

90. S. Pontremoli, E. Grazi and A. Accorsi, *Biochemistry*, *5* (1966), 3568.
91. O. M. Rosen, S. M. Rosen and B. L. Horecker, *Arch. Biochem. Biophys.*, *112* (1965), 411.
92. S. M. Rosen and B. L. Horecker, *Biochem. Biophys. Res. Comm.*, *20* (1965), 279.
93. D. G. Fraenkel and B. L. Horecker, *J. Bacteriol.*, *90* (1965), 837.
94. D. G. Fraenkel, S. Pontremoli and B. L. Horecker, *Arch. Biochem. Biophys.*, *114* (1966), 4.
95. R. A. Field, *The Metabolic Basis of Inherited Disease*, New York, McGraw-Hill, (1960).
96. W. J. Arion and R. C. Nordlie, *J. Biol. Chem.*, *239* (1964), 2752.
97. M. R. Stetten and H. L. Taft, *J. Biol. Chem.*, *239* (1964), 4041.
98. L. F. Leloir, *Biochem. J.*, *91* (1964), 1.
99. A. Munch-Petersen, H. Kalckar, E. Cutolo and E. E. B. Smith, *Nature*, *172* (1953), 1936.
100. L. F. Leloir, J. M. Olavarria, S. H. Goldemberg and H. Carminatti, *Arch. Biochem. Biophys.*, *81* (1959), 508.
101. D. L. Friedman and J. Larner, *Biochemistry*, *2* (1963), 669.
102. R. R. Traut and F. Lipmann, *J. Biol. Chem.*, *238* (1963), 1213.
103. W. H. Danforth, *J. Biol. Chem.*, *240* (1965), 588.
104. H. A. Barker, *Bacterial Fermentations*, New York, Wiley, (1956).
105. S. J. Wakil, *J. Am. Chem. Soc.*, *80* (1958), 6465.
106. S. J. Wakil and D. M. Gibson, *Biochim. Biophys. Acta*, *41* (1960), 122.
107. R. O. Brady, R. M. Bradley and E. G. Trams, *J. Biol. Chem.*, *235* (1960), 3093.
108. P. Goldman and P. R. Vagelos, *Biochem. Biophys. Res. Comm.*, *5* (1962), 414.
109. P. W. Majerus, A. W. Alberts and P. R. Vagelos, *Proc. Natl. Acad. Sci. U.S.*, *51* (1964), 1231.
110. P. W. Majerus, A. W. Alberts and P. R. Vagelos, *J. Biol. Chem.*, *240* (1965), 4723.
111. E. L. Pugh and S. L. Wakil, *J. Biol. Chem.*, *240* (1965), 4727.
112. F. Lynen, in *New Perspectives in Biology*, p. 132, M. Sela, ed., Amsterdam, Elsevier Publishing Co., (1964).
113. P. R. Vagelos, A. W. Alberts and D. B. Martin, *J. Biol. Chem.*, *238* (1963), 533.
114. W. M. Bortz and F. Lynen, *Biochem. Z.*, *337* (1963), 505; *ibid.*, *339* (1963), 77.
115. G. P. Ailhaud and P. R. Vagelos, *J. Biol. Chem.*, *241* (1966), 3866.
116. S. B. Weiss, E. P. Kennedy and J. Y. Kiyasu, *J. Biol. Chem.*, *235* (1960), 40.
117. G. Ehrensvärd, *2e Congrès International de Biochimie*, Symposium sur le métabolisme microbien, Paris, Sedes ed., 1952.
118. B. D. Davis, *Proc. Natl. Acad. Sci. U.S.*, *35* (1945), 1.
119. B. N. Ames and P. E. Hartman, *Cold Spring Harbor Symp. Quant. Biol.*, *28* (1963), 349.
120. G. N. Cohen and F. Jacob, *Comptes rendus*, *248* (1959), 3490.
121. A. M. H. Al-Dawody and J. E. Varner, *Federation Proceedings*, *20* (1961), 10c.
122. J. M. Ravel, S. J. Norton, J. S. Humphreys and W. Shive, *J. Biol. Chem.*, *237* (1962), 2845.
123. S. Black and N. G. Wright, *J. Biol. Chem.*, *213* (1955), 27.
124. G. N. Cohen, M.-L. Hirsch, S. B. Wiesendanger and B. Nisman, *Comptes rendus*, *238* (1954), 1746.
125. E. R. Stadtman, G. N. Cohen, G. Le Bras and H. de Robichon-Szulmajster, *J. Biol. Chem.*, *236* (1961), 2033.
126. S. Black and N. G. Wright, *J. Biol. Chem.*, *213* (1955), 39.
127. Y. Yugari and C. Gilvarg, *J. Biol. Chem.*, *240* (1965), 4710; W. Farkas and C. Gilvarg, *ibid.*, *240* (1965), 4717.
128. B. Peterkofsky and C. Gilvarg, *J. Biol Chem.*, *236* (1961), 1432.
129. S. H. Kindler and C. Gilvarg, *J. Biol. Chem.*, *235* (1960), 3532.

130. M. Antia, D. S. Hoare and E. Work, *Biochem. J.*, *65* (1957), 448.
131. B. D. Davis, *Nature*, *169* (1952), 534.
132. D. Dewey and E. Work, *Nature*, *169* (1952), 533.
133. S. Black and N. G. Wright, *J. Biol. Chem.*, *213* (1955), 51.
134. J.-C. Patte, G. Le Bras, T. Loviny and G. N. Cohen, *Biochim. Biophys. Acta*, *67* (1963), 16.
135. R. J. Rowbury and D. D. Woods, *J. Gen. Microbiol.*, *36* (1964), 341.
136. M. M. Kaplan and M. Flavin, *J. Biol. Chem.*, *241* (1966), 4463.
137. G. N. Cohen and M.-L. Hirsch, *J. Bacteriol.*, *67* (1954), 182.
138. B. Nisman, G. N. Cohen, S. B. Wiesendanger and M.-L. Hirsch, *Comptes rendus*, *238* (1954), 1342.
139. Y. Watanabe, S. Konishi and K. Shimura, *J. Biochem. Tokyo*, *43* (1955), 283.
140. M. Flavin and C. Slaughter, *Biochim. Biophys. Acta*, *36* (1959), 554.
141. H. E. Umbarger and B. Brown, *J. Bacteriol.*, *73* (1957), 105.
142. R. I. Leavitt and H. E. Umbarger, *J. Bacteriol.*, *80* (1960), 18.
143. H. E. Umbarger, B. Brown and E. J. Eyring, *J. Biol. Chem.*, *235* (1960), 1425.
144. J. W. Myers and E. A. Adelberg, *Proc. Natl. Acad. Sci. U.S.*, *40* (1954), 493.
145. A. Meister, *Biochemistry of the Amino Acids*, 2nd ed., New York, Academic Press, (1965).
146. P. Truffa-Bachi and G. N. Cohen, *Biochim. Biophys. Acta*, *113* (1961), 531.
147. J.-C. Patte, G. Le Bras and G. N. Cohen, *Biochim. Biophys. Acta*, *136* (1967), 245.
148. J.-C. Patte, P. Truffa-Bachi and G. N. Cohen, *Biochim. Biophys. Acta*, *128* (1966), 426.
149. G. N. Cohen and J.-C. Patte, *Cold Spring Harbor Symp. Quant. Biol.*, *28* (1963), 513.
150. J.-C. Patte and G. N. Cohen, *Comptes rendus*, *259* (1964), 1255.
151. Y. Yugari and C. Gilvarg, *Biochim. Biophys. Acta*, *62* (1962), 612.
152. G. N. Cohen, J.-C. Patte and P. Truffa-Bachi, *Biochem. Biophys. Res. Com.*, *19* (1965), 546.
153. P. Truffa-Bachi, G. Le Bras and G. N. Cohen, *Biochim. Biophys. Acta*, *128* (1966), 440.
154. P. Truffa-Bachi, G. Le Bras and G. N. Cohen, *Biochim. Biophys. Acta*, *128* (1966), 450.
155. J. Janin, P. Truffa-Bachi and G. N. Cohen, *Biochem. Biophys. Res. Comm.*, *26* (1967), 429.
156. R. J. Rowbury and D. D. Woods, *J. Gen. Microbiol.*, *42* (1966), 155.
157. J.-P. Changeux, *Bull. Soc. Chim. Biol.*, *46* (1964), 927, 947 and 1151.
158. M. Freundlich, R. O. Burns and H. E. Umbarger, *Proc. Natl. Acad. Sci. U.S.*, *48* (1962), 1804.
158*a*. P. Truffa-Bachi, R. van Rapenbusch, J. Janin, C. Gros and G. N. Cohen, *European J. Biochem.*, *5* (1968), 73.
158*b*. P. Truffa-Bachi, R. van Rapenbusch, J. Janin, C. Gros and G. N. Cohen, *European J. Biochem.*, in the press.
158*c*. J. Janin, R. van Rapenbusch, P. Truffa-Bachi and G. N. Cohen, *European J. Biochem.*, in the press.
158*d*. F. Falcoz-Kelly, R. van Rapenbusch and G. N. Cohen, *European J. Biochem.*, in the press.
158*e*. R. O. Burns and M. H. Zarlengo, *J. Biol. Chem.*, *243* (1968), 178.
158*f*. M. H. Zarlengo, G. W. Robinson and R. O. Burns, *J. Biol. Chem.*, *243* (1968), 186.
159. P. Datta and H. Gest, *Proc. Natl. Acad. Sci. U.S.*, *52* (1964), 1004.
160. H. Paulus and E. Gray, *J. Biol. Chem.*, *239* (1964), 4008.
161. L. Burlant, P. Datta and H. Gest, *Science*, *148* (1965), 1351.
162. P. Datta and H. Gest, *Nature*, *203* (1964), 1259.
163. P. Datta, H. Gest and H. J. Segal, *Proc. Natl. Acad. Sci. U.S.*, *51* (1964), 125.
164. Y. Karassevitch and H. de Robichon-Szulmajster, *Biochim. Biophys. Acta*, *73* (1963), 414.

165. T. Nara, H. Samejima, G. Fujita, M. Ito, J. Nakayama and S. Kinoshita, *Agr. Biol. Chem. Tokyo*, *25* (1961), 532.
166. J. R. S. Fincham, *J. Gen. Microbiol.*, *11* (1954), 236.
167. J. R. S. Fincham, *Genetic complementation*, New York, W. A. Benjamin (1966).
168. G. M. Tomkins, K. L. Yielding, N. Talal and J. F. Curran, *Cold Spring Harbor Symp. Quant. Biol.*, *28* (1963), 461.
169. C. A. Woolfolk and E. R. Stadtman, *Biochem. Biophys. Res. Comm.*, *17* (1964), 313.
170. C. A. Woolfolk, R. Shapiro and E. R. Stadtman, *Arch. Biochem. Biophys.*, *116* (1966), 177; *ibid.*, *118* (1967), 736.
171. D. Mecke and H. Holzer, *Biochim. Biophys. Acta*, *122* (1966), 341.
172. D. Mecke, K. Wulff and H. Holzer, *Biochim. Biophys. Acta*, *128* (1966), 559.
172*a*. G. N. Cohen and P. Truffa-Bachi, *Ann. Rev. Biochemistry*, *37* (1968), 79.
172*b*. B. M. Shapiro and E. R. Stadtman, *J. Biol. Chem.*, *243* (1968), 3769.
172*c*. B. M. Shapiro and E. R. Stadtman, *Biochem. Biophys. Res. Comm.*, *30* (1968), 32.
173. H. J. Vogel and B. D. Davis, *J. Am. Chem. Soc.*, *74* (1952), 109.
174. T. Yura and H. J. Vogel, *J. Biol. Chem.*, *203* (1953), 143.
175. H. J. Vogel, in *A Symposium on Amino Acid Metabolism*, Baltimore, Johns Hopkins Univ. Press, (1955).
176. M. E. Jones, L. Spector and F. Lipmann, *J. Am. Chem. Soc.*, *77* (1955), 819.
177. J. B. Walkers and J. Myers, *J. Biol. Chem.*, *203* (1953), 143.
178. H. J. Vogel, in *Control Mechanisms in Cellular Processes*, D. M. Bonner, ed., New York, Ronald Press Co., (1961).
179. D. R. Morris and A. B. Pardee, *J. Biol. Chem.*, *241* (1966), 3129.
180. H. Tristram and C. F. Thurston, *Nature*, *212* (1966), 74.
181. H. E. Umbarger, M. A. Umbarger and P. M. L. Siu, *J. Bacteriol.*, *85* (1963), 1431.
182. R. L. Kisliuk and W. Sakami, *J. Biol. Chem.*, *214* (1955), 47.
183. H. E. Umbarger and M. A. Umbarger, *Biochim. Biophys. Acta*, *62* (1962), 193.
184. P. W. Robbins and F. Lipmann, *J. Am. Chem. Soc.*, *78* (1956), 2652 and 6410.
185. J. Mager, *Biochim. Biophys. Acta*, *41* (1960), 553.
186. L. G. Wilson, T. Asahi and R. S. Bandurski, *J. Biol. Chem.*, *236* (1961), 1822.
187. T. Asahi, R. S. Bandurski and L. G. Wilson, *J. Biol. Chem.*, *236* (1961), 1830.
188. N. M. Kredich and G. M. Tomkins, *J. Biol. Chem.*, *241* (1966), 4955.
189. P. C. De Vito and J. Dreyfuss, *J. Bacteriol.*, *88* (1964), 1341.
190. A. Piérard and J. M. Wiame, *Biochim. Biophys. Acta*, *37* (1960), 490.
191. C. Jungwirth, S. R. Gross, P. Margolin and H. E. Umbarger, *Biochemistry*, *2* (1963), 1.
192. S. R. Gross, R. O. Burns and H. E. Umbarger, *Biochemistry*, *2* (1963), 1046.
193. R. O. Burns, H. E. Umbarger and S. R. Gross, *Biochemistry*, *2* (1963), 1053.
194. P. R. Srinivasan and D. B. Sprinson, *J. Biol. Chem.*, *234* (1959), 716.
195. P. R. Srinivasan, M. Katagiri and D. B. Sprinson, *J. Biol. Chem.*, *234* (1959), 713.
196. S. Mitsuhashi and B. D. Davis, *Biochim. Biophys. Acta*, *15* (1954), 54.
197. H. Yaniv and C. Gilvarg, *J. Biol. Chem.*, *213* (1955), 787.
198. P. R. Srinivasan, H. T. Shigeura, M. Sprecher, D. B. Sprinson and B. D. Davis, *J. Biol. Chem.*, *220* (1956), 477.
199. A. Rivera Jr, and P. R. Srinivasan, *Biochemistry*, *2* (1963), 1063.
200. P. M. Morgan, M. I. Gibson and F. Gibson, *Biochem. J.*, *89* (1963), 229.
201. M. I. Gibson and F. Gibson, *Biochem. J.*, *90* (1964), 248.
202. B. D. Davis, *Science*, *118* (1953), 251.
203. M. I. Gibson and F. Gibson, *Biochim. Biophys. Acta*, *65* (1962), 160.
204. I. Schwinck and E. Adams, *Biochim. Biophys. Acta*, *36* (1959), 102.
205. R. G. H. Cotton and F. Gibson, *Biochim. Biophys. Acta*, *100* (1965), 76.

206. C. H. DOY and F. W. GIBSON, *Biochem. J.*, *72* (1959), 586.
207. O. H. SMITH and C. YANOFSKY, *J. Biol. Chem.*, *235* (1960), 2051.
208. C. YANOFSKY, *Bacteriol. Revs.*, *24* (1960), 221.
209. I. P. CRAWFORD and C. YANOFSKY, *Proc. Natl. Acad. Sci. U.S.*, *44* (1958), 1161.
210. M. E. GOLDBERG, T. E. CREIGHTON, R. L. BALDWIN and C. YANOFSKY, *J. Mol. Biol.*, *21* (1966), 71.
211. L. C. SMITH, J. M. RAVEL, S. R. LAX and W. SHIVE, *J. Biol. Chem.*, *237* (1962), 3566.
212. K. D. BROWN and C. H. DOY, *Biochim. Biophys. Acta*, *77* (1963), 170.
213. R. A. JENSEN and E. W. NESTER, *J. Biol. Chem.*, *241* (1966), 3365 and 3373.
214. J. A. DE MOSS and J. WEGMAN, *Proc. Natl. Acad. Sci. U.S.*, *54* (1965), 241.
215. J. ITO and C. YANOFSKY, *J. Biol. Chem.*, *241* (1966), 4112.
216. B. N. AMES, R. G. MARTIN and B. J. GARRY, *J. Biol. Chem.*, *236* (1961), 2019.
217. H. S. MOYED and B. MAGASANIK, *J. Biol. Chem.*, *235* (1960), 149.
218. B. N. AMES, *J. Biol. Chem.*, *228* (1957), 131.
219. B. N. AMES and B. L. HORECKER, *J. Biol. Chem.*, *220* (1956), 113; *ibid.*, MARTIN *et al.*, *242* (1967), 1168 and 1175.
220. B. N. AMES, *J. Biol. Chem.*, *226* (1957), 583.
221. E. ADAMS, *J. Biol. Chem.*, *209* (1954), 829; *ibid.*, *217* (1955), 325.
221*a*. J. C. LOPER, *J. Biol. Chem.*, *243* (1968), 3264.
221*b*. J. YOURNO, *J. Biol. Chem.*, *243* (1968), 3277.
222. J. C. LOPER and E. ADAMS, *J. Biol. Chem.*, *240* (1965), 788.
223. B. N. AMES and R. G. MARTIN, *Ann. Rev. Biochem.*, *33* (1964), 235.
224. R. G. MARTIN, *J. Biol. Chem.*, *237* (1963), 257.
225. P. P. COHEN, in *The Enzymes*, P. D. BOYER, H. LARDY and K. MYRBÄCK, ed., vol. 6, p. 477, New York, Academic Press, (1963).
226. A. PIÉRARD and J. M. WIAME, *Biochem. Biophys. Res. Comm.*, *15* (1964), 76.
227. F. LACROUTE, A. PIÉRARD, M. GRENSON and J. M. WIAME, *J. Gen. Microbiol.*, *40* (1965), 127.
228. P. REICHARD and G. HANSHOFF, *Acta Chem. Scand.*, *10* (1956), 548.
229. M. SHEPHERDSON and A. B. PARDEE, *J. Biol. Chem.*, *235* (1960), 3233.
230. I. LIEBERMAN and A. KORNBERG, *Biochim. Biophys. Acta*, *12* (1953), 223.
231. H. C. FRIEDMANN and B. VENNESLAND, *J. Biol. Chem.*, *235* (1960), 1526.
232. I. LIEBERMAN, A. KORNBERG and E. S. SIMMS, *J. Biol. Chem.*, *215* (1955), 403.
233. J. HURWITZ, *J. Biol. Chem.*, *234* (1959), 2351.
234. P. BERG and W. K. JOKLIK, *J. Biol. Chem.*, *210* (1954), 657.
235. I. LIEBERMAN, *J. Biol. Chem.*, *222* (1956), 765.
236. C. LAURENT, E. MOORE and P. REICHARD, *J. Biol. Chem.*, *239* (1964), 3436.
237. C. MOORE, P. REICHARD and L. THELANDER, *J. Biol. Chem.*, *239* (1964), 3445.
238. E. C. MOORE and P. REICHARD, *J. Biol. Chem.*, *239* (1964), 3453.
239. E. SCARANO, *J. Biol. Chem.*, *235* (1960), 706.
240. J. C. GERHART and A. B. PARDEE, *Cold Spring Harbor Symp. Quant. Biol.*, *28* (1963), 491.
241. J. C. GERHART, in *Subunit structure of proteins. Biochemical and Genetic Aspects. Brookhaven Symp. Biol.*, *17* (1964).
242. J. C. GERHART and H. K. SCHACHMAN, *Biochemistry*, *4* (1965), 1054.
242*a*. K. WEBER, *Nature*, *218* (1968), 1116.
242*b*. D. C. WILEY and W. N. LIPSCOMB, *Nature*, *218* (1968), 1119.
242*c*. J.-P. CHANGEUX, J. C. GERHART and H. K. SCHACHMAN, *Biochemistry*, *7* (1968), 531.
243. A. LARSSON and P. REICHARD, *J. Biol. Chem.*, *241* (1966), 2533.
244. A. LARSSON and P. REICHARD, *J. Biol. Chem.*, *241* (1966), 2540.
245. E. SCARANO, G. GERACI and M. ROSSI, *Biochem. Biophys. Res. Comm.*, *16* (1964), 239.

246. R. Okazaki and A. Kornberg, *J. Biol. Chem.*, *239* (1964), 275.
247. D. P. Nierlich and B. Magasanik, *J. Biol. Chem.*, *236* (1961), PC 32.
248. S. C. Hartman, B. Levenberg and J. M. Buchanan, *J. Am. Chem. Soc.*, *77* (1955), 501.
249. S. C. Hartman, B. Levenberg and J. M. Buchanan, *J. Biol. Chem.*, *221* (1956), 1057.
250. B. Levenberg and J. M. Buchanan, *J. Biol. Chem.*, *224* (1957), 1005 and 1019.
251. L. N. Lukens and J. M. Buchanan, *J. Am. Chem. Soc.*, *79* (1957), 1511.
252. R. W. Miller, L. N. Lukens and J. M. Buchanan, *J. Am. Chem. Soc.*, *79* (1957), 1513.
253. J. G. Flaks, M. J. Erwin and J. M. Buchanan, *J. Biol. Chem.*, *229* (1957), 603.
254. C. E. Carter and L. H. Cohen, *J. Biol. Chem.*, *222* (1956), 17.
255. B. Magasanik, H. S. Moyed and L. B. Gehring, *J. Biol. Chem.*, *226* (1957), 339.
256. B. Magasanik, H. S. Moyed and D. Karibian, *J. Am. Chem. Soc.*, *78* (1956), 1510.
257. J. B. Wyngaarden and D. M. Ashton, *J. Biol. Chem.*, *234* (1959), 1492.
258. D. P. Nierlich and B. Magasanik, *J. Biol. Chem.*, *240* (1965), 358.
259. J. Mager and B. Magasanik, *J. Biol. Chem.*, *235* (1960), 1474.
260. I. Lieberman, *J. Biol. Chem.*, *223* (1956), 327.
261. R. D. Berlin and E. R. Stadtman, *J. Biol. Chem.*, *241* (1966), 2679.
262. I. G. Leder, *J. Biol. Chem.*, *236* (1961), 3066.
263. Y. Kaziro, R. Tanaka, Y. Mano and N. Shimazono, *J. Biochem. Japan*, *49* (1961), 472.
264. G. W. E. Plaut, *Ann. Rev. Biochem.*, *30* (1961), 409.
265. P. C. Newell and R. G. Tucker, *Biochem. J.*, *100* (1966), 512 and 517.
266. L. J. Wickerham, M. H. Flickinger and R. M. Johnston, *Arch. Biochem.*, *9* (1946), 95.
267. W. McNutt, *J. Biol. Chem.*, *219* (1956), 363.
268. J. Sadique, J. Shanmugasundaram and E. R. B. Shanmugasundaram, *Naturwissenschaften*, *53* (1966), 282.
269. J. Sadique, J. Shanmugasundaram and E. R. B. Shanmugasundaram, *Biochem. J.*, *101* (1966), 2C.
270. H. Katagiri, I. Takeda and K. J. Imai, *J. Vitaminol. Japan*, *5* (1959), 287.
271. G. W. E. Plaut, *J. Biol. Chem.*, *235* (1960), PC 41.
272. B. B. McCormick and R. C. Butler, *Biochim. Biophys. Acta*, *65* (1962), 326.
273. A. W. Schrecker and A. Kornberg, *J. Biol. Chem.*, *182* (1950), 795.
274. A. C. Wilson and A. B. Pardee, *J. Gen. Microbiol.*, *28* (1962), 283.
275. T. Tanaka and W. E. Knox, *J. Biol. Chem.*, *234* (1959), 1162.
276. A. H. Mehler and W. E. Knox, *J. Biol. Chem.*, *187* (1950), 431.
277. F. T. De Castro, J. M. Price and R. R. Brown, *J. Am. Chem. Soc.*, *78* (1956), 2904.
278. W. B. Jakoby and D. M. Bonner, *J. Biol. Chem.*, *221* (1956), 689.
279. R. H. Decker, H. H. Kang, F. R. Leach and L. M. Henderson, *J. Biol. Chem.*, *236* (1961), 3076.
280. L. V. Hankes and L. M. Henderson, *J. Biol. Chem.*, *225* (1957), 349.
281. M. V. Ortega and G. M. Brown, *J. Am. Chem. Soc.*, *81* (1959), 4437.
282. E. Mothes, D. Gross, H. R. Scwelte and K. Mothes, *Naturwissenschaften*, *48* (1961), 623.
283. F. Lingens, *Angew. Chem.*, *72* (1960), 920.
284. P. Handler, in *Proceedings of the 4th International Congress of Biochemistry*, Vienna, vol. XI, p. 39, London, Pergamon Press, (1959).
285. A. Kornberg, *J. Biol. Chem.*, *182* (1950), 805.
286. J. Imsande and A. B. Pardee, *J. Biol. Chem.*, *237* (1962), 1305.
287. J. Imsande, *Biochim. Biophys. Acta*, *85* (1964), 255.
288. J. Imsande and L. S. Prestidge, *Biochim. Biophys. Acta*, *85* (1964), 265.
289. M. I. Gibson and F. Gibson, *Biochem. J.*, *90* (1964), 248.
290. E. Viera and E. Shaw, *J. Biol. Chem.*, *236* (1961), 2507.

291. J. J. REYNOLDS and G. M. BROWN, *J. Biol. Chem.*, *237* (1962), PC 2713.
292. L. ZIEGLER, *Naturwissenschaften*, *48* (1961), 458.
293. R. NATH and D. M. GREENBERG, *Biochemistry*, *1* (1962), 435.
294. U. W. KENKARE and B. M. BRAGANCA, *Biochem. J.*, *86* (1963), 160.
295. W. B. DEMPSEY and P. F. PACHLER, *J. Bacteriol.*, *91* (1966), 642.
296. W. B. DEMPSEY, *J. Bacteriol.*, *90* (1965), 431.
297. J. H. MUELLER, *Science*, *85* (1937), 502.
298. M. A. EISENBERG, *Biochem. Biophys. Res. Comm.*, *8* (1962), 437.
299. V. G. LILLY and L. H. LEONIAN, *Science*, *99* (1944), 205.
300. J. KNAPPE, E. RINGELMAN and F. LYNEN, *Biochem. Z.*, *335* (1961), 168.
301. D. P. KOSOW and M. D. LANE, *Biochem. Biophys. Res. Comm.*, *5* (1961), 191.
302. D. P. KOSOW, S. C. HUANG and M. D. LANE, *J. Biol. Chem.*, *237* (1962), 3633.
303. D. P. KOSOW and M. D. LANE, *Biochem. Biophys. Res. Comm.*, *7* (1962), 439.
304. W. K. MAAS and B. D. DAVIS, *J. Bacteriol.*, *60* (1950), 733.
305. D. BILLEN and H. C. LICHSTEIN, *J. Bacteriol.*, *58* (1949), 215.
306. E. R. STADTMAN, *J. Am. Chem. Soc.*, *77* (1955), 5765.
307. E. N. MCINTOSH, M. PURKO and W. A. WOOD, *J. Biol. Chem.*, *228* (1957), 499.
308. R. KUHN and T. WIELAND, *Ber. dtsch. chem. Ges.*, *75 B* (1942), 121.
309. W. K. MAAS, *J. Biol. Chem.*, *198* (1952), 23.
310. W. K. MAAS and G. D. NOVELLI, *Arch. Biochem. Biophys.*, *43* (1953), 236.
311. W. K. MAAS, in *Proceedings of the 4th International Congress of Biochemistry*, Vienna, vol. XI, p. 161, London, Pergamon Press, (1959).
312. T. E. KING and F. M. STRONG, *J. Biol. Chem.*, *189* (1951), 315.
313. G. M. BROWN, *J. Biol. Chem.*, *234* (1959), 370 and 379.
314. I. W. CHEN and F. C. CHARALAMPOUS, *J. Biol. Chem.*, *241* (1966), 2194.
315. J. J. FERGUSON, JR., and H. RUDNEY, *J. Biol. Chem.*, *234* (1959), 1072.
316. P. R. STEWART and H. RUDNEY, *J. Biol. Chem.*, *241* (1966), 1222.
317. H. RUDNEY, P. R. STEWART, P. W. MAJERUS and P. R. VAGELOS, *J. Biol. Chem.*, *241* (1966), 1226.
318. F. LYNEN, B. W. AGRANOFF, H. EGGERER, U. HENNING and E. M. MÖSLEIN, *Angew. Chem.*, *71* (1959), 657.
319. T. T. TCHEN, *J. Biol. Chem.*, *233* (1958), 1100.
320. U. HENNING, E. M. MOSLEIN and F. LYNEN, *Arch. Biochem. Biophys.*, *83* (1959), 259.
321. A. DE WAARD, A. H. PHILLIPS and K. BLOCH, *J. Am. Chem. Soc.*, *81* (1959), 2913.
322. G. SUZUE, *J. Biochem. Japan*, *51* (1962), 246.
323. G. SUZUE, K. ORIHARA, H. MORISHIMA and S. TANAKA, *Radioisotopes*, *13* (1964), 300.
324. A. A. KANDUTSCH, H. PAULUS, E. LEVIN and K. BLOCH, *J. Biol. Chem.*, *239* (1964), 2507.
325. T. W. GOODWIN, in *The Biosynthesis of Vitamins and Related Compounds*, 294–299, London and New York, Academic Press, (1963).
326. M. GRIFFITHS, W. R. SISTROM, G. COHEN-BAZIRE and R. Y. STANIER, *Nature*, *176* (1955), 1211.
327. M. DWORKIN, *J. Gen. Physiol.*, *41* (1958), 1099.
328. M. J. BURNS, S. M. HAUGE and F. W. QUACKENBUSH, *Arch. Biochem. Biophys.*, *30* (1951), 341 and 347.
329. A. F. BLISS, *Arch. Biochem. Biophys.*, *31* (1951), 197.
330. F. LYNEN, U. HENNING, C. BUBLITZ, B. SORBO and L. KROPLEN-RUEFF, *Biochem. Z.*, *330* (1958), 269.
331. G. POPJÀK and J. W. CORNFORTH, *Adv. Enzymology*, *22* (1960), 281.
332. R. G. GOULD, *Amer. J. Med.*, *11* (1951), 209.

333. M. D. SIPERSTEIN and V. M. FAGAN, in *Advances in Enzyme Regulation*, vol. 2, p. 249, ed., G. Weber, London, Pergamon Press, (1964).
334. G. KIKUCHI, A. KUMAR, P. TALMAGE and D. SHEMIN, *J. Biol. Chem.*, *233* (1958), 1214.
335. K. D. GIBSON, A. NEUBERGER and J. J. SCOTT, *Biochem. J.*, *61* (1955), 618.
336. B. F. BURNHAM and J. LASCELLES, *Biochem. J.*, *87* (1963), 462.
337. L. BOGORAD, *J. Biol. Chem.*, *233* (1958), 501.
338. D. B. HOARE and H. HEATH, *Biochem. J.*, *73* (1959), 679.
339. L. BOGORAD, *J. Biol. Chem.*, *233* (1958), 510.
340. D. MAUZERALL and S. GRANICK, *J. Biol. Chem.*, *232* (1958), 1141.
341. S. SANO and S. GRANICK, *J. Biol. Chem.*, *236* (1961), 1173.
342. R. J. PORRA and J. E. FALK, *Biochem. J.*, *90* (1963), 69.
343. P. FILDES, *Brit. J. Exptl. Pathol.*, *2* (1921), 16.
344. S. GRANICK and H. GILDER, *J. Gen. Physiol.*, *30* (1946), 1; *ibid.*, *31* (1947), 103.
345. S. GRANICK and D. MAUZERALL, *J. Biol. Chem.*, *232* (1958), 1119.
346. J. JENSEN and E. THOFERN, *Naturforsch.*, *8 B* (1953), 599 and 604; *ibid.*, *9 B* (1954), 596.
347. M. BELJANSKI and M. BELJANSKI, *Ann. Institut Pasteur*, *92* (1957), 396.
348. J. LASCELLES, *Biochem. J.*, *62* (1956), 78.
349. J. LASCELLES, *J. Gen. Microbiol.*, *23* (1960); 487.
350. S. GRANICK, *Harvey Lectures*, *44* (1950), 220.
351. K. D. GIBSON, A. NEUBERGER and G. H. TAIT, *Biochem. J.*, *88* (1963), 325.
352. S. GRANICK, *J. Biol. Chem.*, *183* (1950), 713.
353. J. H. C. SMITH, in *Biological Structure and Function*, vol. 2, p. 325; Goodwin and Lindberg, ed., New York, Academic Press, (1961).
354. G. COHEN-BAZIRE, W. R. SISTROM and R. Y. STANIER, *J. Cellular Comp. Physiol.*, *49* (1957), 25.
355. J. LASCELLES, *Tetrapyrrole biosynthesis, and its regulation*, p. 99, New York, W. A. Benjamin, (1964).
356. J. E. FALK and R. J. PORRA, *Biochem. J.*, *90* (1963), 66.
357. R. C. BRAY and D. SHEMIN, *J. Biol. Chem.*, *238* (1963), 1501.
358. K. BERNHAUER, F. WAGNER, H. MICHNA, H. BEISBARTH and P. RIETZ, *Biochem. Z.*, *345* (1966).
359. H. C. FRIEDMANN and D. L. HARRIS, *J. Biol. Chem.*, *240* (1965), 406.
360. P. BARBIERI, G. BORETTI, A. DI MARCO, A. MIGLIACCI and C. SPALLA, *Biochim. Biophys. Acta*, *57* (1962), 599.
361. R. O. BRADY, E. C. CASTERNA and H. A. BARKER, *J. Biol. Chem.*, *237* (1962), 2325.
362. H. WEISSBACH, B. REDFIELD and A. PETERKOFSKY, *J. Biol. Chem.*, 237 (1962), 3217.
363. H. A. BARKER, F. SUZUKI, A. A. IODICE and V. ROOZE, *Ann. N.Y. Acad. Sci.*, *112* (1964), 644.
364. H. EGGERER, E. R. STADTMAN, P. OVERATH and F. LYNEN, *Biochem. Z.*, *333* (1960), 1.
365. B. D. DAVIS and E. S. MINGIOLI, *J. Bacteriol.*, *60* (1950), 17.
366. D. D. WOODS, M. A. FOSTER and J. R. GUEST, in *Transmethylation and Methionine Biosynthesis*, p. 138, S. K. Shapiro and F. Schlenk, ed., Univ. of Chicago Press, (1965).

Index

A

T

U

V

X